History of Geophysics

History of Geophysics

Volume 3

C. Stewart Gillmor
Series Editor

The History of Hydrology

Edited by
Edward R. Landa and Simon Ince

With a Foreword by William Back

American Geophysical Union
1987

C. Stewart Gillmor, Editor
Professor of History and Science
Wesleyan University, Middletown, CT 06457

History of Geophysics is a collection of new as well as previously published articles covering the social and intellectual history of the geophysical sciences. The series is published approximately once each year in a single volume and is available by subscription.

ISSN: 8755-1217
ISBN: 0-87590-277-4

Send orders and inquiries to:
AMERICAN GEOPHYSICAL UNION
2000 Florida Avenue, NW
Washington, DC 20009

Printed in the United States of America

"Science Without Its History Is Like a Man Without a Memory. The Results of Such Collective Amnesia Are Dire."

Colin Russell
Nature (1984) 308:778

TABLE OF CONTENTS

FOREWORD

This book is a compilation of the papers presented at the first two Symposia sponsored by the Committee on History and Heritage of Hydrology. This foreword is based primarily on the welcoming comments for the first History of Hydrology Symposium, in San Francisco, December 1984. The Committee has subsequently sponsored two more Symposia on History of Hydrology, the third at the San Francisco meeting of 1985, organized by Dr. T. N. Narisimhan, University of California, Berkeley, and the fourth at the Baltimore meeting, May 1986, organized by Drs. Gerry Meyer, U.S. Geological Survey, and George Davis, Woodward and Clyde., Inc. The Symposium in San Francisco, 1984, was the first activity of the newly formed Committee that R. A. Freeze appointed as soon as he became President-Elect of the Hydrology Section.

The Committee has three main purposes: One, to encourage the study of the classical history of hydrology in order to provide practicing scientists with a sense of continuity by knowing their professional roots. This is done primarily by providing a forum for presentation of papers and providing a means for publication. The second goal, is to develop a body of knowledge that could be considered contemporary history. Because hydrology is a relatively young science, many living hydrologists are either founders of the science or worked closely with the founders. The history of the past 50 years should be documented before data are lost and memories fade. The third objective is to develop some means of preserving the hydrologic data that will be of scientific significance in the future. I make the plea now that we welcome any suggestions on how to achieve these goals most effectively.

This Committee is a subcommittee of the History of Geophysics Committee organized and chaired by David Stern, NASA. Dr. Stern has encouraged other sections to establish similar committees on history. The Geophysics Committee was instrumental in establishing the History of Geophysics series of which this book is the third volume. These committees and activities are a manifestation of the resurgence of interest in the history of science. During the past 5 years, many associations of history have been formed including groups in electrical engineering, information processing, chemistry, and astronomy. The reasons for this great amount of activity are not clear at the present time. Several of these associations are of direct interest to hydrologists, including the History of Geology Division of the Geological Society of America that is more than 10 years old; INHIGO, the International Commission on History of Geology, has been active for several years, and held its 11th Symposium at the International Geologic Congress in Moscow, August 1983; HESS, the History of Earth Sciences Society, was formed 5 years ago, and has an active publication program. One of the first modern books on history of hydraulics was by Hunter Rouse and Simon Ince, one of the editors of this

volume [1957].[1] The other book on the history of hydrology that has been widely used is by Biswas [1970].[2]

Because the history of science is a history of ideas and the people who had these ideas, it is a study of how these ideas were generated, what the scientists did and why they did it. When the history of science is considered in these terms, it is obvious that we are also talking about the philosophy of science. I think that in addition to the study of history of science having an intellectual fascination of its own, it provides a way for us to develop our own personal philosophy of science.

One book that I have found extremely helpful and would recommend to you is the little book by Sir Peter Medawar [1979][3], the British biologist. He has expressed a lot of the concerns and attitudes that many of us have long recognized but have been reluctant to promote because they smack of heresy; however, their credibility is greatly enhanced when they are espoused by a Noble Laureate such as Sir Peter. His advice is primarily to young scientists, but experienced scientists should well pay heed. For example, many of us are concerned that we do not "keep up with the literature." He makes a point that this is not necessarily a desirable activity. "Too much book learning may crab and confine the imagination and the endless pouring over the research of others is sometimes psychologically a research substitute, much as reading romantic fiction may be a substitute for real-life romance . . . The beginner must read, but intently and choosily and not too much."(pp. 16–17). He is deplored by the sight of a young research worker always seen hunched over journals in the library; by far the best way to become proficient in research is to get on with it. You can either do science or read about it.

He also expounds on the idea of how critical it is to identify important problems. Anyone who wants to make important discoveries must work on important problems. "Dull or piffling problems yield dull or piffling answers."(p. 13). If an experiment is not worth doing, it is not worth doing well.

Many of us often wish that we were brighter, well, Sir Peter makes a point that this is not necessarily a desirable attribute either. One does not need to be terrifically brainy to be a good scientist. He states, "An antipathy or a total indifference to the life of the mind and an impatience of abstract ideas can be taken as contraindications, to be sure, but there is nothing in experimental science that calls for great feats of ratiocination or a preternatural gift for deductive reasoning. Common sense one cannot do without, and one would be the better for owning some of those old fashioned virtues . . . application, diligence, a sense of

---

[1]"History of Hydraulics" by Hunter Rouse and Simon Ince, 1957, Iowa Institute of Hydraulic Research, State University of Iowa, 269 p.

[2]"History of Hydrology" by A. K. Biswas, 1970, American Elsevier Publishing Co., New York, 336 p.

[3]"Advice to a Young Scientist" by Sir Peter Medawar, 1979, Harper and Row, New York, 109 p.

purpose, the power to concentrate, to persevere and not be cast down by adversity.'' (pp. 8–9). I believe the most important characteristics of a good scientist are imagination and intuition which have little to do with intelligence. Although Sir Peter does not discuss Leonardo da Vinci, I am sure that he would agree with George Sarton's (the acknowledged father of the history of science), analysis that Leonardo, one of the great geniuses of all time and widely recognized as a man of science, was in fact a total failure as a practicing scientist. His genius was his undoing. Although Leonardo made many important observations and drawings in human anatomy, geology, aerodynamics, and hydrodynamics, he did not have an impact on the course of science because his notes were never made available until many centuries later, so his many discoveries were essentially nondiscoveries because no one knew about them. Leonardo was a nonpragmatic dreamer, whose intellectual curiosity was satisfied when he had made some discovery, observation, or solved some significant engineering or military problem. ''He was one of the greatest men of science, but remained unknown. . . . The fault of his being unappreciated rests entirely with him; he did only part of the work which should have been done and stopped half way.'' [Sarton, 1962, p. 141].[4] If he had been less of a genius, he could have changed the course of science in many disciplines.

Another point on which I agree with Sir Peter, is that it is not wise to be too critical. I do not mean to be tolerant of sloppy science or sloppy scholarship, but a critical attitude is not conducive to your own creativity, likewise, a negative attitude inhibits inspired creativity and is self-defeating.

Sir Peter discusses the excess of hubris in that success sometimes has a bad effect on young scientists, in that they sometimes believe that all previous work was done slovenly and that only their own work has been competently carried out. Sir Peter says that the old-fashioned remedy for hubris was a smart blow on the head with an inflated pig's bladder and suggests this done in spirit by a rebuke before the young scientist injures himself. Similar failings exist in some older scientists with an excess of confidence in the rightness of their own views and can be considered a sort of senile hubris.

Sir Peter warns that although ambition as a motive or force to get things done is not necessarily a deadly sin, ''excessive ambition can certainly be a disfigurement. An ambitious young scientist is marked out by having no time for anybody or anything that does not promote or bear upon his work. Seminars or lectures that do not qualify are shunned, and those who wish to discuss them are dismissed as boors. The

ambitious make too obvious a point of being polite to those who can promote their interests and are proportionately uncivil to those who cannot.''[Medawar, 1979, p.52].[3] He goes on to suggest that young scientists should not make overt attempts to ingratiate themselves with their seniors. ''A senior scientist is much more flattered by finding that his views are the subject of serious criticism than by sycophantic and sometimes obviously simulated respect. A young scientist will not, however, ingratiate himself with a prospective patron by exposing his views to scathing public criticism. Older scientists expect nothing more from the young than civility.''[Medawar, 1979, p. 55].[3]

''Young scientists wishing to be thought even younger and more inexperienced than they really are should lose no opportunity to jibe at and belittle the administration, whatever it may be. It would help them to grow up if they realized that scientific administrators are problem-solvers as they are—and are working, too, for the advancement of learning. In some ways, a young scientist should reflect, the administrator's task is the more difficult, for whereas well-established laws of nature discourage a young scientist from attempting to circumvent the Second Law of Thermodynamics, no comparable body of administrative common law assures the administrator that he can't get a quart into or out of a pint pot, or money out of a stone—feats executed or attempted daily by administrators trying to raise funds.'' [Medawar, 1979, p. 56].[3]

The one final point that I want to make is the expression of Sir Peter Medawar on the importance of the history of science: ''an indifference to the history of ideas is widely interpreted as a sign of cultural barbarism—and rightly, too, I should say, because the person who is not interested in the growth and flux of ideas is probably not interested in the life of the mind. A young scientist working in an advancing field of research should certainly try to identify the origin and growth of current opinions. Although self-interest should not be his motive, he will probably end with a stronger sense of personal identity if he can see where fits into the scheme of things.''[Medawar, 1979, p. 30].[3]

So I hope that the papers in this book and the symposia sponsored by the Committee on History and Heritage of Hydrology will help reinforce your philosophy of science and your awareness for the need to know the origin of many ideas that we now accept in our paradigm of hydrology.

William Back
Chairman of Committee on History and Heritage,
Hydrology Section, American Geophysical Union

U.S. Geological Survey
Reston, Virginia

---

[4]''Sarton on the History of Science'' (Essays by George Sarton) edited by Dorothy Stimson, 1962, Harvard University Press, Cambridge, Massachusetts, 383 p.

PREFACE

For society as a whole, and more specifically, for a subgroup of society composed of the practitioners of a specific scientific discipline such as hydrology, the preservation and study of the record of how our understanding of natural processes has developed is not only a worthy and noble goal in itself, but has a didactic role in the education of scientists. However, for such preservation and study of this record to occur requires the action of individuals—either historians of science or practitioners of science. Both have a role, and both are represented in this volume. For the historians of science, such activities represent the focus of their profession. In contrast, for the practicing scientist, such historical activities are necessarily peripheral. In addition, for most such individuals the last formal contact with history came in high school or early in college. The exposure was to political history, all too often with an emphasis on the rote memorization of names and dates, and occasional platitudes regarding history as a key to understanding the future. In the typical university-level science class, there is generally little or no discussion of the historical development of the field. Where such discussion does occur, it more-often-than-not is a proforma, first lecture or part thereof, used more as an ice-breaker than a serious attempt at discussing the development of the present state-of-knowledge. Except for a few advanced seminars, there is generally little emphasis on reading the original literature that forms the foundation of the science summarized in current texts.

Despite such a limited historical treatment in the education of scientists, an increasingly apparent interest in the history of science exists in most disciplines. We think the reasons for this are three-fold, and stem from the professional and personal benefits thus derived. Such activities can be: (1) technically productive, (2) intellectually broadening, and (3) enjoyable. Scientific investigations in the 1980's are generally aimed at answering very specific questions. The historical perspective gives an otherwise highly-focused investigator, the opportunity to view how his/her contribution fits into the accumulated and evolving body of facts and concepts that make up our present inventory of knowledge. This is of inherent value to the individual and can help a scientist to explain the relevance of his/her work to others—a discussion of an increment of new information as it relates to the larger body of knowledge is of far more value than a bare exposition on the increment alone. As to the second point—that of intellectual broadening—historians of science such as Thomas Kuhn, Colin Russell, and Bruce Wheaton, have pointed out how the development of science follows a tortuous path with many diversions and deadends, rather than the linear development which most science texts suggest by their highly abridged treatment of the subject. Following this tortuous road for even brief segments can be a real learning experience. Personal enjoyment surely has a role here too; for many persons, there is something inherently fascinating in reading the account of scientific investigations done decades or centuries earlier—the techniques involved, the interpretations offered, the language used, and the personalities involved. It is the same lure that draws people to museums and genealogy. Indeed an interest in processes acting through times is what has drawn many to their chosen career in the geophysical sciences.

For these reasons—the learning experience and pure enjoyment—the study of the history of science can be gratifying. It may remain an amateur interest, pursued only for self-fulfillment, or be carried one step beyond into the public arena of formal scholarship and publication. Taking this step into the history of a science requires the same commitment to rigorous data collection and interpretive synthesis as expected in the science itself. We hope that society-sponsored symposia and publications such as this will provide forums for discussion and encourage future efforts in the history of hydrology.

Edward R. Landa
U.S. Geological Survey
Reston, Virginia

Simon Ince
University of Arizona
Tucson, Arizona

Editors

Darcy's Law: Its Physical Theory and Application to Entrapment of Oil and Gas

M. King Hubbert

5208 Westwood Drive, Bethesda, Maryland 20816

Darcy's law in its primitive form, generalized for flow in any direction in a water-filled sand in three-dimensional space, may be expressed by

$$\mathbf{q} = -K \operatorname{grad} h, \tag{a}$$

where $\mathbf{q}$ is the volume of water crossing unit area normal to the flow direction in unit time at a given point, and h is the height of water in a manometer terminated at that point. This is a kinematic equation, involving the dimensions only of length and time, which expresses the coupling between the flow field of the vector $\mathbf{q}$ and the scalar field h. It lacks, however, any explicit expression of the dynamical quantities, the energies and forces involved. This deficiency can be removed by noting that h is related to the fluid pressure p at a given point of elevation z, and to the fluid density ρ and gravity g, by

$$h = z + p/\rho g. \tag{b}$$

Multiplying both sides of equation (*b*) by g then gives

$$gh = gz + p/\rho, \tag{c}$$

each term of which is a potential energy per unit mass of the water at the given point, gz being the gravitational energy, p/ρ the pressure energy, and gh the total energy per unit mass, which is also the potential Φ of the water. Then, since

$$gh = \Phi, \tag{d}$$

$$-\operatorname{grad} h = -(1/g) \operatorname{grad} \Phi. \tag{e}$$

This, when substituted into equation (a), gives Darcy's law in the dynamical forms,

$$\left. \begin{aligned} \mathbf{q} &= (K/g)\,(-g \operatorname{grad} h), \\ &= (K/g)\,(-\operatorname{grad} \Phi). \end{aligned} \right\} \tag{f}$$

Here,

$$-g \operatorname{grad} h = -\operatorname{grad} \Phi = \mathbf{E} \tag{g}$$

is the force per unit mass acting upon the water at a given point. Then, substituting σ for the constant (K/g) in equations (f), gives

$$\left. \begin{aligned} \mathbf{q} &= -\sigma g \operatorname{grad} h, \\ &= -\sigma \operatorname{grad} \Phi, \\ &= +\sigma \mathbf{E}, \end{aligned} \right\} \tag{h}$$

as equivalent expressions of Darcy's law.

For an incompressible liquid,

$$\Phi = gz + p/\rho, $$

but, in general, for both liquids and gases, so long as ρ is a function of p only,

$$\Phi = gz + \int_0^p (1/\rho)\,dp. \tag{i}$$

The potential Φ of any fluid at a particular point, as given by equation (i). is the work that would be required to transport a unit mass of the fluid from a standard reference elevation and pressure to the elevation and pressure at the given point. At each point in a water-filled regional sandstone, not only will there be a definite potential Φ_w for water, but also definite potentials, Φ_o and Φ_g. for oil and gas, with those three potentials having different values:

$$\left.\begin{aligned}
\Phi_w &= gz + \int_0^{p_w} (1/\rho_w)dp, \\[2em]
\Phi_O &= gz + \int_0^{p_w+p_{co}} (1/\rho_O)dp, \\[2em]
\Phi_g &= gz + \int_0^{p_w+p_{cg}} (1/\rho_g)dp.
\end{aligned}\right\}$$

(j)

Here, p_w is the pressure of the water at the given point and p_{co} and p_{cg} are the additional capillary pressures of water against oil, or water against gas, at that point.

Thus, in a regional sandstone, if the water is static, the water potential Φ_w will be constant in space, whereas the equipotential surfaces for both oil and gas will be horizontal with the potentials, Φ_o and Φ_g, each decreasing upward, but with the gradient of that for gas being greater than that for oil. If the water is flowing, the water equipotential surfaces will be perpendicular to the water flowlines and essentially perpendicular to the sandstone stratum, whereas the equipotential surfaces for both oil and gas will be inclined downward in the water-flow direction, those for oil being more steeply inclined than those for gas.

Since the forces acting upon discrete particles of oil or gas will be in the direction of decrease of their respective potentials, a trap for either oil or gas will be a space of minimum potential for that fluid, enclosed jointly by an impermeable barrier and an equipotential surface of the given fluid. If the water is static, the equipotential surfaces of both oil and gas being horizontal, the traps for these two fluids will coincide in space. The traps will be the space enclosed jointly by a downwardly concave impermeable barrier and a horizontal surface—the conventional closed structure of the anticlinal theory. If the water is flowing, the equipotential surfaces for oil and gas no longer will coincide but will be inclined downward in the flow direction, that for oil more steeply than that for gas. In this case, neither will the traps for oil and gas coincide. They may partially overlap or they may be separated completely, a trap for oil being unable to hold gas and vice versa.

The exploration for oil and gas thus reduces in part to the location of those regions in underground space of minimum potential for the respective fluids.

INTRODUCTION

On January 2, 1985, I received a telephone call from William Back of the U.S. Geological Survey informing me of the plans to hold a History of Hydrology Symposium during the American Geophysical Union Spring Meeting in Baltimore, May 19–23, 1985, and inviting me to be one of the contributors to that program. This paper has been written in response to that request. However, in view of my state of retirement from the Survey, and the brevity of time before the meeting, I was seriously in need of technical assistance in the preparation of demonstration equipment for the presentation at the meeting. As a result, I am indebted to the U.S. Geological Survey for providing this assistance, and particularly to David Pollock of the Ground-Water Branch, and to Rudolph Raspet of the Branch of Theoretical and Applied Geophysics, for reconditioning experimental demonstration apparatus, and producing a 16-millimeter film of a live experiment on the migration and entrapment of oil and gas for use in the presentation.

The present paper is essentially a synthesis and condensation of results that were developed over a period of about three decades, and published originally in the following papers: *Hubbert* [1940], "The Theory of Ground-Water Motion"; [1953], "Entrapment of Petroleum under Hydrodynamic Conditions"; [1956, 1957], "Darcy's Law and the Field Equations of the Flow of Underground Fluids"; and [1967], "Application of Hydrodynamics to Oil Exploration." In some cases the present theoretical analyses differ from those made originally but the over-all results remain essentially the same.

DARCY'S LAW

The Darcy experiment

In Paris in the year 1856 there was published by Victor Dalmont as a part of the *Libraire des Corps Impériaux des Ponts et des Mines* a monograph by the French engineer, Henry Darcy (correct spelling), Inspector General of Bridges and Highways. This was entitled:

«LES FONTAINES PUBLIQUES
DE LA VILLE DE DIJON
Exposition et Application
DES PRINCIPES A SUIVRE ET DES FORMULES A EM-
PLOYER
Dans les Questions
de
DISTRIBUTION D'EAU
Ouvrage terminé
par un Appendice Relatif aux Fournitures d'Eau de Plusieurs
Villes
AU FILTRAGE DES EAUX
et
A la Fabrication des Tuyaux de Fonte, de Plomb, de Tole et de
Bitume»

For several years previously Henry Darcy had been engaged in modernizing and enlarging the waterworks of the City of Dijon and this treatise comprising a 647-page volume of text and an accompanying *Atlas* of lithographed illustrations, constitutes an engineering report of that enterprise.

The item of present interest represents only a detail of the general work and appears in an appendix on pages 590 to 594 under the heading, "Determination of the Law of Flow of Water through Sand." This pertains to a problem encoun-

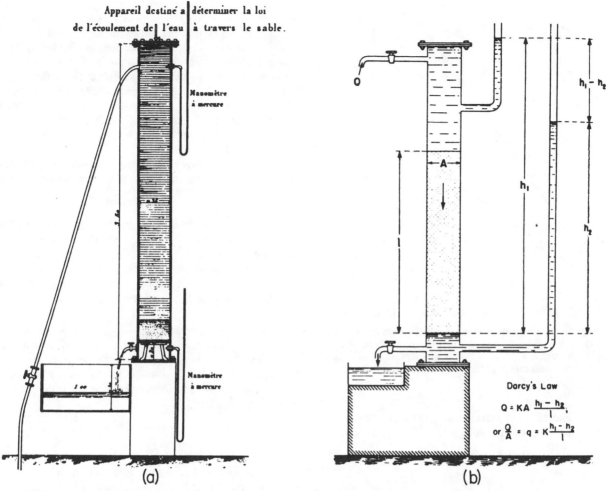

Fig. 1. Henry Darcy's experiment on flow of water through sands. (*a*) Darcy's original apparatus with mercury manometers. (*b*) Equivalent apparatus with water manometers and Darcy's own statement of law expressed in notation of present paper. [*Hubbert*, 1953, Figure 8.]

tered by Darcy in designing a filter for the system. It was customary at that time to filter the water by flowing it through a bed of sand. Darcy needed to know how large a filter would be required for a given volume of water per day. Unable to find the required information in the published literature, he proceeded to obtain it experimentally.

A drawing of the apparatus used is shown as Figure 3 in the *Atlas*, and it is here reproduced in facsimile as Figure 1 (*a*). This consists of a vertical iron pipe 0.35 meters in diameter and 3.50 meters in length (the figure gives 3.50 meters but the text gives 2.50 meters), flanged at both ends. At a height of 0.20 meters above the base of the column, there was placed a horizontal screen supported by an iron grillwork upon which rested a column, a meter or so in height, of siliceous sand. Water could be admitted into the system by means of a pipe from the building water supply, with a control valve, tapped into the column near the top, and it could be discharged through a faucet from the open chamber near the bottom of the column. The faucet discharged into a measuring tank 1 meter square and 0.50 meters deep. Into the open chambers above and below the sand U-tube mercury manometers were tapped for the measurement of pressures.

Five different series of observations were made, using five different sizes and different thicknesses of sand beds. For each sand a series of fixed flow rates was used. The flow rate

was determined by measuring the volume of water discharged during a measured time. Also, for each flow rate, the differences in the heights of the mercury in the upper and lower U-tubes were recorded, and these were then converted by computation into the heights of equivalent water manometers. The observations were then assembled in two tables: the first comprising the four series of experiments on the first four sands, made during October 29 and 30, and November 2, 1855. The second table contained the results of the fifth series made during February 17 and 18, 1856.

In Figure 1 (*b*), is shown the Darcy apparatus with equivalent water manometers instead of mercury U-tubes. The reason that Darcy used mercury U-tubes instead of water manometers must have been that the water heights, some as high as 12 to 14 meters, would have been higher than the ceiling of the laboratory room.

Darcy published no graphs of his results, but I have constructed graphs in Figure 2 of the results of his first and fifth series of experiments in which the total discharge rate Q is plotted as an ordinate against the differences $(h_1 - h_2)$ between the heights above the base of the sand of the upper and lower water manometers. A very good linear relation is shown between the discharge rates and the manometer drops, the slopes of the two curves being different for the two different sands. When the cross-sectional area A of the sand column and the length l, or thickness, of the sand bed

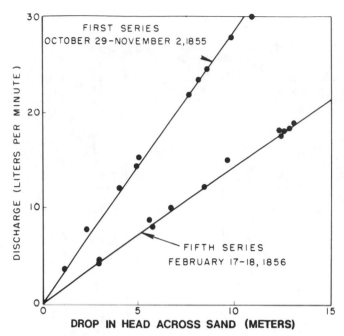

Fig. 2. Graphs compiled from Darcy's tabular data on his expeiments of Oct. 29 to Nov. 2, 1855, and of Feb. 17–18, 1856, showing linear relation between flow rate and differences in heights of equivalent water manometers. [*Hubbert*, 1956, Figure 2.]

were taken into account Darcy's final result was expressed (using present notation) by the equation

$$Q = K(A/l)(h_1 - h_2),$$

or

$$Q/A = q = K(h_1 - h_2)/l. \quad (1)$$

However, since the cross-sectional area of the pipe is uniform,

$$(h_1 - h_2)/l = -(h_2 - h_1)/l = -dh/dl. \quad (2)$$

and

$$q = -K(dh/dl). \quad (3)$$

What Darcy determined experimentally and stated was that, when water flows vertically downward through a bed of sand, the discharge rate Q is directly proportional to the cross-sectional area of the sand normal to the flow direction, to the difference in the heights of water above a common datum in manometers terminated above and below the sand bed, and inversely proportional to the thickness l of the sand. The factor of proportionality, K, he referred to as a "coefficient depending upon the permeability of the sand."

Generalization of Darcy experiment

The relationship expressed by equation (1) soon became known among Darcy's colleagues as "Darcy's law." It is an experimentally determined relationship that can be verified at will so there can be no question regarding its validity, but how general is it? Would it still be true if the flow were in some other direction, say, horizontal or vertically upward? This too can be determined experimentally by means of a moveable apparatus such as that shown in Figure 3. This consists of a rectilinear glass tube of uniform cross-section

closed at both ends and containing a sand-pack between two screens. Two water manometers, connected by flexible tubing, are tapped into the sand at upstream and downstream positions. Inlet and outlet connections are made with flexible tubing whereby water flows into one end of the tube, passes through the sand and discharges through the outlet tube. The flow rate can be controlled by adjustable valves in both the inlet and outlet tubes. The flow-tube may be inclined, with the flow direction making a variable angle θ with the downward vertical direction. The angle θ may be set at any value from 0 to π radians.

With $\theta = 0$, the flow is vertically downward and the results are exactly the same as those obtained by Darcy, namely,

$$q = -Kdh/dl.$$

Now, to test the validity of equation (1) or (3) for flows in directions other than vertically downward, first, with the flow downward and $\theta = 0$, we adjust the flow to a fixed rate q_0 corresponding to which $(h_2 - h_1)$ will have the value Δh_0. Next, with the tube rotated to a fixed angle θ greater than 0, we again adjust the flow rate until

$$\Delta h_\theta = \Delta h_0.$$

Then we measure q_θ and find that it is exactly the same as q_0. We repeat this for horizontal flow when $\theta = \pi/2$ radians, and for vertically upward flow with $\theta = \pi$ radians. Again, in each instance the results are the same as for vertically downward flow, namely, when

$$\Delta h_\theta = \Delta h_0,$$

$$q_\theta = q_0.$$

Hence, for any direction of flow making an angle θ with the direction of gravity,

$$q_\theta = -Kdh/dl. \quad (4)$$

Therefore Darcy's law is valid for the flow in any direction in three-dimensional space.

We can generalize this still further by considering a uniform sand in three-dimensional space the pore space of which is completely filled with water. The water may be either static or in a steady state of flow through the sand. In

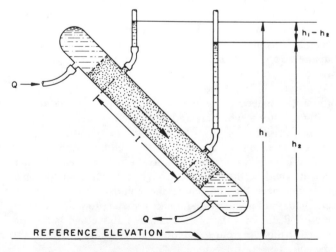

Q ∝ (h₁ - h₂) FOR ALL DIRECTIONS OF FLOW

Fig. 3. Apparatus for verifying Darcy's law for flow in various directions. [*Hubbert*, 1956, Figure 3.]

either case, in a vertical manometer terminated at any given point $P(x, y, z)$ the water will stand at a static height h above the reference level $z = 0$. This will be true for every point in the three-dimensional space. Hence, to each point may be assigned a value $h(x, y, z)$ and the totality of all such values constitutes a scalar field h.

In case the water is not flowing, the heights h of water in manometers terminated at every point will be the same and $h(x, y, z)$ will be constant. If the water is in a state of steady flow through the sand, then, from the Darcy experiment, h will not be constant in space but will decrease in the downstream direction of the flow, and there will be a family of surfaces along each of which h will be constant. Let two of these surfaces have the values h and $h + \Delta h$ and let Δn be their distance of separation along their normal n. Also let Δs be the distance from the surface h to that of $h + \Delta h$ in a direction s making an angle θ with normal n in the direction of increase of h.

According to the Darcy experiment, the rate of flow q_n parallel to the positive-directed normal n will be

$$q_n = -K\Delta h/\Delta n, \qquad (5)$$

and that in direction s will be

$$q_s = -K\Delta h/\Delta s. \qquad (6)$$

But

$$\Delta s = \Delta n/\cos \theta.$$

Therefore

$$-\Delta h/\Delta s = -(\Delta h/\Delta n)\cos \theta, \qquad (7)$$

and

$$q_s = -K(\Delta h/\Delta n)\cos \theta \qquad (8)$$

$$= q_n \cos \theta.$$

When θ is $\dfrac{\pi}{2}$ the direction s is along a surface $h = $ const and

$$\Delta h/\Delta s = 0.$$

This is the relationship of rectangular vector resolution so that we may let $\mathbf{q}$ be the vectorial expression of the total flow rate normal to the equiscalar surfaces $h = $ const. Also, passing to the limit,

$$\lim_{\Delta n \to 0} \Delta h/\Delta n = \text{grad } h,$$

which is a vector in the direction of increase of h along its positive normal, having a magnitude dh/dn. Therefore, in three-dimensional space Darcy's law may be expressed by

$$\mathbf{q} = -K \text{ grad } h. \qquad (9)$$

The components of the flow vector $\mathbf{q}$ in the directions of the rectangular Cartesian axes x, y, and z, are accordingly

$$\left. \begin{array}{l} q_x = -K\partial h/\partial x, \\ q_y = -K\partial h/\partial y, \\ q_z = -k\partial h/\partial z. \end{array} \right\} \qquad (10)$$

Hence, for flow in three-dimensional space, we deal with two fields, a vector field of the flow-vector $\mathbf{q}$, and a scalar field of the manometer height h. At every point in space the flow-vector $\mathbf{q}$ has a particular magnitude and direction. Curves which at every point are tangential to $\mathbf{q}$ constitute the family of flowlines of the flow field. Likewise, at every point there exists a particular value of the manometer height h and through each point there passes a surface on which all values of h are equal. Darcy's law, as expressed by equation (9), gives the manner in which these two fields are mutually related. The flowlines are everywhere perpendicular to the surfaces $h = $ const, with the flow in the direction of decrease of h and proportional to the rate of decline of h in the flow direction.

Equations (1), (3), (4), and (9) are all equivalent expressions of increasing generality of what may be regarded as the primitive form of Darcy's law. The form principally used in ground-water hydrology has been that of equation (3), although the more general form expressed by equation (9) was developed and made use of by *Philipp Forchheimer* [1914] in his comprehensive monograph *Hydraulik*.

MISSTATEMENTS OF DARCY'S LAW

Velocity-potential equation

Despite the importance and simplicity of Darcy's law, especially when expressed in the general form of equation (9), in this primitive form it is still seriously deficient in several important respects. Although the flow of a viscous fluid through the three-dimensional network of channels in porous solids is a dynamical phenomenon involving forces and energies, Darcy's law in its primitive form is a purely kinematic expression involving explicitly only the dimensions of length and time. For example, the dimensions of q are

$$[q] = [(\text{Volume/Area})/\text{Time}] = [(L^3/L^2)/T] = [LT^{-1}]. \quad (11)$$

Those of grad h are

$$[\text{grad } h] = [L/L] = [L^0], \qquad (12)$$

and K, being a derived quantity,

$$K = q/\text{grad } h,$$

has the same dimensions as q,

$$[K] = [q] = [LT^{-1}]. \qquad (13)$$

There is also lacking any explicit expression as to how the fluid properties, the density ρ and dynamic viscosity μ, are involved in the flow, or how the flow rate is affected by the geometrical properties of the porous solid.

Attempts during the last century have been made by many different authors to remove these deficiencies. Unfortunately, these attempts have led to a variety of different expressions, some of which have been mutually contradictory, but all have been called "Darcy's law." These have fallen principally into two groups, one based upon the assumption that the flow-vector $\mathbf{q}$ is derivable from a velocity potential, and the other upon the assumption that the water flows in the direction of decrease of pressure.

The velocity-potential procedure appears to have originated from a theorem in classical hydrodynamics where it was shown that for the irrotational flow of an ideal nonviscous liquid the flow velocity is given by the equation,

$$\mathbf{v} = -\text{grad } \Omega, \qquad (14)$$

where Ω is the velocity potential of the flow field. Assuming this to be true for the Darcy flow through porous solids, Darcy's law in its valid form

$$\mathbf{q} = -K \text{ grad } h \tag{9}$$

has been transformed into

$$\mathbf{q} = -\text{grad } (Kh), \tag{15}$$

where (Kh) would be the velocity potential of the flow field $\mathbf{q}$ analogous to Ω in equation (14). This equation can only be valid provided that

$$\text{grad } (Kh) = K \text{ grad } h. \tag{16}$$

Expanding the left-hand side of equation (16) gives

$$\text{grad } (Kh) = K \text{ grad } h + h \text{ grad } K. \tag{17}$$

Hence, equation (15) can only be equivalent to equation (9) provided that the last term in equation (17)

$$h \text{ grad } K = 0.$$

This would require that in all cases of flow of water through sands or other porous rocks

$$\text{grad } K = 0.$$

and that $K(x, y, z)$ in three-dimensional space be constant. But Darcy's experiments showed that K varies with the permeabilities of the sands through which the flow occurs. In general, in underground space the flow occurs through rocks of widely variable permeabilities in which K is not constant. Therefore, equation (15), which is valid only for the special case of

$$K(x, y, z) = \text{const,}$$

is not equivalent to equation (9) and therefore is not a valid statement of Darcy's law.

Pressure-gradient equation

Let us now consider expressions based upon the assumption that the flow of water through a sand is in the direction from higher to lower pressure. These assume that the water pressure p is a physical analogue of the Darcy manometer height h and lead to equations of the form

$$\mathbf{q} = -K_p \text{ grad } p, \tag{18}$$

in which the factor of proportionality K_p is analogous to K in the Darcy equation although differing from K for the same flow system in both magnitude and dimensions.

According to equation (18) the flowlines should be everywhere perpendicular to the equipressure surfaces with the flow in the direction of decreasing pressure and at a rate proportional to the negative gradient of the pressure. Whether this is true, we shall now investigate.

TRANSITION FROM KINEMATIC TO DYNAMIC EQUATION

The transformation of the Darcy kinematical equation into an equivalent dynamical equation becomes simple after we examine the physical significance of the manometer height h. When a vertical manometer is terminated at a point P of elevation z in the flow system, the water rises to a height h above the reference level $z = 0$. This height is therefore the sum of two parts, the elevation z and the length of the water column $(h - z)$, or

$$h = z + (h - z). \tag{19}$$

The water column will exert a pressure at its base of

$$p = \rho g(h - z), \tag{20}$$

where ρ is the density of the water and g the scalar magnitude of the acceleration, or force per unit mass, of the gravity vector $\mathbf{g}$. This pressure will be in equilibrium with the pressure p at the point P in the field of flow. Then by transposition of equation (20) we obtain

$$(h - z) = p/\rho g,$$

according to which the length $(h - z)$ of the water column becomes a measuring instrument for the water pressure at the terminus of the manometer. Then, substituting $p/\rho g$ for $(h - z)$ in equation (19), we obtain

$$h = z + p/\rho g, \tag{21}$$

which affords an explicit introduction of the fluid pressure p into the Darcy equation.

Experimental demonstration of flow from lower to higher, or from higher to lower pressure

However, before proceeding to a more general treatment, it will be instructive to re-examine the Darcy experiment in the light of equation (21). Consider again the moveable flow tube shown in Figure 3. Let the tube be set, as shown in Figure 3, with the flow direction θ at a fixed angle of about $\pi/4$ radians from the downward vertical. Let z_1 and z_2 be the elevations of the termini at points P_1 and P_2 of the upstream and downstream manometers, and h_1 and h_2 be the corresponding manometer heights. Then, from equation (21), the pressures at P_1 and P_2 will be

$$\left. \begin{array}{l} p_1 = \rho g(h_1 - z_1), \\ p_2 = \rho g(h_2 - z_2). \end{array} \right\} \tag{22}$$

and, from equation (22),

$$p_2 = p_1 + \rho g[(z_1 - z_2) - (h_1 - h_2)]. \tag{23}$$

According to this the length of the water column in the downstream manometer has been increased by the amount $(z_1 - z_2)$ and decreased by $(h_1 - h_2)$ with respect to that of the upstream manometer. Of these two quantities, the first remains fixed and only the second increases as the flow rate is increased.

For brevity, let

$$\Delta z = (z_1 - z_2)$$

and

$$\Delta h = (h_1 - h_2).$$

Then equation (23) becomes simplified to

$$p_2 = p_1 + \rho g(\Delta z - \Delta h). \tag{24}$$

Now, beginning with an initial flow rate of 0, let the flow rate be gradually increased by a succession of small increments. At 0 flow rate

$$\Delta h = 0,$$

and

$$p_2 = p_1 + \rho g \Delta z. \tag{25}$$

In this case, the water is not flowing, yet p_2 is greater than p_1. As the flow rate is increased, Δh increases and the downstream pressure p_2, while still greater than the upstream pressure p_1, steadily decreases. Eventually, as the flow rate is further increased,

$$\Delta h = \Delta z.$$

When that occurs,

$$p_2 = p_1 \tag{26}$$

and the water will be flowing with no pressure difference between the upstream and the downstream points.

For all higher rates of flow,

$$\Delta h > \Delta z,$$

and

$$p_2 < p_1. \tag{27}$$

The flow will then be from higher to lower pressure.

Thus, in this single, simple flow experiment the following relationships can be obtained:

$$\left. \begin{array}{l} (a) \ q = 0; \ \Delta h = 0; \ p_1 < p_2, \\ (b) \ q > 0; \ 0 < \Delta h < \Delta z; \ p_1 < p_2, \\ (c) \ q > 0; \ \Delta h = \Delta z; \ p_1 = p_2, \\ (d) \ q > 0; \ \Delta h > \Delta z; \ p_1 > p_2. \end{array} \right\} \tag{28}$$

Since these results contradict the pressure-gradient equation (18) in just about every possible way, they demonstrate unequivocally the physical invalidity of that equation. It is not an expression of Darcy's law.

What actually does happen physically is this: When the flow rate is 0 and the water in the flow tube is hydrostatic, the equipressure surfaces are horizontal with the pressure increasing downward at a rate

$$\text{grad } p = \rho \, \mathbf{g}. \tag{29}$$

This is the fundamental equation of hydrostatics.

Then, when the flow rate has been increased until

$$\Delta h = \Delta z,$$

the upstream and downstream pressures are equal and the equipressure surfaces are now parallel to the lines of flow. Hence, as the flow rate has been progressively increased, the equipressure surfaces must have rotated from their initial horizontal orientation until they are now parallel to the flowlines, with no decrease or increase of the pressure along the flowlines. Within this interval, for which

$$0 < \Delta h < \Delta z,$$

the flowlines will cross the family of equipressure surfaces obliquely in the direction from lower to higher pressure. Then, when the flow rate has been increased until

$$\Delta h > \Delta z,$$

the equipressure surfaces will have rotated until their inclination from the horizontal is greater than that of the flow-lines. The latter will now intersect the equipressure surfaces obliquely, but in the direction from higher to lower pressure.

In no case, in this particular example, will the flowlines be perpendicular to the equipressure surfaces. This could only occur if the flow direction were either vertically downward or upward.

THE SCALAR FIELDS h, z, AND h_p

As we have seen, in the three-dimensional space of a sand filled with flowing water, we deal with two separate superposed fields, a vector field of the flow-vector $\mathbf{q}$, and a scalar field of the manometer-height h. The coupling between these two fields is expressed by Darcy's law in the form of equation (9), according to which the lines of flow are everywhere orthogonal to the family of equiscalar surfaces, $h = $ const, with the flow in the direction of decreasing h, and at a rate proportional to the negative gradient of h.

The manometer height h at each point is the sum of two parts, the elevation z and the length of the water column supported by the pressure at the terminus of the manometer. Letting h_p represent the length of this water column, then at each point in the field we have three different scalar quantities, h, z, and h_p, each having the dimension of length. These are related by the equation

$$h = z + h_p. \tag{29}$$

Of these quantities, only two are mutually independent, the third being either the sum or difference of the first two. It will be convenient for our purposes to choose h and z as the independent quantities. Then h_p, the dependent quantity, is given by

$$h_p = h - z.$$

We thus have three scalar fields with three different families of equiscalar surfaces. To see how these are related in space, consider two pairs of surfaces, h_0 and $h_0 + \Delta h$, and z_0 and $z_0 + \Delta z$, with

$$\Delta z = \Delta h = \text{const.}$$

The pair of surfaces h_0 and $h_0 + \Delta h$ will be perpendicular to the lines of flow with the latter upstream from the former. The distance of separation between these two surfaces is obtainable from Darcy's law in a finite form,

$$q = -K(\Delta h / \Delta n),$$

or

$$\Delta n = -(K \Delta h)/q. \tag{30}$$

Then, for constant Δh, we see that as the flow rate q approaches 0,

$$\Delta n \to \infty.$$

In order for Δn to become 0, q would have to become infinite, which is physically impossible. Therefore, in a region of uniform sand, for which K would be constant, the distance of separation between the surfaces h_0 and $h_0 + \Delta h$ varies inversely as the local flow rate, but can never be 0. Therefore, the two surfaces can never coincide.

The other pair of surfaces, z_0 and $z_0 + \Delta z$, is simply a pair of horizontal surfaces of elevations z_0 and $z_0 + \Delta z$ with a constant distance of separation, Δz.

Except for the case when the flow direction is either

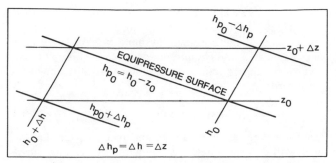

Fig. 4. Cross section of $\Delta z \Delta h$-solenoid showing equipressure surface h_p = const.

vertically upward or downward, these two pairs of surfaces will be nonparallel and will intersect one another forming a curvilinear prism whose bottom and top surfaces are the planes z_0 and $z_0 + \Delta z$, and whose lateral surfaces are formed by the surfaces h_0 and $h_0 + \Delta h$. This prism, which we shall call a $\Delta h \Delta z$-solenoid, cannot contract along its axis to a zero cross-sectional area, but must continue to an impermeable boundary of the flow field, or else form a closed loop. If, in the entire field the families of surfaces h = const and z = const be drawn with constant intervals Δh and Δz, then the entire space would be divided into a family of $\Delta h \Delta z$-solenoids.

On a vertical plane perpendicular to the h- and z-surfaces the cross section of the $\Delta h \Delta z$-solenoid, as shown in Figure 4, will be a curvilinear parallelogram. On this parallelogram, let A be the point of intersection of the lines h_0 and z_0. Then, traversing the periphery in the direction in which an increase of z precedes that of h, let succeeding points of intersection be B, C, and D. At each of these points the value of h_p will be given by the difference between the corresponding values of h and z. Then, letting

$$\Delta h_p = \Delta h = \Delta z, \qquad (31)$$

the values of h_p at the successive points A, B, C, and D will be:

$$\left. \begin{array}{l} (A) \ h_{p0} = h_0 - z_0, \\ (B) \ h_p = h_{p0} - \Delta h_p, \\ (C) \ h_p = h_{p0}, \\ (D) \ h_p = h_{p0} + \Delta h_p. \end{array} \right\} \qquad (32)$$

It is thus seen that the family of surfaces Δh_p = const, with the constant interval

$$\Delta h_p = \Delta h = \Delta z,$$

coincides with the diagonals of the $\Delta h \Delta z$-solenoids along which Δh and Δz both increase or decrease together. Since h_p at every point is proportional to the fluid pressure at that point, the family of surfaces h_p = const, is also a family of equipressure surfaces.

ENERGIES AND FORCES

Energy per unit mass

For a more general treatment of the flow of water through sand, we make use of a fundamental principle of mechanics first formulated in the late 18th century by the French-Italian

physicist, Joseph Louis Lagrange. According to this principle, a mechanical system of whatever complexity will be in a state of stable equilibrium with respect to local displacements if its kinetic energy is zero and its potential energy a minimum. If the kinetic energy is zero and the potential energy is not a minimum, then a force will act upon the system tending to drive it in the direction of decrease of potential energy.

For the system with which we are concerned, water-filled sand in three-dimensional space, let us consider a unit mass of water at a given point P in the field. This will be either at rest or in motion. If at rest, its kinetic energy will be zero, but even if it is in motion the velocity will be so small that the kinetic energy will be almost infinitesimal with respect to the potential energy. Therefore, for present purposes, only the potential energy per unit mass at a given point needs to be considered. This quantity, as defined by *Hubbert* [1940, p. 797], is the *potential* Φ of the water with respect to its environment. It represents the work required to transport a unit mass of water from a reference **elevation** and pressure,

$$\left. \begin{array}{l} z = 0, \\ p = 0, \end{array} \right\} \qquad (33)$$

to the elevation z and the pressure p at the point considered. For the pressure p it is convenient to use the gauge pressure, defined as the absolute pressure minus that of the local atmosphere. At atmospheric pressure, the gauge pressure p will be zero.

The work Φ required to transport a unit mass of water from the reference elevation and pressure, ($z = 0$; $p = 0$), to the final elevation and pressure, (z, p), will be Φ_{gr} and Φ_p, the work against gravity and against pressure respectively. Hence,

$$\Phi = \Phi_{gr} + \Phi_p. \qquad (34)$$

The work against gravity will be that required to lift a unit mass a height z, or

$$\Phi_{gr} = gz. \qquad (35)$$

The work against pressure will be that required to inject a unit mass of water from an outside pressure of $p = 0$ against the pressure p. This would be

$$\Phi_p = vp \qquad (36)$$
$$= (1/\rho)p,$$

where v is the specific volume, or volume per unit mass, of water. Hence,

$$\Phi = gz + p/\rho \qquad (37)$$

is the potential of the water at a point of elevation z and a pressure p. But, since

$$p = \rho g h_p,$$
$$p/\rho = g h_p,$$

then

$$\Phi = gz + g h_p = gh. \qquad (38)$$

This would represent the work required to lift a unit mass of water at atmospheric pressure to the elevation h of the water in the manometer and then bring it down the tube with zero work to elevation z and the pressure p at the terminus of the tube.

What we see now is that, since

$$\Phi = gh,$$

the manometer height h becomes a measure of the potential of the water at the point at which the manometer is terminated. If the water is not flowing, $h(x, y, z)$ is constant and a static body of water represents an equipotential region. If the water is flowing, then from Darcy's law,

$$\mathbf{q} = -K \operatorname{grad} h.$$

but since

$$h = \Phi/g,$$

and

$$\operatorname{grad} h = (1/g) \operatorname{grad} \Phi,$$

Darcy's law becomes

$$\mathbf{q} = -(K/g) \operatorname{grad} \Phi \qquad (39)$$

$$= -(K/g)g \operatorname{grad} h.$$

If we let

$$\sigma = (K/g)$$

be the new factor of proportionality, we obtain

$$\mathbf{q} = -\sigma(g \operatorname{grad} h), \qquad (40)$$

$$= -\sigma \operatorname{grad} \Phi,$$

where σ is the volume conductivity of the system.

Forces per unit mass

According to equation (40) the lines of flow are orthogonal with the family of equipotential surfaces $\Phi = $ const. To determine the impelling force which acts upon a unit mass of the water at a given point P_1, let Φ be the equipotential surface passing through that point and $\Phi + \Delta\Phi$ be that passing through a second point P_2 a small distance Δn upstream from P_1. Also let $\mathbf{E}$ be the force per unit mass acting on the water at P_1. The work required to move the mass from P_1 to P_2 will be

$$-E\Delta n = \Delta\Phi,$$

or

$$E = -\Delta\Phi/\Delta n, \qquad (41)$$

where E is the scalar magnitude of $\mathbf{E}$. Then, passing to the limit,

$$\lim_{\Delta n \to 0} \Delta\Phi/\Delta n = \operatorname{grad} \Phi,$$

which is a vector normal to the surface $\Phi = $ const and in the direction of increasing Φ. Accordingly, the impelling force per unit mass acting upon the water at P_1 will be

$$\mathbf{E} = -\operatorname{grad} \Phi \qquad (42)$$

and will be directed downstream. Substituting this into equation (40) then gives Darcy's law in the form,

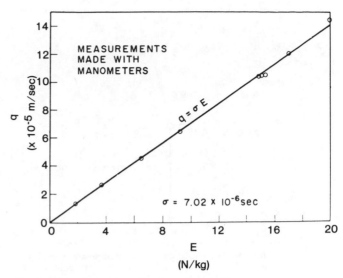

Fig. 5.   Experimental verification of $\mathbf{q} = \sigma\mathbf{E}$.

$$\mathbf{q} = \sigma\mathbf{E}, \qquad (43)$$

according to which the flow rate at every point is proportional to, and in the direction of, the driving force per unit of mass acting upon the fluid at that point. An experimental verification of equation (43) is shown in Figure 5.

Now, since

$$\Phi = gz + p/\rho,$$

each term of which is an energy per unit mass, a similar analysis applied to each of the scalar fields, gz and p/ρ, gives the results,

$$\mathbf{E_{gr}} = -\operatorname{grad}(gz) = -g\operatorname{grad} z = \mathbf{g}, \qquad (44)$$

and

$$\mathbf{E_p} = -\operatorname{grad}(p/\rho) = -(1/\rho)\operatorname{grad} p. \qquad (45)$$

Each of these is directed perpendicularly to its equiscalar surface and in the direction of decrease of the scalar quantity. The vector $\mathbf{E}$, therefore, is the vector sum,

$$\mathbf{E} = \mathbf{g} - (1/\rho)\operatorname{grad} p. \qquad (46)$$

In Figure 6 is shown the family of flowlines and the corresponding family of equipotential surfaces, $\Phi = $ const (and $h = $ const). There is also shown the three force vectors, $\mathbf{g}$, $-(1/\rho)\operatorname{grad} p$, and $\mathbf{E}$ which act upon a unit mass of fluid at their common point of origin. The equipressure surface, $p = $ const, is perpendicular to the pressure vector. There is also shown the relation between the flow vector $\mathbf{q}$ and the impelling force $\mathbf{E}$ per unit mass of the fluid.

Of these three force vectors, only two are independent, the third being either the sum or difference of the other two. For most purposes, it is convenient to choose $\mathbf{g}$ and $\mathbf{E}$ as the independent vectors, since $\mathbf{g}$ is known already and $\mathbf{E}$ is determinable by means of the equation,

$$\mathbf{E} = -g\operatorname{grad} h.$$

Then

$$\mathbf{E_p} = \mathbf{E} - \mathbf{g} \qquad (47)$$

$$= (-\mathbf{g}) + \mathbf{E}$$

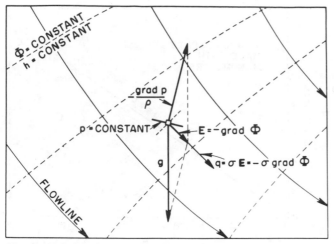

Fig. 6. Relations between flowlines, equipotential surfaces, forces acting upon the fluid, and the rate of flow of water through a sand.

where $-\mathbf{g}$ is a vector of magnitude g directed vertically upward.

Application to the flow experiment of Figure 3

Let us return now to the flow experiment shown in Figure 3. With the flow tube set at a fixed angle of about $\pi/4$ radians to the downward vertical, and beginning with a zero flow rate, we increase the rate and hence the difference of manometer heights $(h_1 - h_2)$ by successive small increments. For any given value of $(h_1 - h_2)$,

$$\mathbf{E} = -g \operatorname{grad} h = -g(h_2 - h_1)/l, \qquad (48)$$

and will be in the direction of the axis of the tube. Hence, at zero flow rate $\mathbf{E}$ will be zero. As the flow rate is increased it will have a fixed direction but an increasing magnitude.

Then, since both $\mathbf{g}$ and $\mathbf{E}$ are known, the force due to the pressure gradient is given by equations (45) and (47),

$$\mathbf{E}_p = -(1/\rho) \operatorname{grad} p = (-\mathbf{g}) + \mathbf{E}. \qquad (49)$$

Thus, if the vector $-\mathbf{g}$ is directed vertically upward from a point on the axis of the flow tube, and the vector $\mathbf{E}$ is placed with its origin at the terminus of $-\mathbf{g}$, the vector $-(1/\rho) \operatorname{grad} p$ will have its origin at the same point as $-\mathbf{g}$ and its terminus at the terminus of $\mathbf{E}$, as shown in Figure 7. Since $\mathbf{E}$ is parallel to the axis of the flow tube, the vector $-(1/\rho) \operatorname{grad} p$ will have a fixed origin, but as $\mathbf{E}$ increases, its terminus will move along a line passing through the terminus of $-\mathbf{g}$ and parallel to the flow direction.

When the flow rate is zero,

$$\mathbf{E} = 0,$$

and the vector $-(1/\rho) \operatorname{grad} p$ will coincide with the vector $-\mathbf{g}$. Hence,

$$(1/\rho) \operatorname{grad} p = \mathbf{g}$$

or

$$\operatorname{grad} p = \rho\mathbf{g}, \qquad (50)$$

which is the fundamental equation of hydrostatics.

Since the equipressure surfaces are perpendicular to the vector $-(1/\rho) \operatorname{grad} p$, the angle of inclination δ of the equipressure surfaces from the horizontal will be the same as

the angle of $-(1/\rho) \operatorname{grad} p$ from the vertical. Hence, when the flow rate is zero, the vector $-(1/\rho) \operatorname{grad} p$ is vertical and the equipressure surfaces are horizontal. As the flow rate is increased, $\mathbf{E}$ increases and the inclination δ of the equipressure surfaces increases. When

$$E = g \cos \theta,$$

the angle of inclination

$$\delta = (\pi/2 - \theta)$$

and the equipressure surfaces will be parallel to the flow lines. For

$$E < g \cos \theta, \; \delta < (\pi/2 - \theta),$$

and the flow will be across the equipressure surfaces from lower to higher pressure. For

$$E > g \cos \theta, \; \delta > (\pi/2 - \theta),$$

and the flow will traverse the equipressure surfaces from higher to lower pressure.

Limitations of the potential Φ

Of the two fields, the scalar field Φ and the vector field $\mathbf{E}$, the field $\mathbf{E}$ is the more general because, regardless of the nature of the fluid, at any given point the forces per unit mass exist and satisfy the equation

$$\mathbf{E} = \mathbf{g} - (1/\rho) \operatorname{grad} p.$$

However, for some important cases, the potential Φ is indeterminate or nonexistent. In order for the field of force to have a potential it is necessary that the work done in transmitting a unit mass from a starting point P_0 in the field to a final point P_1 be independent of the path along which the mass is transported. Thus, if W_1 is the work required to transport unit mass from P_0 to P_1 along path s_1 and W_2 that along any other path s_2, then if

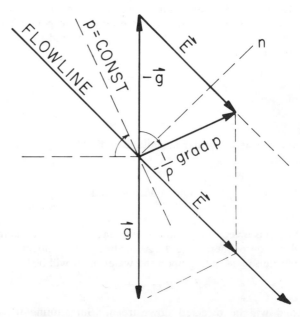

Fig. 7. Pressure vector, $-(1/\rho) \operatorname{grad} p$, as function of $\mathbf{E}$ and $\mathbf{g}$.

$$W_2 = W_1 = W,$$

a definite potential Φ at P_1 exists and is given by

$$\Phi_1 = \Phi_0 + W. \tag{51}$$

In that case, the work done in transporting the mass from P_0 and P_1 along path s_1 would be W_1 and by returning from P_1 and P_0 by path s_2 would be $- W_2$. Then the work around the closed path $s_1 + s_2$ would be

$$W = W_1 - W_2 = 0. \tag{52}$$

However, if

$$W_2 \neq W_1$$

the work around the closed path would be

$$W = W_1 - W_2 \neq 0. \tag{53}$$

Hence, the necessary and sufficient condition for a field of force to have a potential is for the line integral

$$\oint E_s ds = 0, \tag{54}$$

where E_s is the component of $\mathbf{E}$ parallel to the path element ds.

Applying this criterion to the vector

$$\mathbf{E} = \mathbf{g} - (1/\rho)\,\text{grad}\,p,$$

$$\oint E_s ds = \oint g_s ds - \oint (1/\rho)(\partial p/\partial s)ds \tag{55}$$

$$= \oint g dz - \oint (1/\rho)dp.$$

Of the two right-hand terms in equation (55),

$$\oint g dz = 0$$

is a fundamental property of the gravity field. This leaves us with the question of under what conditions is

$$\oint (1/\rho)dp = 0 \text{ ?}$$

One obvious condition would be for the density of the fluid to be constant, which is closely approximated by water or other homogeneous liquids under the pressures of present interest. In that case,

$$\oint (1/\rho)dp = (1/\rho)\oint dp = 0,$$

and the potential,

$$\Phi = gz + p/\rho,$$

exists.

If the density is not constant but is a function of pressure only, such as that of a gas under isothermal or adiabatic conditions, then the surfaces of equal density coincide with the surfaces of equal pressure and again

$$\oint (1/\rho)dp = 0.$$

In this case the potential would be

$$\Phi = gz + \int_0^p (1/\rho)dp, \tag{56}$$

which would be valid for both homogeneous liquids and gases.

The cases for which a potential does not exist are those for which the fluid density is not constant, and the surfaces of equal density are not parallel to those of equal pressure. This can arise from temperature differences, causing thermal convection, or in the case of ground water, with density differences caused by variable salinity.

For our present purposes we shall assume that the fluids of interest either have very nearly constant densities or, if gases, that the density is a function of the pressure only. For either of these conditions the potential is given by equation (56).

Analysis of the factor σ

In equation (43), the factor σ is the factor of proportionality between the flow vector $\mathbf{q}$ and the impelling force per unit mass $\mathbf{E}$. Accordingly the dimension of σ will be

$$[\sigma] = [q/E] = [LT^{-1}/LT^{-2}] = [T]. \tag{57}$$

The factor σ is a lumped parameter composed of all the remaining physical factors affecting the flow rate not previously considered. These represent the mechanical properties of the fluid, and the geometrical properties of the porous solid. The mechanical properties of the fluid which could affect the flow rate would be the dynamic viscosity μ and the density ρ, or their combination, the kinematic viscosity ν, defined by

$$\nu \equiv \mu/\rho, \tag{58}$$

which has the dimensions

$$[\nu] = [\mu/\rho] = [ML^{-1}T^{-1}/ML^{-3}] = [L^2T^{-1}]. \tag{59}$$

Obviously, for the same sand and the same force $\mathbf{E}$, a fluid of higher viscosity would flow more slowly than one of lower viscosity.

The geometrical properties of the sand that affect the flow rate are two, the size scale of the grain or pore structure, and the geometrical shape of the pore system. The size scale may be represented by a characteristic length of grain or pore structure. For our purposes, the mean grain diameter, d, of the sand would be a suitable choice. This has the dimension

$$[d] = [L]. \tag{60}$$

The second geometrical factor is that of shape. Bodies that are geometrically similar have corresponding angles that are equal. We may accordingly represent the shape factor by an undefined number N of dimensions

$$[N] = [L/L] = [L^0]. \tag{61}$$

The factor σ must be composed of the combined factors N, d, and ν, the last two raised to unknown powers a and b, respectively, whose combined dimensions must be the same as those of σ. Hence

$$[Nd^a\nu^b] = [\sigma] = [T] \tag{62}$$

or

$$[L^0 L^a(L^2T^{-1})^b] = [T]. \tag{63}$$

Equating the exponents of T in the left and right terms of equation (63) gives

$$-b = 1, \text{ or } b = -1. \tag{64}$$

Likewise, for L,

$$a + 2b = a - 2 = 0, \text{ or } a = 2. \tag{65}$$

Therefore,

$$\sigma = (Nd^2)/\nu = (Nd^2)(\rho/\mu). \qquad (66)$$

With these substitutions, Darcy's law may be expressed in any of the following equivalent forms:

$$\mathbf{q} = (Nd^2)(\rho/\mu)\mathbf{E}, \qquad (67)$$

$$= (Nd^2)(\rho/\mu)(-\operatorname{grad} \Phi), \qquad (68)$$

$$= (Nd^2)(\rho/\mu)(-g \operatorname{grad} h). \qquad (69)$$

Each of these involves the geometrical property of the sand (Nd^2), the mechanical properties of the fluid (ρ/μ), and the impelling force per unit mass. The only undefined quantity is the shape factor N whose value is obtainable from any of the equations (67) to (69) when all the other quantities are known. For a series of random-packed sands of uniform grain size the average value of N has been found to be approximately 6.0×10^{-4}. For other shapes, the values of N would be somewhat different.

For most purposes, it is convenient to represent the combined geometric properties by

$$(Nd^2) \equiv k \qquad (70)$$

where k with dimension $[L^2]$ is defined as the *permeability* of the solid.

PROPERTIES OF THE COMBINED POTENTIAL AND FLOW FIELDS

Before proceeding to the consideration of oil and gas in a water-rock environment, a few summary statements concerning the combined flow and potential fields in a water-filled porous space are in order.

The volume of water flowing out of a space enclosed by a fixed surface during a given time is equal to that flowing into the space. As a consequence, in a flow system in which the porous solid is rigid, the potential can not have either a maximum or a minimum. Were a maximum or a minimum to exist it would be enclosed by equipotential surfaces that were either lower or higher than that of the enclosed region, and the water would be flowing only out of or into such a region.

Along an impermeable boundary to a flow field, except at stagnant points where the velocity is zero, the normal component of the flow is zero and the flowlines are tangent to the boundary. Upon such a boundary, the equipotential surfaces must terminate perpendicularly.

The boundary of an open body of water, such as a lake or reservoir, will be an equipotential surface. Therefore the flowlines entering or leaving such a body must be perpendicular to the boundary.

In a continuously permeable space filled with water of constant density, it is impossible to have the water flowing in part of the space and stagnant in an adjacent part. In the flowing part, along the mutual interface, the potential would increase or decrease, whereas in the stagnant part the potential would be constant. This would produce potential gradients or discontinuities across the boundary without a corresponding flow normal to the boundary.

Refraction of flowlines

Let region 1, filled with a uniform sand of conductivity σ_1, be adjacent to a region 2, of conductivity σ_2, with a plane

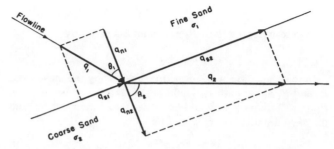

Fig. 8.   Refraction of flowline at interface of two sands of different permeabilities. [*Hubbert*, 1953, Figure 9.]

interface between the two regions. Let water flow obliquely across this interface from region 1 into region 2. Let θ_1 be the angle between the flowlines in region 1 and the normal to the interface and θ_2 be the corresponding angle in region 2, as shown in Figure 8.

Across the interface at adjacent points the potential Φ_1 in region 1 will be the same as Φ_2 in region 2. Therefore, along the interface

$$(\partial\Phi/\partial s)_1 = (\partial\Phi/\partial s)_2, \qquad (71)$$

and the corresponding tangential components of flow will be

$$\left.\begin{array}{l} q_{s1} = -\sigma_1(\partial\Phi/\partial s), \\ q_{s2} = -\sigma_2(\partial\Phi/\partial s). \end{array}\right\} \qquad (72)$$

The normal components of flow will be

$$q_{n1} = q_{n2}. \qquad (73)$$

Then

$$\left.\begin{array}{l} \tan\theta_1 = q_{s1}/q_{n1}, \\ \tan\theta_2 = q_{s2}/q_{n2}, \end{array}\right\} \qquad (74)$$

and

$$\left.\begin{array}{l} \tan\theta_2/\tan\theta_1 = q_{s2}/q_{s1}, \\ \qquad\qquad = \sigma_2/\sigma_1, \\ \qquad\qquad = k_2/k_1. \end{array}\right\} \qquad (75)$$

The flowlines will accordingly be refracted as they cross the interface, those in the region of higher conductivity having a larger angle θ than those in the region of lower conductivity. If the flow be obliquely across a stratum of uniform coarse sand embedded between two regions of uniform fine sand, or silt, the conductivity in the coarse stratum would be much larger than that in the boundary regions. Consequently, in the coarse stratum, the flowlines would be nearly parallel and the equipotential surfaces nearly perpendicular to its boundaries. The converse would occur for the flow across a stratum of fine sand between two regions of coarse sand.

Both of these effects are shown experimentally in Figure 9, (*a*) and (*b*).

APPLICATION TO MIGRATION AND ENTRAPMENT OF OIL AND GAS

Geologic background

The foregoing analysis affords an essential theoretical basis for the analysis of the mechanics of migration and

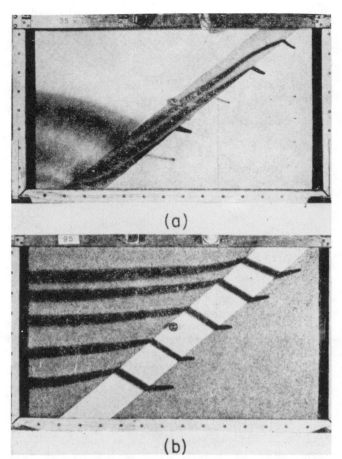

Fig. 9. Experiments on refraction of flowlines. Front of box is Plexiglas and flowlines are marked by injections of dye in sand. Flow is from right to left. (a) Thin bed of high-permeability sand between low-permeability sands. (b) Thin bed of low-permeability sand between high-permeability sands. [*Hubbert*, 1953, Figure 10.]

accumulation of oil and gas in underground space. As to their modes of occurrence, oil and gas at present are found as concentrations occupying the pore volumes of coarse-textured rocks in limited regions of underground space within or adjacent to basins of sedimentary rocks.

In petroleum geology, if a well is drilled at any point, it commonly will penetrate various thicknesses of sedimentary rocks—sandstones, shales or mudstones, limestones, and evaporates such as rock salt and gypsum. Eventually, if drilled deep enough, the well will reach the bottom of the sediments and will encounter the underlying older, nonporous crystalline rocks which are commonly known as the *basement complex*, or the "basement." The upper surface of the basement complex is a continuous world-wide surface. In certain large regions—a large part of Africa, most of the eastern half of Canada, much of Scandinavia, and many mountainous areas—the sedimentary cover is either very thin or else absent altogether. In these regions the surface of the basement rocks coincides approximately with the surface of the ground. In other regions, the top of the basement is depressed and the depressions are filled with younger sedimentary rocks having thicknesses ranging from zero at the edges to a maximum in their interiors. Commonly, this maximum thickness does not exceed 4 to 5 kilometers, but in a few cases it has been found to be as great as 10 to 15 kilometers.

Unmetamorphosed sedimentary rocks are porous, with the pore volume ranging usually between 10 and 30 percent of the total volume. Beneath shallow depths of a few meters or tens of meters beneath the earth's surface the pore space of the sedimentary rocks is filled with water, except where the water is displaced by oil or gas. This water extends to depths below which the porosity becomes zero. Oil and natural gas, and also coal, are found in the sedimentary rocks. They are derived from plants and animals which lived at the time the sediments were being deposited. They became buried in the accumulating sediments in an oxygen-deficient environment and have subsequently become transformed chemically into the present fossil fuels.

On land, the topographic surface of sedimentary rock outcrops varies widely in elevation from mountains to sea level. Consequently the potentials of the water in these rocks must vary widely, with the result that, except in the cases of static bodies of dense brines, much of the body of ground water is in a state of flow. In fine-textured rocks such as silts or clays the permeability is commonly orders of magnitude less than in sandstones. As a consequence, although water may be leaking into or out of a regional sandstone from overlying or underlying shales, most of the flow occurs in the sandstones or other comparably permeable coarse-textured rocks. In a stratum of sandstone of regional extent, along which water is flowing, the flow lines will be essentially parallel, and the equipotential surfaces h = const perpendicular, to such a stratum.

As evidence of the degree of dispersion of the oil prior to its having been concentrated into present oil accumulations, suppose that the oil initially contained in present reservoirs in the U.S. Lower-48 states and adjacent continental shelves were to be returned and uniformly distributed in the shales from which it came originally. According to Cram (1971, v. 1, p. 5), the volume of potentially oil-bearing sediments in this area is about $13 \times 10^{15} \text{m}^3$.

Assuming that the shales comprise 80 percent of the sedimentary rocks [*Clarke*, 1924, p. 34] with an average porosity of 20 percent, then the pore volume of the shales would be about $2 \times 10^{15} \text{m}^3$. The oil originally present in the reservoir rocks is estimated to have been about 425×10^9 bbl, or $68 \times 10^9 \text{m}^3$. Assuming that the natural gas under subsurface conditions had a volume of about 3 times that of the oil, then the volume of oil and gas combined would have been about $300 \times 10^9 \text{m}^3$. The fraction of the total,

$$(300 \times 10^9 \text{m}^3)/(2 \times 10^{15} \text{m}^3) = 1.5 \times 10^{-4}.$$

It appears, therefore, that the oil and gas in their initial state of dispersion could only have occupied a few parts in 10,000 of the total pore volume of the shale. The rest was water.

Expulsion of oil and gas from source rock to reservoir rock

As remarked before, two fundamental differences between the source rocks (shales) and the reservoir rocks (sandstones) are that the shales were organic-rich and the sandstones organic-lean; and the shales are very fine grained and of low permeability, whereas the sandstones are coarse grained and of high permeability. The expulsion of oil and gas from the shales to the sandstones involves two separate physical factors, the compactibility of the clays of which the shales are composed, and capillary forces in the rock-water-hydrocarbon system.

Regarding compactibility, sediments are deposited under surface pressures and temperatures. Gradually they become buried under an increasing overburden of younger sediments and are also depressed to greater depths and higher temperatures. This causes the clays to compact, reducing the pore volume and expelling a part of the contained water and associated oil and gas. If there is a regional stratum of sandstone embedded between thick shales, the water with its entrained liquid and gaseous hydrocarbons will be expelled from both below and above into the sandstone stratum.

For an idea of the magnitude of this process, in the young Tertiary sediments of the Texas-Louisiana Gulf Coastal region, the clays near the surface have a bulk density of clay plus contained water of about 1.9 kg/dm^3 with a porosity of about 50 percent. At a depth of about 5 kilometers the shales have become compacted to about one-half their original thickness, with a bulk density of about 2.5 kg/dm^3 and a porosity of only about 12 percent. Hence, about 75 percent of the initial water has been expelled.

The capillary effect results from the fact that nearly all rock minerals are hydrophilic, or oleophobic. This means that in sedimentary rocks, the capillary interface between water and oil within the pore spaces is concave toward the oil, similar to that of water and air in a capillary tube. According to an equation derived by the French mathematician *Pierre Simon Laplace* [1806], the difference of the pressure on opposite sides of a capillary interface between two nonmiscible fluids is given by

$$p_c = \gamma[(1/r_1) + (1/r_2)], \qquad (76)$$

where γ is the surface tension of the interface and r_1 and r_2 are the principal radii of curvature of the capillary surface. The highest pressure will be on the side having the smallest radius of curvature.

If a small volume of oil should be injected into a water-filled sand, because the sand is preferentially water-wet with respect to the oil, the capillary interfaces will be concave toward the oil, and the pressure inside the oil will be greater than that of the surrounding water by the amount of the capillary pressure p_c. Because of this additional capillary pressure, the oil will have an incremental capillary potential

$$\Phi_c = p_c/\rho_{oil}. \qquad (77)$$

The oil would accordingly assume a configuration such as to minimize Φ_c. That would require that

$$1/r_1 + 1/r_2 = \text{minimum},$$

or that the oil-water interfaces must occupy the largest pore spaces available.

For the oil-water system in porous rocks [*Hubbert*, 1953, p. 1975–1979], the minimum capillary pressure at a given point is given approximately by

$$p_c = (C \gamma \cos \theta)/d, \qquad (78)$$

where γ is the oil-water surface tension, θ the acute angle of contact of the capillary surface with the rock surface, d the mean grain diameter of the rock, and C a dimensionless factor of proportionality.

If the porous rock is statistically uniform, then

$$d(x, y, z) = \text{const}.$$

But if the rock is nonuniform, and d varies with position,

there will be a capillary force acting upon any enclosed volume of oil, surrounded by water, tending to drive it in the direction of increase of d. The magnitude of this force per unit of mass of the oil will be

$$E_c = - \text{ grad } \Phi_c \qquad (79)$$
$$= - (1/\rho_{oil}) \text{ grad } p_c.$$

Then, from equation (78) in conjunction with equation (79),

$$E_c = [(C \gamma \cos \theta)/(\rho_{oil}d^2)] \text{ grad } d. \qquad (80)$$

For the approximate magnitudes of the quantities in equations (78) and (80), it has been found experimentally that, for the oil-water-rock system,

$$\gamma \cos \theta \cong 25 \times 10^{-3} \, N/m,$$

and

$$C \cong 16,$$

or

$$C \gamma \cos \theta \cong 400 \times 10^{-3} \, N/m. \qquad (81)$$

Various sedimentary rocks (Pettijohn, 1949, p. 13) have the following ranges of grain diameter:

clays: $< 3.91 \, \mu m,$

silts: $(3.91 \text{ to } 62.5) \, \mu m,$

sands: $(62.5 \text{ to } 2\,000) \, \mu m.$

Then, from equation (78) the capillary pressure of water against oil in rocks of these grain sizes would be:

clays: $> 10^5 \, Pa,$

silts: $(100 \text{ to } 6.4) \times 10^3 \, Pa,$

sands: $(6.4 \times 10^3 \text{ to } 2 \times 10^2) \, Pa.$

Hence, as shown in Figure 10, if a slug of oil should extend across a clay-sand interface, within the clay it would be subjected to a pressure of 10^5 Pa or more, whereas in the sand the pressure would be only (6 400 to 200) Pa. Accordingly, the oil would be forcefully expelled from the clay into the sand. It could only be driven back into the clay by a pressure of 10^5 Pa or more. As a consequence of this difference of capillary pressures, oil in the fine-textured source rocks tends to be driven into the coarse-textured reservoir rocks. The clay- or shale-sand interface accordingly acts toward oil like a one-way valve. The oil can flow from the shale into the sand, but not from the sand into the shale. Water, on the other hand, can cross this boundary with equal facility in either direction.

MIGRATION AND ENTRAPMENT IN RESERVOIR ROCKS

We now direct our attention to the mechanical forces and energies that cause the initially dispersed oil and gas, after these fluids have been expelled into the reservoir rocks, to become concentrated into the restricted spaces of these rocks. For purposes of analysis, we shall consider a regional sandstone stratum such as that depicted in Figure 11, through which water is flowing. Although water will be leaking into and out of this formation, the principal flow will be parallel to the bedding with the equipotential surfaces, gh = constant, perpendicular to the formation boundaries.

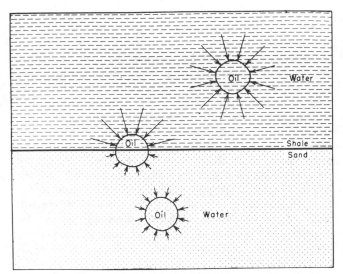

Fig. 10. Diagram showing how capillary pressure of water against oil in preferentially water-wet environment facilitates passage of oil globules from fine- to coarse-textured rocks. [*Hubbert*, 1953, Figure 14.]

Forces per unit mass acting upon water, oil, and gas

Now, consider the forces per unit mass that would act upon elementary volumes of oil or gas injected into the sandstone from the underlying shale. These forces, as in the case of water, will be gravity plus the force due to the negative gradient of the pressure. The pressure in the oil or gas will be

$$\left.\begin{array}{l} p_o = p_w + p_{co}, \\ p_g = p_w + p_{cg}, \end{array}\right\} \qquad (82)$$

where the subscripts w, o, and g signify water, oil, and gas, respectively. But, as we have shown previously the capillary pressures in the sand-water environment, while not zero, are so small that they may be neglected. In that case, the pressure common to all three fluids will be the water pressure p_w, from which we may drop the subscript and use simply p.

With this simplification, the forces per unit mass that would act upon an elementary volume of water, oil, or gas, respectively, at a given point would be

$$\left.\begin{array}{l} \mathbf{E_w} = \mathbf{g} - (1/\rho_w)\ \mathrm{grad}\ p, \\ \mathbf{E_o} = \mathbf{g} - (1/\rho_o)\ \mathrm{grad}\ p, \\ \mathbf{E_g} = \mathbf{g} - (1/\rho_g)\ \mathrm{grad}\ p. \end{array}\right\} \qquad (83)$$

In each of these cases, each fluid would be acted upon by the same gravity vector $\mathbf{g}$ and by pressure forces each having the same direction, that of $-$ grad p. The magnitudes of the pressure forces will be different, however, because of the factor $1/\rho$. This factor increases as ρ decreases. Consequently, the pressure-gradient force acting upon oil will be greater than that upon water, and that upon gas will be the greatest of all.

The vector diagram for equations (83) is shown in Figure 12. What is most significant is that, if the water is flowing, the forces that would act upon water, oil, or gas, if placed at the same point, all have different magnitudes and divergent directions. If the water were static, then $\mathbf{E_w}$ would be zero and both $\mathbf{E_o}$ and $\mathbf{E_g}$ would be directed vertically upward. Under these conditions elements of both oil and gas would tend to migrate vertically upward to the upper boundary of the sandstone stratum, and then updip along this to the highest structural position where accumulations would occur. A trap under these conditions, for either oil or gas, or both, would be the same namely, a space completely enclosed jointly by a downwardly concave impermeable surface and a horizontal surface. Within this trap gas, oil, and water would occur in horizontal stratification in the downward order of increasing densities. This, of course, is the classical trap of the anticlinal theory.

Beginning with this hydrostatic state, let the water flow rate in the downdip direction be increased by successive small increments. From Figure 12, it will be seen that for each increment of flow rate the water vector $\mathbf{E_w}$ will increase and the oil and gas vectors will be deflected further from the vertical in the direction of the flow, with the deflection of $\mathbf{E_o}$ greater than that of $\mathbf{E_g}$. Eventually, as $\mathbf{E_w}$ is increased, a state will be reached, as is illustrated in Figure 13, for which the deflection of $\mathbf{E_o}$ will be greater than that of the normal to the bedding of the sandstone, while that of $\mathbf{E_g}$ will still be less than that of the normal. For the range of flow rates for which this occurs, gas will migrate upward to the upper surface of

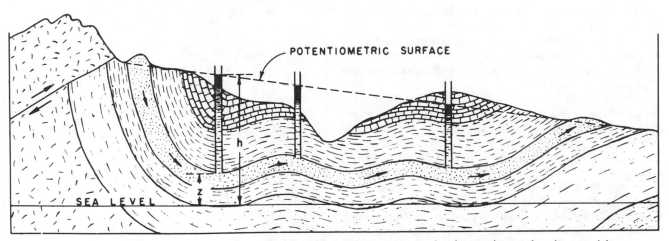

Fig. 11. Regional flow of water through sand from higher to lower outcrop, showing continuous drop in potential. [*Hubbert*, 1953, Figure 11.]

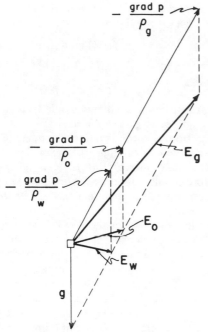

Fig. 12. Force vectors **E** at the same point in water-filled space acting upon water, oil, and gas.

the sandstone and then continue updip in the direction opposite to that of the flow of the water. Oil at the same time will migrate in the direction of E_o to the upper surface of the sandstone, and then downdip in the direction of the water flow. In this case, there will be a two-way traffic for oil and gas along the upper surface of the sandstone stratum, the gas migrating updip and the oil in the opposite direction.

A trap for gas will occur updip when the deflection of the vector E_g from the vertical is less than that of the normal to the bedding. Similarly the migration of the oil downdip will be arrested when the dip of the formation steepens until the deflection from the vertical of its normal is greater than that of E_o. In this case, we deal with a situation where gas migrates to a gas trap that will not hold oil, while the oil migrates to a separate oil trap that will not hold gas. Neither trap need be a closed structure as in the hydrostatic case.

Hydrodynamic tilts of the oil- and gas-water interfaces.

After a volume of oil or gas has already accumulated, this will constitute a hydrostatic body of oil or gas resting upon water that may be either motionless or flowing. We need to consider only the hydrodynamic case, when the water is flowing, of which the hydrostatic case is the special solution when the flow rate is zero.

Consider a static body of oil of density ρ_o resting upon a flowing body of water of density ρ_w. Because of capillary effects the actual interface between the water and oil will be very irregular with stringers of water penetrating into the oil space. This is physically analogous to the air-water interface in ground-water hydrology. There, the capillary effect can be eliminated by a hollow space, such as a hand-dug well, extending across the boundary. In this hollow space, the air-water interface will be a smooth horizontal surface on which the water pressure is equal to that of the atmosphere, or

$$p_w = p_{atm}.$$

This equipressure surface, which has a definite elevation z for each point of horizontal coordinates, x and y, is known as the *water table*.

In petroleum reservoir engineering, the term "water table" has been borrowed from ground-water hydrology, and is also applied to an oil-water or gas-water contact. In the oil-water case, the water table would be a surface whose elevation at a particular point would be that of the oil-water interface in a vertical hollow cylinder of large enough diameter to eliminate capillary disturbances. Regardless of the capillary effects, the pressure along a vertical line in the interpenetrating oil and water phases will each be continuous. Hence, if these be plotted on a graph of pressure versus elevation, the curve for the pressure in the oil phase will have a slope different from that for the water phase. The elevation of the point of intersection of these two curves will be the elevation z of the water table, or what we shall call the oil-water interface.

Consider now the intersection of this surface with the vertical xz-plane parallel to the water flowlines, with the horizontal x-axis positive in the flow direction. At each point $P(x,z)$ along this interface, the pressures of the oil and water phases must be the same,

$$p_o = p_w. \qquad (84)$$

To determine p_w, let a water manometer be terminated at the interface at the point $P(x,z)$. In this the water will rise to an elevation h_w, and the pressure p will be

$$p_w = \rho_w g(h_w - z). \qquad (85)$$

Then

$$(dp/dx)_w = \rho_w g[(dh_w/dx) - (dz/dx)]. \qquad (86)$$

Along the interface, for the static oil phase,

$$(dp/dx)_o = (dp/dz)_o(dz/dx). \qquad (87)$$

However, in the static oil phase,

$$(dp/dz)_o = -\rho_o g. \qquad (88)$$

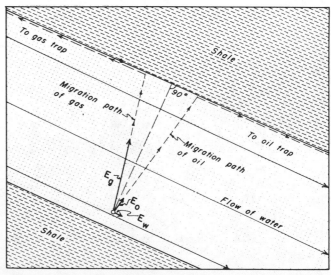

Fig. 13. Divergent migration of oil and gas in hydrodynamic environment. [*Hubbert*, 1953, Figure 17.]

Hence

$$(dp/dx)_o = -\rho_o g(dz/dx). \qquad (89)$$

Then, since

$$(dp/dx)_o = (dp/dx)_w, \qquad (90)$$

from equations (86) and (89),

$$\rho_w g[(dh_w/dx) - (dz/dx)] = -\rho_o g(dz/dx). \qquad (91)$$

Eliminating g and solving equation (91) for dz/dx, gives

$$(dz/dx)_o = [\rho_w/(\rho_w - \rho_o)] (dh_w/dx). \qquad (92)$$

According to this, the slope of the interface, dz/dx, has the same sign as dh_w/dx but is multiplied by the dimensionless factor, $\rho_w/(\rho_w - \rho_o)$. Since, in the direction of the water flow, dh_w/dx is negative, the tilt of the oil-water interface will also be downward in the flow direction. When the water is static, both dh_w/dx and dz/dx will be zero and the interface horizontal.

The tilt equation for the gas-water interface is identical with that for oil except that ρ_g is substituted for ρ_o, giving, for gas,

$$(dz/dx)_g = [\rho_g/(\rho_w - \rho_g)] (dh_w/dx). \qquad (93)$$

In case the water is static and the oil or gas is flowing, by means of the same kind of analysis as that used for the opposite case, the corresponding tilt equations are:

$$\left. \begin{array}{l} (dz/dx)_o = -[\rho_o/(\rho_w - \rho_o)] (dh_o/dx), \\ (dz/dx)_g = -[\rho_g/(\rho_w - \rho_g)] (dh_g/dx), \end{array} \right\} \qquad (94)$$

where h_g is the manometer elevation of a liquid having the constant density ρ_g.

A more general expression that includes each of the foregoing tilt equations as a special case is obtained if we let ρ_f be the density of the flowing fluid and ρ_{st} be that of the static fluid. When these are substituted into any of the equations (92), or (94), we obtain

$$dz/dx = [\rho_f/(\rho_f - \rho_{st})](dh_f/dx). \qquad (95)$$

The dimensionless factor, $\rho_f/(\rho_f - \rho_{st})$ is a *tilt-amplification factor* by means of which dh_f/dx is amplified to give the angle of tilt. In the case of water and oil, with the water flowing, ρ_f would be the density of water and ρ_{st} that of oil. The density of water is approximately 1.0 kg/dm³. The density of crude oil may have any value from about 0.66 kg/dm³ for very light crude oils to as much as 1.0 for extremely heavy oils. Representative values characteristic of most crude oils would be about 0.8 to 0.9. Assuming a value of 0.8 for the static oil, the tilt-amplification factor would have a magnitude of 5.0. For a more dense oil of density 0.9, this factor would be 10.

For natural gas, on the other hand, the densities at the pressures and temperatures prevailing in gas reservoirs are commonly in the range of 0.1 to 0.2 kg/dm³. These values would give tilt amplification factors of only 1.1 to 2.5. Hence, for a given hydraulic gradient, dh_w/dx, an oil-water interface would be tilted by an amount several times greater than a gas-water interface. This is consistent with the force-vector analyses given previously. The oil-water interface, or gas-water interface, will be perpendicular to the corresponding force-per-unit-mass vector $\mathbf{E_o}$ or $\mathbf{E_g}$.

If the tilt is greater than the dip of the reservoir sandstone, the oil or gas will move downdip; if less than the dip, it will move updip. If, in the downdip direction, the dip increases from an angle less than the tilt angle to one greater than the angle of tilt, the oil or gas would be trapped in the region of increase of dip. This would be in an unclosed structure with water both updip and downdip from the entrapped oil or gas.

OIL OR GAS TRAPS IN TERMS OF EQUIPOTENTIAL SURFACES

Heretofore we have discussed the potential of water in a water-filled space, but no recognition has been given to the fact that the potential of any fluid is much more general than that. Any fluid whose density ρ is either constant or a function of pressure only has a definite potential Φ at any point of elevation z and ambient fluid pressure p, which is given by

$$\Phi = gz + \int_0^p (1/\rho)dp,$$

or, when ρ is constant, by

$$\Phi = gz + p/\rho.$$

Hence, at a given point of elevation z and pressure p, regardless of what fluid occupies that space, different fluids, if placed at that point, would each have a different potential. In particular, elementary volumes of oil or gas, if placed at a given point in a water-filled reservoir sandstone, would each have a separate potential. Within the three-dimensional space of the sandstone, there would be separate families of surfaces, $\Phi = $ const. Perpendicular to these respective surfaces the forces per unit mass, $\mathbf{E_o}$ and $\mathbf{E_g}$, would tend to drive the elements of oil or gas in the direction of their decreasing potentials. A trap for oil or gas would accordingly be either a region in space of minimum potential completely enclosed by a family of equipotential surfaces of outwardly increasing potential, or else, a space of lower potential enclosed jointly by an equipotential surface and an impermeable lithologic boundary. In either case, an element of oil or gas driven into such a space would be unable to escape, and the accumulation of such elements would lead to a reservoir of oil or gas. Accordingly, the search for oil or gas accumulations is reduced to the mapping of oil or gas equipotential surfaces, in conjunction with the geometry of reservoir rocks, in order to determine the positions of the regions of enclosed minimum potential for the respective fluids.

To do this, we now consider the separate potentials of water, oil, and gas at a particular point of elevation z and water pressure p in the reservoir rock. Water and oil will have constant densities, ρ_w and ρ_o, but the density of gas is variable and increases with pressure. Hence, the potential for gas includes the work required to compress the gas from an initial pressure 0 to a final pressure p. However, for our purposes, we require only the geometry of the gas equipotential surfaces in a restricted region of underground space in which the pressure variation is small as compared with the total pressure. Consequently, within this space the gas density also will be nearly constant. Accordingly, we may with negligible error treat the gas as if it were a liquid of constant density ρ_g corresponding to the mean pressure of the region considered.

With this simplification, the separate potentials for water, oil, and gas at the given point will be,

$$\left.\begin{array}{l} \Phi_w = gz + p/\rho_w, \\ \Phi_o = gz + p/\rho_o, \\ \Phi_g = gz + p/\rho_g. \end{array}\right\} \tag{96}$$

Equipotential surfaces of water, oil, and gas

If $p(x, y, z)$ were known at every point in the field the potentials for oil and gas at each point could be computed by means of equations (96). Unfortunately, although p at elevation z is one of the primary quantities measurable in a well located at x and y, there is no simple rationale for the direct determination of p from measurements at widely separated points. However, there is such a rationale for the determination of Φ_w. If the water is static, then $\Phi_w(x, y, z)$ is constant. If the water is flowing in a stratum, the flowlines will be parallel and the surfaces $\Phi_w = $ const perpendicular to the boundaries of the stratum, with the potential decreasing in the downstream direction, and with the spacing of the equipotential surfaces approximately constant. This permits fairly accurate linear interpolations of Φ_w along the stratum, and hence its determination in three-dimensional space.

For this reason, it is preferable to eliminate p from equations (96) and to express Φ_o and Φ_g in terms of Φ_w and z. From equation (38),

$$\left.\begin{array}{l} \Phi_w = gh_w, \\ \Phi_o = gh_o, \\ \Phi_g = gh_g. \end{array}\right\} \tag{97}$$

When these are substituted into equations (96) and each is solved for p, we obtain

$$\left.\begin{array}{l} p = \rho_w gh_w - \rho_w gz, \\ p = \rho_o gh_o - \rho_o gz, \\ p = \rho_g gh_g - \rho_g gz. \end{array}\right\} \tag{98}$$

Then, equating the first and second of the expressions for p in equations (98) and solving for gh_o, and equating the first and third expressions and solving for gh_g gives,

$$\left.\begin{array}{l} \Phi_o = gh_o = (\rho_w/\rho_o)gh_w - [(\rho_w - \rho_o)/\rho_o]gz, \\ \Phi_g = gh_g = (\rho_w/\rho_g)gh_w - [(\rho_w - \rho_g)/\rho_g]gz. \end{array}\right\} \tag{99}$$

Thus if h_w and z are known at every point, then Φ_o and Φ_g are given by equations (99), every term of which has the dimension of [energy/mass].

However, since we are interested only in the space geometry of the oil and gas equipotential surfaces, no change in this geometry will be produced if every term of each equation is multiplied by a constant. Thus, if each of equations (99) is multiplied by $1/g$, we obtain equations of which each term has the simple dimension of length. Unfortunately, this still leaves us with the elevation z which must be multiplied by the density ratio $(\rho_w - \rho_o)/\rho_o$ or by $(\rho_w - \rho_g)/\rho_g$ for oil and gas potentials, respectively. However, since z is a primary geometrical measurement, it is highly desirable that each of equations (99) be multiplied by a factor which leaves the coefficient of z equal to 1. This can be done by multiplying each of equations (99) by the reciprocal of the coefficient of z. By this means, when g is eliminated from each of the equations, we obtain for oil and gas respectively,

$$\left.\begin{array}{l} [\rho_o/(\rho_w - \rho_o)]h_o = [\rho_w/(\rho_w - \rho_o)]h_w - z, \\ [\rho_g/(\rho_w - \rho_g)]h_g = [\rho_w/(\rho_w - \rho_g)]h_w - z. \end{array}\right\} \tag{100}$$

These can be further simplfied if we let

$$\left.\begin{array}{l} [\rho_o/(\rho_w - \rho_o)]h_o = u_o;\ [\rho_w/(\rho_w - \rho_o)]h_w = v_o; \\ [\rho_g/(\rho_w - \rho_g)]h_g = u_g;\ [\rho_w/(\rho_w - \rho_g)]h_w = v_g. \end{array}\right\} \tag{101}$$

We then have

$$\left.\begin{array}{l} u_o = v_o - z, \\ u_g = v_g - z, \end{array}\right\} \tag{102}$$

each term of which is measurable in a unit of length. When dealing with only one fluid, oil or gas, at a time, we may drop the subscripts and simply write

$$u = v - z. \tag{103}$$

In this equation, u is proportional to the oil (or gas) potential and v is proportional to the water potential. Hence, the surface $u = $ const is also an oil (or gas) equipotential surface; the surface $v = $ const is a water equipotential surface; and the surface $z = $ const is a horizontal plane of elevation z.

Space geometry of equiscalar surfaces, u, v, and z

Now consider the two pairs of intersecting equiscalar surfaces, z and $z + \Delta z$, and v and $v + \Delta v$, with

$$\Delta v = \Delta z.$$

These will enclose a $\Delta z \Delta v$-solenoid whose lower and upper boundaries are the horizontal planes z and $z + \Delta z$, and whose lateral surfaces u and $u + \Delta u$, are water equipotential surfaces. At each intersection, the value of u, from equation (103), will be the difference between the values of v and z. As shown in Figure 14, the family of equiscalar surfaces, $u = $ const, passes through the $\Delta z \Delta v$-solenoids along their diagonals for which both z and v increase or decrease, with the constant interval

$$\Delta u = \Delta z = \Delta v. \tag{104}$$

These surfaces also are inclined downward in the direction of decrease of v.

Figure 15 shows the families of equiscalar surfaces, v, z, and u, and the family of $\Delta z \Delta v$-solenoids in a vertical cross section normal to the strike and to the axis of the solenoids. The water flows downdip, and, due to a variation in the permeability of the sandstone in the dip direction, the water equipotentials are unevenly spaced. This produces a concave-upward curvature of the oil equipotentials, causing the upper two surfaces to intersect the upper surface of the sandstone. The space enclosed between the oil equipotential surface, $u - 5\Delta u$, and the upper surface of the sandstone is accordingly an area of low oil potential. If this intersection forms a closed curve on the upper surface of the sandstone, the volume enclosed would be a trap for oil.

The intersections of the surfaces $z = $ const and $v = $ const with the upper surface of the sandstone comprises a family of curves $z = $ const and $v = $ const upon that surface which can be projected vertically upon the xy-plane as a map. The curves $z = $ const are then the familiar structure contour lines

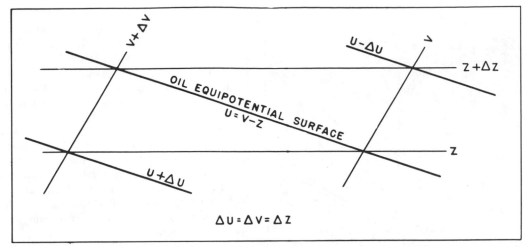

Fig. 14. Cross section of $\Delta z \Delta v$-solenoid showing oil equipotential surfaces, $u = $ const. [*Hubbert*, 1967, Figure 1.]

of the upper surface of the sandstone. The curves $v = $ const are water equipotential curves. These families of curves intersect forming a family of curvilinear $\Delta z \Delta v$-parallelograms. These are the intersections on the surface of the sandstone of the corresponding $\Delta z \Delta v$-solenoids, whose diagonals in the direction of simultaneous increase of z and v comprise the curves $u = $ const of the intersections of the oil equipotential surfaces. If the oil equipotential curves enclose an area of minimum potential, this represents the horizontal boundary of an oil trap in the sandstone.

Figure 16 is a block diagram showing the use of this technique for locating the position of an oil trap on a plunging structural anticlinal nose with a steepening axis in the direction of water flow. Figure 17 shows how an oil trap can be formed in a sandstone stratum of uniform homoclinal dip, but with variable permeability. In this case, the structure contour lines are rectilinear but the water-potential contours are curved and concave in the downdip direction because of a local region of high permeability.

In each of these cases, the structure contours are fixed, but the curves $v = $ const, from the defining equations (101), would have a different configuration for gas from that for oil, and also for different assumed values for the oil density. For this reason, if the water is flowing, traps for oil and traps for gas can not coincide. They may partially overlap or be separated from one another entirely.

EXPERIMENTAL VERIFICATION

The theoretical analysis given in the present paper is a synthesis of results achieved from a continuing study of the mechanics of underground fluids during the period 1937 to 1968. This study was begun at Columbia University, and the fundamental principles were established in the paper, "The

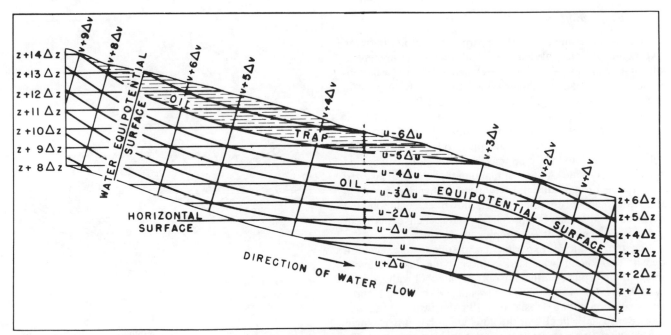

Fig. 15. Homoclinically dipping reservoir bed with variable permeability, showing oil trap formed by termination of oil equipotential surfaces against upper surface of bed. (Reproduced by permission of Shell Development Company.) [*Hubbert*, 1967, Figure 2.]

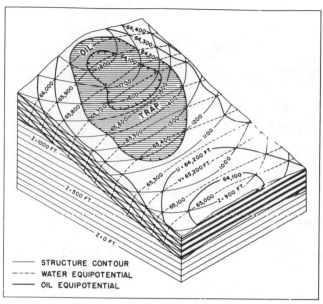

Fig. 16. Block diagram of plunging nose showing oil trap on unclosed structure formed by suitable combination of structure and hydrology. (Reproduced by permission of Shell Development Company.) [*Hubbert*, 1967, Figure 3.]

Theory of Ground-Water Motion,'' [*Hubbert*, 1940]. Later, at the Exploration and Production Research Laboratory of Shell Oil Company in Houston, the study was extended to the problem of migration and entrapment of oil and gas under hydrodynamic conditions.

By 1948 the study had advanced to the state that experimental verification of the theoretical deductions became desirable. For this purpose a graduate student of physics from Rice Institute, Jerry P. Conner, was employed as my research assistant and, during the summers of 1948 and 1949, he was given the assignment of verifying experimentally the entire suite of theoretical deductions.

Sand-box experiments

For the experiments on the hydrodynamic tilts between two liquids of unequal densities, and for the entrapment of oil under various conditions, a closed sand box was constructed. This had the dimensions of 0.81 m wide, 0.46 m high, and 0.064 m deep. It had a transparent Plexiglass front and a plywood rear, with screened vertical open chambers at each end between which water could be made to flow through the sand. Through the plywood in the rear, dye tubes were inserted for mapping the water flowlines behind the Plexiglass plate. A bank of manometers was also inserted from the rear to measure the elevations h at various points in the flow field. From these data, flowlines, equipotential surfaces, and equipressure surfaces for each experiment were computed and drawn graphically.

For the two-fluid experiments, distilled water with a density of 1 kg/dm³ was used as the moving fluid. To avoid undesirable capillary effects, isopropyl alcohol with a density of 0.9 kg/dm³ was used as the less dense static fluid, and a sugar solution with a density of 1.1 kg/dm³ was used for the more dense static fluid. For the flowing fluid, in order to map the flowlines with injected dye, clear water was used. To make the two-liquid interfaces visible, the static fluids were tinted with a dark dye.

Hydrostatic conditions are shown in Figure 18(*a*). Hydrodynamic tilting of the oil-water interface, simulating water coning in a producing oil well, with the less dense liquid flowing, is shown in Figure 18(*b*). The measured equipotential surfaces of the flowing liquid are shown graphically in Figure 18(*c*). The migration of a hydrostatic oil accumulation into a hydrodynamic trap in an unclosed structure is shown in Figure 19.

Many experiments such as these, with various structural configurations and rates of flow, were performed. Afterwards, measurements were made of the observed angles of tilt when the corresponding values of dh/dx were known. A graph of the calculated angles of tilt versus the observed angles for tilts as high as 0.87 radians is shown in Figure 20. Excellent agreement, within a narrow range of experimental error, is indicated.

Hele-Shaw type experiments

The sand-box experiments were thoroughly satisfactory for the purpose for which they were intended, but, because each required about a day and night to stabilize, they were not satisfactory for making a working demonstration. For the latter purpose, in the year 1950 the Hele-Shaw type of apparatus shown in Figure 21 was constructed. This could be used for direct demonstration before small groups, but its primary purpose was for demonstration before large audiences by projecting live experiments upon a screen by means of a lantern-slide projector.

The cell consisted of a brass frame with a glass Hele-Shaw window representing a sandstone with an anticline and a plunging nose which steepened in the down-plunge direction. This was designed to fit into the space of the slide carrier of an American Optical Company projector for the 3¼ × 4-inch glass slides in current use at that time. As shown in the photograph of Figure 21, water at variable rates could be made to flow through the cell from left to right. Oil, represented by tinted isopropyl alcohol, could be admitted

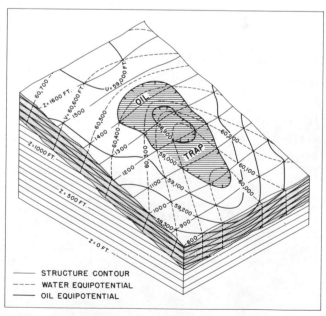

Fig. 17. Block diagram showing combination of structure, permeability, and hydrology forming oil trap in permeable homoclinically dipping bed. (Reproduced by permission of Shell Development Company.) [*Hubbert*, 1967, Figure 4.]

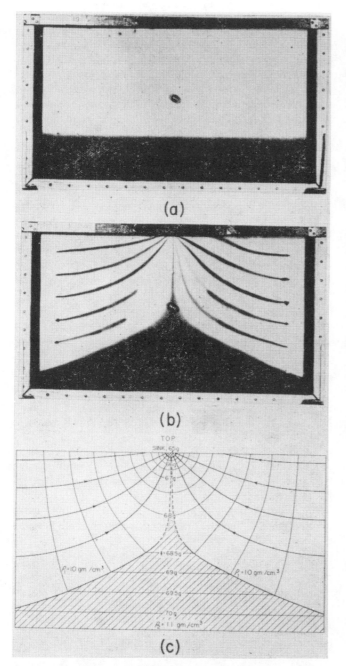

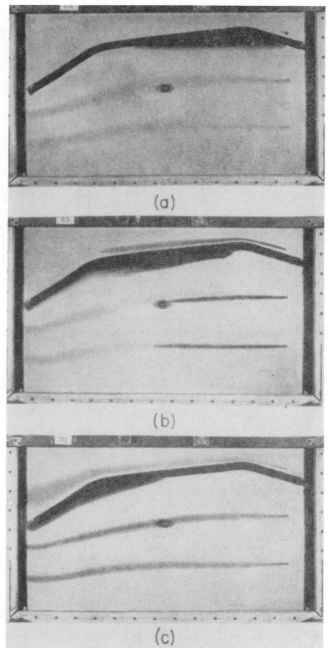

Fig. 18. Experimental relations between flowing fresh water and static sugar solution (colored). (*a*) Fresh water at rest; (*b*) fresh water flowing; (*c*) measured fresh-water equipotentials for state (*b*). [*Hubbert*, 1953, Figure 31.]

Fig. 19. Experimental oil traps, using colored alcohol and water. (*a*) Hydrostatic conditions. (*b*) Flushing of alcohol from anticline by water flowing left. (*c*) Alcohol trapped on nose. [*Hubbert*, 1953, Figure 32.]

through inlets at either end of the cell. Likewise, gas, represented by air, could be injected as bead-sized bubbles by means of rubber-bulb syringes at each end of the cell.

If projected directly upon the screen, this would have presented a disturbing inverted image of the experiment. This was precluded by deflecting the lantern beam by two $\pi/2$-radian reflections in the vertical plane by means of first-surface mirrors, resulting in an upright image on the screen.

By varying the rates of flow of the water, all of the effects deduced theoretically theretofore could be produced in this cell. For hydrostatic conditions, water, oil, and gas would assume a horizontally stratified arrangement at the crest of the anticline. At an appropriate rate of flow, the gas would remain trapped in the anticline, but with an inclined gas-

water interface, while the oil would be trapped in the plunging nose of the structure, entirely separate from the gas trap.

With the system in this state, gas bubbles injected into the cell at its upstream end would migrate along the upper edge of the cell directly to the gas trap. When gas was injected into the downstream end of the cell, the gas bubbles would move updip along the top of the cell to the oil accumulation, pass through the oil, and continue updip to the gas trap. Similarly, oil admitted into the cell from either end would migrate to the oil trap.

Photographs of several stable configurations of oil and gas in this cell are shown in Figure 22. Figure 22(*a*) shows the horizontal stratification under hydrostatic conditions. Figure

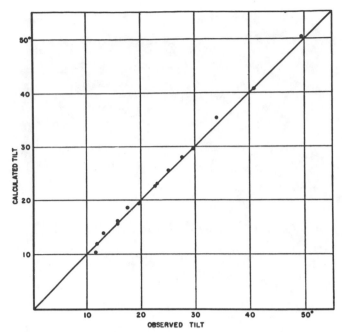

Fig. 20. Experimental confirmation of tilt equation. [*Hubbert*, 1953, Figure 34.]

22(*b*), (*c*), and (*d*) show the configurations for successively increased rates of flow of the water from right to left. At the flow rate of Figure 22(*d*), while the gas is still in the anticline, the tilt of the oil-water interface has exceeded the steepest dip of the axial plunge and the oil has migrated farther down the plunge and out of the cell.

A public demonstration of this was first made when my paper, "Entrapment of Petroleum under Hydrodynamic Conditions," was presented during the Annual Meeting of the American Association of Petroleum Geologists in Los Angeles on March 26, 1952. It was used later during the same year on a six-week Distinguished Lecture circuit of the AAPG across the United States and western Canada.

For my paper on the present subject, given as a part of the History of Hydrology Symposium during the Spring Meeting of the American Geophysical Union in Baltimore on May 28, 1985, it was intended to repeat this live demonstration. Unfortunately a suitable projector could not be found. I am indebted to David Pollock and his colleagues in the U.S. Geological Survey for making a 16-mm colored motion picture of the experiment which was used instead.

GEOLOGIC CONFIRMATION OF HYDRODYNAMIC
ENTRAPMENT

Review of field occurrences

Following the completion during 1948 and 1949 of the laboratory verification of previous theoretical deductions, the investigation was extended to the field. The theoretical and laboratory studies indicated that almost certainly, in regions of high topographic relief, the ground water in sands and permeable limestones of regional extent should be in a state of flow. Should this be so, then oil and gas accumulations in these formations should have oil- and gas-water interfaces inclined downward in the flow direction. Accumulations might also occur in unclosed structures, such as plunging anticlinal noses or structural terraces.

Concerning regional ground-water flow, from the classical studies of *N. H. Darton* [1905; 1909; 1918*a*; 1918*b*], it was known that there was a regional flow of ground water eastward from the Rocky Mountains and the Black Hills in the Dakota and other Cretaceous sandstones under the Great Plains. A review of the literature disclosed many accounts, some as early as the 1880-decade, of fields with inclined oil- or gas-water interfaces, and accumulations on unclosed structural terraces and plunging anticlinal axes. When this literature review was supplemented by unpublished company reports and drilling data, it became unmistakable that hydrodynamic effects in existing oil and gas fields are of frequent occurrence and of world-wide distribution. In nearly all cases these effects have been consistent either with the known ground-water flow, or with the inferred flow direction based upon the regional topography and geology. Space here does not permit a review of these results in detail, but many have been described in my two earlier papers [*Hubbert*, 1953; 1967]. For the present, only one conspicuous example will be discussed.

The Panhandle-Hugoton Field

In my paper of 1953 (p. 2013–2015), one of the fields discussed was the Hugoton gas field of western Kansas and the Oklahoma Panhandle. This field was conspicuous in being the largest gas field in the United States. It was roughly oval in shape with an east-west width of about 72 km, and a north-south length of about 160 km. It was also conspicuous in another respect. It was described by *Garlough and Taylor* [1941] in a paper included in the American Association of Petroleum Geologists volume on stratigraphic traps, *Stratigraphic type oil fields*, as an outstanding example of a stratigraphic trap.

According to these authors, the gas is trapped at a mean depth of about 830 meters in porous and permeable Permian

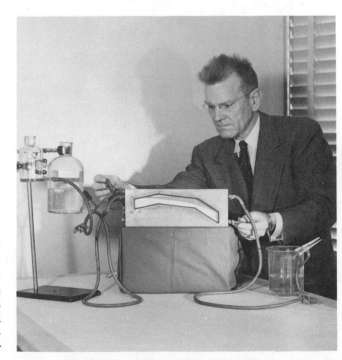

Fig. 21. Hubbert demonstrating oil and gas migration and entrapment with Hele-Shaw-type apparatus in 1950 at Shell Exploration and Production Research Laboratory in Houston.

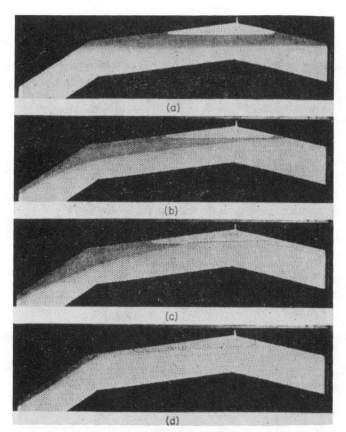

Fig. 22. Experiments with Hele-Shaw apparatus. (a) Hydrostatic conditions. (b) Dynamic conditions; oil-water interface tilted, gas-oil interface horizontal. (c) Higher rate of flow, oil highly tilted, with gas cap resting partly on oil and partly on water; gas-oil interface horizontal, gas-water interface tilted. (d) Complete separation of oil and gas traps under still higer rate of flow, with oil trapped in downstructure nose and gas in anticline but tilted. [*Hubbert*, 1953, Figure 35.]

limestones and dolomites with a homoclinal eastward dip of about 2.8 to 4.7 m/km, and with no structural closure. The reservoir carbonate rocks were reported to grade into red shales and silts about 32 km west of the field. These red shales and silts were supposed to provide the lithologic updip barrier which retained the gas in the unclosed structure as a stratigraphic trap.

However, in the same paper, the following additional information was given. The gas-water interface had an elevation of about 152 m above sea level in the westernmost wells of the field, about 76 m in a well near the center, and 37 m in a well near the eastern edge.

The initial pressure of the gas in the field was stated to have been 435 lb/in^2 (3.00×10^6 N/m^2) and nearly constant throughout the field. This was evidently the gauge pressure. The absolute pressure would have been 450 lb/in^2, or 3.10×10^6 N/m^2. The temperature was not given, but a more recent independent source [*Mason*, 1968, p. 1545] gives 90° F, or 305.4 K, as the average temperature throughout the field.

That the initial pressure should have been nearly constant is evident when we consider the density of the gas at the initial temperature and pressure. The gas in the Hugoton field is principally methane, CH$_4$, with a molecular mass of 16.04×10^{-3} kg. At the pressure of only 3.10×10^6 N/m^2 and a temperature of 305.4 K, the pressure, volume, and temperature relations for methane should agree closely with those for an ideal gas as given by the gas equation,

$$pV = nRT, \qquad (105)$$

in which p is the pressure and V the volume of n moles of the gas at the absolute temperature T, and R is the universal gas constant.

For 1 mole of methane, its mass will be M, the molecular mass, and its density will be

$$\rho = M/V.$$

To determine this, divide both sides of equation (105) by M and solve the equation for M/V. This gives

$$\rho = M/V = pM/RT, \qquad (106)$$

for which the numerical values of p, M, and T have already been given. This leaves only R as an unknown, whose value in S.I. units is

$$R = 8.3144 \text{ Nm/mol K}.$$

With these numerical data for the right-hand term of equation (106), the density of methane is

$$\rho = \frac{(3.10 \times 10^6 \, N/m^2) \times (16.04 \times 10^{-3} \, kg)}{8.3144 \, (Nm/K) \times 305.K}$$

$$= 19.6 \text{ kg/m}^3.$$

This calculated value of the density of methane at the given pressure and temperature agrees closely with the measured value given graphically by *Amyx, Bass, and Whiting* [1960, Fig. 4-17, p. 421]. Since the density of water is 1000 kg/m^3, the density of methane at the initial reservoir pressure and temperature would have been only about 2 percent of that of water. With a density of 19.6 kg/m^3 and a value of gravity of 9.80 N/kg, the initial pressure gradient in the Hugoton gas would have been

$$dp/dz = -\rho g$$

$$= -19.6 \text{ kg/m}^3 \times 9.80 \text{ N/kg}$$

$$= -192 \text{ Pa/m}.$$

In an east-west cross section of the Hugoton field in southwestern Kansas, after the field was fully developed, the gas-water contact has been found to terminate upon the upper surface of the reservoir at an elevation of about 30 m at the eastern edge of the field, and at about 330 m at the western edge. This gives an elevation range of about 300 m for the gas-water contact, with a median elevation of about 180 m and a range of elevations of 180 m $\pm$ 150 m. If we let $\bar{p}$ be the pressure at the median elevation, then the maximum and minimum pressures would be $\bar{p} \pm \Delta p$, where

$$\Delta p = -(dp/dz)\Delta z$$

$$= 192 \text{ Pa/m} \times 150 \text{ m}$$

$$= 2.88 \times 10^4 \text{ Pa}.$$

Then, if we take the initial pressure of 3.10×10^6 Pa for $\bar{p}$,

$$\Delta p/\bar{p} = (2.88 \times 10^4)/(3.10 \times 10^6)$$

$$= 9.29 \times 10^{-3}$$

$$\cong 10^{-2}$$

Thus, the ratio of the extreme variations of the initial pressure in the field to the median pressure could not have been more than about 2 percent, which would have been about the range of accuracy of the initial pressure measurements. This is consistent with the statement of Garlough and Taylor that the initial reservoir pressure was nearly constant throughout the field. The same would have been true for the pressure along the gas-water interface. At the eastern edge of the field, the maximum pressure would have been

$$p_{max} = \bar{p} + \Delta p$$
$$= (3.10 \times 10^6 + 2.88 \times 10^4) \text{ Pa}$$
$$= 3.129 \times 10^6 \text{ Pa}.$$

The minimum pressure,

$$p_{min} = (3.10 \times 10^6 - 2.88 \times 10^4) \text{ Pa}$$
$$= 3.071 \times 10^6 \text{ Pa},$$

would have occurred at the western edge of the field.

The height h above sea level of water in a manometer terminated at the gas-water contact would be

$$h = z + p/\rho_w \, g.$$

Accordingly, the minimum value of h at the eastern edge of the field would have been

$$h_{min} = 30 \text{ m} + [(3.129 \times 10^6 \text{ Pa})/(10^3 \text{ kg/m}^3 \times 9.80 \text{ N/kg})]$$
$$= 349.3 \text{ m}.$$

At the western edge of the field, the manometer height would have had the maximum value

$$h_{max} = 330 \text{ m} + [(3.071 \times 10^6 \text{ Pa})/(10^3 \text{ kg/m}^3 \times 9.80 \text{ N/kg})]$$
$$= 643.4 \text{ m}.$$

In a diagonal NW-SE cross section of the field, this corresponds to an average hydraulic gradient to the southeast of

$$\overline{dh/dx} \cong -294 \text{ m}/80 \text{ km}$$
$$\cong -3.7 \text{ m/km}.$$

This again indicates that along this cross section, the water is flowing in a southeasterly direction.

From equation (93), the tilt of the gas-water interface is

$$dz/dx = [\rho_w/(\rho_w - \rho_g)](dh/dx).$$

In this case, the tilt-amplification factor

$$\rho_w/(\rho_w - \rho_g) = 1000 \text{ kg/m}^3/(1000 - 19.6) \text{ kg/m}^3$$
$$= 1.02.$$

Accordingly the slope, dz/dx, of the gas-water interface in the Hugoton field and the hydraulic gradient, dh/dx, should have been almost identical. Because the gas was initially in hydrostatic equilibrium, the gas potential within the reservoir must have been constant. Hence, the gas-water interface must have been a gas equipotential surface. Within the water immediately below the gas-water interface the gas equipotentials would have been parallel to the interface with a steep negative gas-potential gradient toward the interface.

In 1953 the Hugoton gas field in Kansas and the Oklahoma Panhandle, and the Panhandle oil and gas field farther south in Texas, were two separate fields. Gas had been discovered in the Texas field in 1918 and the oil in 1921. Subsequent drilling showed that the field occurred principally in the

Pennsylvanian "granite wash" along the northeast side of the buried Amarillo Granite Ridge, and the field extended in a slightly southeasterly direction, with a length of 170 km. The associated gas field bounded the oil field to the southwest and west and then extended northward almost to the Oklahoma boundary, a distance of about 145 km.

The Hugoton field, while discovered a year or two earlier, had its initial development in 1927 and then rapidly grew by 1950 to the size described earlier in the present paper. During the period of development of the separate Panhandle and Hugoton fields, because the initial gas pressure in both fields was known to have been the same, it had long been suspected that the two fields were actually connected. Also during that period, oil geologists often wondered about what could have become of the oil that should have been associated with the Hugoton gas field.

During the 1950-decade, subsequent drilling did establish the connection between the Panhandle and the Hugoton gas fields and showed that the single very large gas field and the associated Panhandle oil field were a unified oil and gas system.

Toward the end of the 1950-decade, Shell geologists J. L. Porter and J. H. Hoyt in Kansas, and S. S. Moran in Texas

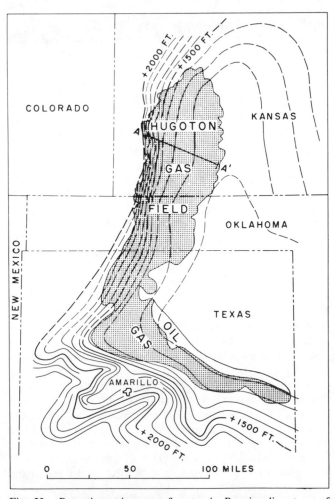

Fig. 23. Potentiometric map of water in Permian limestone of Wolfcamp age in western Kansas and Oklahoma, and northern Texas Panhandle, showing relation of Hugoton-Panhandle gas field and Panhandle oil field to regional hydrology. (Map by J. L. Porter and J. H. Hoyt, Kansas, and S. S. Moran, Texas, reproduced by permission of Shell Oil Company.) [*Hubbert*, 1967, Figure 5.]

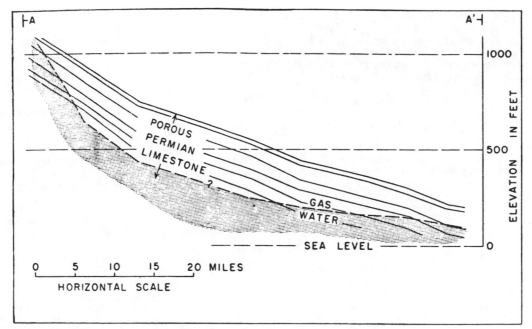

Fig. 24. Cross section A—A' from Fig. 23, showing the southeastward tilt of the gas-water interface in the Hugoton gas field in western Kansas, and its closure against overlying impermeable strata. (Cross section by J. L. Porter and J. H. Hoyt reproduced by permission of Shell Oil Company.) [*Hubbert*, 1967, Figure 6.]

were given the assignments of making regional potentiometric maps of the waters associated with the gas, and gas and oil fields in their respective areas. For my invited review paper before the World Petroleum Congress in 1967, Shell Oil Company permitted me to use the results of these combined studies, the figures from which are reproduced here as Figures 23 and 24.

Figure 23 is a map of the integrated fields with the potentiometric contours, h = const, of the associated waters in the reservoir formations within and around the areas of the gas and oil accumulations. It is seen that these are roughly parallel to the southwestern boundary of the gas field in Texas and then make a nearly right-angle turn to the northward along the western edge of the field. Finally, at the north end of the field, they make a U-turn eastward and southward. Along the southwestern and western borders of the field the water is flowing with a steep negative gradient toward the field. Along the eastern boundary of the Hugoton field a very weak southward negative gradient exists.

Figure 24 is a nearly east-west cross section of the Hugoton field, showing the gas-water interface and the reservoir formations, with the steeper hydrodynamic tilt at the western edge of the field, and with the interface becoming nearly horizontal near the eastern edge.

From these maps, the question of what has become of the oil that should have been associated with the Hugoton gas field is now resolved. It is contained in the Panhandle oil field, which is the oil that corresponds to the entire gas field. Moreover, in accordance with its hydrodynamic environment, it occurs at the lowest structural position on the northeastern edge of the Panhandle gas field.

CONCLUSION

Despite its simplicity and its fundamental importance with respect to the flow of underground fluids, Darcy's law has been one of the most misstated and misunderstood relationships in recent scientific history. For example, during the

quarter-century period from about 1930 to the 1950-decade, petroleum-reservoir engineering in the United States was based almost exclusively on the physically erroneous flow equation,

$$\mathbf{v} = -(k/\mu) \ \text{grad} \ p,$$

which was called "Darcy's law."

The Darcy formulation generalized to flow in three-dimensional space,

$$\mathbf{q} = -K \ \text{grad} \ h,$$

is a kinematic expression of the linear coupling between the vector field of flow q and the scalar field of the quantity h, but it is lacking in explicit dynamical content. This deficiency is removed, however, when it is recognized that h is related to the pressure field by the equation,

$$h = z + p/\rho g.$$

Using this as a transition, the energies and forces relating to the entire array of underground fluids become immediately apparent, and simple methods are provided for dealing with problems which otherwise are almost intractable.

REFERENCES

Amyx, James W., Bass, Daniel M., Jr., and Whiting, Robert L., 1960, *Petroleum reservoir engineering*: New York, McGraw Hill, Fig. 4-17, p. 241.

Bartle, Glen G., and Smith, Rufus M., 1940, Relative porosity and permeability of producing formation of the Hugoton field as indicated by gas withdrawal and pressure decline: *American Association of Petroleum Geologists Bulletin*, v. 24, no. 10, p. 1798–1804.

Cram, Ira H., 1971, editor, Future petroleum provinces of the United States—their geology and potential: Summary: *American Association of Petroleum Geologists, Memoir 15*, v. 1, preface xiii; p. 1–34.

Darcy, Henry, 1856, *Les fontaines publiques de la ville de Dijon*, Victor Dalmont, Paris, p. 590–94; also Atlas, Fig. 3.

Darton, N. H., 1905, Preliminary report on the geology and underground water resources of the central great plains: *U.S. Geological Survey Professional Paper 43*, 433 p.

—— 1909, Geology and underground waters of South Dakota, *U.S. Geological Survey Water-Supply Paper 227*, 156 p.

—— 1918a, Artesian waters in the vicinity of the Black Hills, South Dakota, *U.S. Geological Survey Water-Supply Paper 428*, 64 p.

—— 1918b, The structure of parts of the central great plains, *U.S. Geological Survey Bulletin 691*, p. 1–26.

Forchheimer, Philipp, 1914, *Hydraulik*: Leipzig and Berlin, B. G. Teubner, p. 436–444.

Garlough, John L., and Taylor, Garvin L., 1941, Hugoton gas field, Grant, Haskell, Morton, Stevens and Seward Counties, Kansas, and Texas County, Oklahoma, in A. I. Levorsen, editor, *Stratigraphic type oil fields*, American Association Petroleum Geologists, p. 78–104.

Hubbert, M. King, 1940, The theory of ground-water motion: *Journal of Geology*, v. 48, no. 8, p. 785–944.

—— 1953, Entrapment of petroleum under hydrodynamic conditions: *American Association of Petroleum Geologists Bulletin*, v. 37, no. 8, p. 1954–2026.

—— 1956, Darcy's law and the field equations of the flow of underground fluids: *Journal of Petroleum Technology*, October, p. 222–239; also 1957, *L'Association Internationale d'Hydrologie Scientifique*, Bulletin no. 5, p. 24–59.

—— 1967, Application of hydrodynamics to oil exploration: *Seventh World Petroleum Congress Proceedings*, v. 1A, p. 59–75.

—— 1969, *The theory of ground-water motion and related papers* (with reprint of 1856 Darcy paper in appendix): New York, Hafner, 311 p.

Laplace, Pierre Simon, 1805, *Traité méchanique céleste*: Paris, Chez Courcier, Imprimeur - Libraire pour les Mathematiques, v. 4, book X, supplement, p. 349–498; also in *Oeuvres complete de Laplace de l'Academie des Sciences*, Paris, Gauthier-Villars, 1880.

Mason, John L., 1968, Hugoton Panhandle field, Kansas, Oklahoma and Texas, in Beebe, B. Warren, editor, *Natural gases of North America*: American Association of Petroleum Geologists, Memoir 9, v. 2, p. 1539–1547.

Pettijohn, Francis J., 949, *Sedimentary rocks*: New York, Harper and Brothers, p. 13.

Purcell, W. R., 1949, *Capillary pressures—Their measurement using mercury and the calculation of permeability therefrom*: American Institute of Mining and Metallurgical Engineers Transactions, v. 186, p. 39–48.

M. K. Hubbert, 5208 Westwood Drive, Bethesda, MD   20816.

The Alexandrian Equation

Luna B. Leopold

Department of Geology and Geophysics, University of California, Berkeley, California

The balance of power in the Aegean region shifted in 360 B.C. Philip the Second became the ruler in Macedon and thence began the remaking of the map of the civilized world. Philip introduced two elements into the struggle for world power that were new and practical—the sarissa and the cavalry-infantry combination. The sarissa was a long, thin, iron pointed spear, much longer and thinner than the heavier short weapon of the Greek hoplite. A solid line of infantry, bristling with this pincushion of horizontal steel, backed up rank on rank by layers of the weapon held at an upward angle, meant that if the front line failed the next rank went into operation.

The flanks of the massed infantry were protected by lightly armed cavalry ready to gallop pell-mell into any part of the field. The fast-moving horsemen were held well to the side until a lightning blow was required.

What are the generalized terms that describe these innovations? The terms I choose are technological advance and strategy.

Interestingly, these two great contributions were not enough. Philip conquered all the surrounding tribes of Macedonia, Thrace, and the country west to the Adriatic. With the threat of his military power, his young son, Alexander, concluded a treaty with Athens, the only real Greek adversary to the Macedonian might. But Philip did not conquer Persia, much less the world.

A third element was needed—leadership. Leadership in this context means a vision, a goal, and the ability to meld various, often disparate, forces into a coherent channel. Young Alexander provided this essential element. Utilizing these three inseparable necessities, he conquered the world. At the death of Alexander in 323 B.C., chaos again reigned, though the imprint of his exploits are seen on the map of the world in the 20th century.

How easy it is to leave the unopened history book on the dusty shelf and suppose that everything is new, everything is different. Hydrologists would do well to look backward as a way of going forward.

Our sarissa is the computer. The long spear did not just come from a single idea, but it developed by trial and error, testing different kinds and lengths of the shaft, different shapes and weights of the iron head. I can remember when the ink trace of the water stage recorder was to be digitized by a scanning device. In the middle of this extended experimentation, Rolland Carter brought the punched tape to the gaging station.

Our first sarissa in groundwater was the electrical analog of Herbert Skibitzke. He even had three dimensional or layered models representing different geologic strata. Then came the digital analog program on the rapidly developing computer, pressed forward by Robert Bennett, Allan Freeze, and Skibitzke himself.

In quality of water, the spear developing was in redox potential and quantitative analytical chemistry—William Back, Frank Clarke, Ivan Barnes, and Donald White. The relation of water chemistry to geology and, through dating, the large scale movement of groundwater was advanced by Meyer Rubin, William Back, Bruce Hanshaw, and more recently by Thomas Winter and Allan Freeze.

Our technological tools are well developed—unfortunately even outdistancing the other essential elements of a healthy science.

Strategy—the science of hydrology has had its ups and downs. In our profession, two aspects of scientific strategy have played an outstanding role in recent history. The first is the recognition that hydrology and geomorphology are so closely related as to be nearly one. When I joined the United States Geological Survey in 1950, I found that no one in the Water Resources Division even knew the word geomorphology. Today it is taken for granted that physical geology of the earth's surface, hydraulics and sediment transport, the occurrence and movement of water and the conduits or channels in which it flows, are inseparable.

The second aspect of strategy for the advancement of our science was the decision on the part of government to send persons to university at government expense for advanced training. University faculties had the theory and the breadth of interest which the practical engineer, geologist, chemist, petrologist or forester needed. For a decade or more this close collaboration was a great stimulus.

Finally, leadership. We have seen it in the past so we ought to recognize what it is. Some examples: Robert E. Horton saw the need for basic measurements of infiltration capacity and accompanying theory required by the Soil Conservation Service in its flood control assignment.

Raymond L. Nace—his International Hydrological Decade was no great scientific success, but it started much new thinking in many countries and made hydrology a household word throughout the world. The International Vigil Network of repeated surveys to measure morphologic change: again, few saw the opportunity, but it was an idea. The Federal Interagency Committee and the development of the suspended load sampler—a goal, and a mechanism for attaining it.

The founding of the first department of hydrology at the University of Arizona is an example. John Harshbarger, Nicholas Matalas, and Walter Langbein made it go by combining academic facilities and philosophy with government personnel and support.

Our field needed a publication outlet of its own. Each issue of the Transactions of A.G.U. was divided into units representing the various sections of the Union—geodesy, terrestrial magnetism, meteorology, hydrology and the others. When this gave way to the Journal of Geophysical Research, hydrology was nearly elbowed out. Through the work of Walter Langbein and Waldo Smith, we finally got our own journal under A.G.U. auspices and it has turned out to be a financial as well as a scientific success.

There has not been in the last decade any initiative in hydrology comparable to these achievements of the 50's and 60's. Agency support of graduate study has diminished to a mere trickle. The dependence on research grants rather than agency-supported research has moved academics increasingly away from the technical agencies of state and federal government. In fact, the agencies seem to have moved into competition with rather than toward cooperation with universities. The situation has not been helped by the formation of many new consulting firms whose use of available theory and data tends to standardize and ossify existing procedures.

Research programs in federal agencies are often directed toward secondary problems while ones important to society and science are bypassed. Some agencies devote their research programs to matters that managers in the same agency consider irrelevant to the agency's main task. As an example, the U.S. Forest Service has spent an inordinate effort by their research arm trying to show how forest management can increase stream flow. Yet I know of no instance where forest management policy has been directed specifically to increasing water yield. Timber production is the dominant goal despite the much advertised multiple-use theme.

The Corps of Engineers and the Soil Conservation Service have massive programs on channelization. The adverse by-products of these programs remain essentially unstudied.

One recent exception to the usual lack of cooperation is the current study of hydraulics and sediment in the Grand Canyon of the Colorado. Reluctant though it may have been, the Bureau of Reclamation did finally seek and obtain the expertise of the U.S. Geological Survey for the sediment aspects of this large effort.

Leadership, as exemplified by Alexander the Great, means a vision, a goal, and willingness to innovate in the face of social and administrative inertia. If a goal is clearly in mind, stratagems for reaching it may follow.

A goal may at first be abstract and non-specific, beginning as a vision and later developing into something more concrete. Let me give a couple of examples drawn from my own experience in the Geological Survey. Our organization in the early 1950's consisted primarily of engineers, chemists, and geologists, doing work that was fairly well standardized in methods and in goals. Data collection was emphasized and data interpretation was subordinate. We visualized that progress would be promoted if new minds, new people were continually fed into the discipline. New people would mean an expanding reservoir of experience and therefore an infusion of new ideas. As a result it became our policy to hire a few young, well trained people every year, with whatever money could be obtained and by any stratagem necessary to circumvent the often-applied personnel freeze.

This goal of an expanding force of new young minds balanced by the ordinary attrition resulting from retirements and resignations was highly successful, for it put the agency into a position where we were no longer standardized but offered opportunity for a much wider range of technical work. As a result, our hiring program became for the first time competitive with universities and industry, and posi-

tions with us were sought after rather than shunned by the best graduates. An annunciation of a goal—a vision made concrete—changed the level of scientific productivity by an order of magnitude.

Another example drawn from the Geological Survey was a strategem that was frozen out before it had time to mature. It was the decision to have people change jobs or positions—recognition that research people can burn out, that new blood brings new ideas, and that intermittent exposure to the practical world of data collecting and administration brings new insights into research. But the trauma of enforcing rotation was more than administrators could stomach, and so there are cohorts of people using hard-to-obtain research funds for but little production. This situation probably is not unique in government, and may also exist in academia and industry.

Leadership is becoming a rare commodity because the constricting forces, always at work in large organizations, are becoming more prevalent, more throttling. Freedom of action seems to be strangled by greater bureaucracy, increasing costs, tight budgets, and greater demands from interest groups. And this disease is not a monopoly of government agencies. The report, just published, by the Commission on Strengthening Presidential Leadership (see Science, 26 October, 1984) says, "our colleges and universities are in desperate need of leadership." University presidents, the report says, devote ever more time to politics and money matters at the expense of substantive academic questions and long term planning. That description could fit nearly every unit I know, from large agencies to the smallest research team.

Leadership is needed to compensate or minimize the effects of isolation. We tend to think that going to scientific meetings is the antidote for isolation. Though there is some truth to that, there are now so many meetings, symposia, workshops, and conferences that the benefits of exposure, considered essential to disseminate our ideas, cut into the time for scientific work.

There is another aspect of isolation. Academics tend to become so distant from practical problems that progress toward solution of societal dilemmas is halted because of the lack of research effort. I am not advocating that priority be given to applied rather than basic research. However, the choice of basic research problems has become so divorced from real needs that much research is devoted to trivia merely because important issues are overlooked. I repeat here a comment I have made on a previous occasion.

There is a widespread and perhaps unthinking assumption that science progresses from the isolation of the ivory tower and that to be a good research man one must disdain the market place and the practical. It is seldom stated that although the ivory tower provides time for thought (or should do so) and freedom from interruption, it also implies isolation, and isolation is the antithesis of interdisciplinary exchange.

I maintain that the good research man is the one who asks himself the right question. The questions to be answered are manifold and the sorting of good from bad, productive from unproductive, important from less important, is greatly assisted by exposure to science and technology far removed from one's own specialty. Mixing it up with the practical problems of the world would do wonders for many research men I know.

Further, it often happens that the very techniques one develops in his own field are just the ones needed for solution of some problems far distant in subject matter.

Let us sharpen our spears, regroup the cavalry, and decide by conscious choice, rather than by a least resistance psychology, what parts of our scientific and engineering world we want to conquer. As a starter, I propose a new combination of forces which I will call the Agency Academic Alliance. The Triple A would be not an organization but a program. There are outstanding scientific and engineering problems that are either being approached in bits and pieces, without coherence, or not being addressed at all. They are, for the most part, too large and too complicated to be handled by a variety of people, each working alone.

The exercise of leadership implies obtaining the cooperation of diverse groups. But leaders need to define goals in order to muster the cooperation required. Government agencies have certain strengths not available in academic institutions—usually more money, more manpower, and the ability to give orders. Academic groups have greater freedom, more independence, and a greater variety of skills and viewpoints. Where government—federal, state, or local—has been able to team with universities, good results have been realized. I visualize the Agency Academic Alliance as a way to revitalize such cooperative effort.

Let us review an example of a large problem facing all parts of our community—government, academics, and consultants. It is the matter of channel stability, sediment characteristics, and discharge. As a sample program for the Alliance, let us establish a small network of bedload sampling stations. If there were one in each state—only one—we would have 50 stations. But, to utilize the results of bedload sampling, we need to measure river slope, grain size on the bed, bank materials, and channel geometry in both plan and cross section.

Thus, the needed information goes far beyond the mere determination of a sediment rating curve and so goes beyond the ordinary practice of the U.S. Geological Survey. Could not these additional parameters be the responsibility of students and professors? A bedload sampler is now available. Cableways and stage recorders are common. But a larger goal is needed—a cooperative network for channel geometry measurement combined with hydraulic and sediment data.

A requisite for success in such a program is the publication of all the data—not merely the final graphs or summary results. The value of published data has a life far longer than any analysis of those data—the Gilbert flume experimental data well demonstrate that fact. Here again, cooperation would be the key. Scientific journals generally have such a limitation on manuscript length that the publication of tabulated data is precluded. But, as an appendix to a Professional Paper of the U.S. Geological Survey, in the Miscellaneous Publication series of the Agricultural Research Service, or in the Potomology Series of the Corps of Engineers, a few pages of tabulated data would greatly enhance the long time value of a field investigation.

I am not going to specify what problems such an Alliance might tackle. To consider the possible subjects is exactly where the cooperation I speak of would come into play. I have given merely one example of the kind of goal that might be considered.

Let us recall that Alexander conquered much of the known world by a unique combination of technology, strategy, and leadership. This is what I call the Alexandrian equation. We hydrologists are used to equations. Let us look hard at this one.

L. B. Leopold, Department of Geology and Geophysics, University of California, Berkeley, CA 94720.

The Last Word on Science

BRUCE R. WHEATON

University of California, Berkeley

While I was growing up, history was presented as a succession of political events stretched on a matrix of dates, elections, battles, and diplomatic coups. I found it all rather boring, so it is somewhat ironic that I find myself now a professional historian.

My own views began to change when I discovered that some people studied the evolution of things other than politics: of ideas and concepts, of the social institutions that affected and were affected by those ideas, of the relationship in general between society and (for the case in point) the sciences. I had always been interested in science but rather more in the process of scientific validation of concepts than in assimilating the currently accepted world view. I was therefore delighted to discover the field of history of science and was fortunate to have several excellent teachers to introduce me to it.

It has been said that there are as many histories as there are observers of history: that each person's view of what was important in the past is unique. Also, the approach, even to the same problems, differs from profession to profession. In the practical realm of "doing" history, that is, actually writing down a coherent and likely reconstruction of past events, the diversity of method and approach to history becomes even more significant than the uniqueness of the individual perspective. Historians do manage to agree about the gross features of the landscape, just as geophysicists agree about the major tenets of their domain of study, even if, in principle, each of them has his or her own unique perceptual contact with nature.

Yet the question of "why do history?" generates markedly different responses to the reconstructive urge. When I started to write history, I was in for a rude shock: I began to perceive how very different the perspectives can be between historians and scientists about the development of science. Beginning from the present understanding of physical law, I visited the past to understand from whence it arose, to pick up a pretty pebble of prescient fact here, a bouquet of wildflower anecdote there, to admire the copse of young trees that would develop later into the giant arbor of 20th century physics.

The trees were there all right, albeit a little hard to recognize in the verdant underbrush, being remarkably similar to other less-recognizable young trees destined to burn down or atrophy before our time. Not only that; the people—the details of their lives—were fascinating: Johannes Kepler, now recognized for his contributions to astronomy, cast horoscopes and made astrological predictions for a living; natural philosopher Isaac Newton reached his inspirations with a tormented and pathologically defensive person-

ality; physicist Albert Einstein did not speak until age 3. Yet the whole of my historical study, once completed, was unsatisfying. All was directed to tracing the paths that led to present-day ideas, embroidered with interesting biographical and scientific facts. Indeed, what emerged was full of facts but lacking in coherence; it was a clever rendition of what was largely already known rather than an enlightening synthetic interpretation of exactly how it had come to be.

I was saved by the prolific undergrowth in that primal forest of the past. The competing young trees were themselves interesting. In some cases, I found them to be even more interesting than those I sought precisely because they failed to appear in the modern forest of scientific theory. Examining the state of knowledge at a point in time and space to understand the wider historical context of the concepts and processes that later assume importance has a great salutary benefit: you come to understand, as in no other way, the contemporary significance of accomplishments of the past. Putting yourself into the time frame of the historical actors, in other words, allows a more accurate historical reconstruction of affairs than does the dissection of the scene to pick out those facts that in retrospect seem to lead to modern understanding.

The historian of ideas Herbert Butterfield has called the latter approach to history "Whig history," in honor of the optimistic progressivist nature of political belief characteristic of the 19th century British Whig party [*Butterfield*, 1931; see also *Butterfield*, 1955]. The viewpoint assumes that we are constantly progressing toward an ever more complete and detailed understanding of nature. The task of history, in this view, is to identify the pathways that have led to our present state of knowledge so as better to encourage progress in the future. To the practicing historian this viewpoint is anathema because it reads into the past motivations and concerns that the historical actors cannot possibly have understood, let alone held.

Since method determines the tools to be used, the Whig intepretation demands different sorts of manuscript and primary documentation than does non-Whig historical research. Because it is the historian's task to interpret past scientific events long after the participants in the research have passed from the scene, it is ultimately the non-Whig interpretation by the historian that prevails in the long-term evaluation of contributions to science. Hence the title of this paper, "the last word on science."

At a meeting that I attended last year of physicists interested in history and historians interested in physics, one of my historical colleagues mentioned this last fact to the scientists present, and as you might imagine, he created quite a stir. Many took great exception to the idea that the historian should, in a sense, outlive the scientist, that the ultimate evaluation of the scientist's contribution could rest in the hands of someone other than a practicing scientist. Yet it is so.

The inevitable difference in viewpoint about history is understandable and, when properly construed, even helpful. However, when it comes to decisions regarding what to save and what to throw out, whom to venerate and whom to forget, when it comes to establishing a set of priorities for encouraging historical research and appreciation of a field as fruitful and diverse as geophysics, the difference in viewpoint can have a marked and long-term influence.

There is a long tradition of historical analysis of developing science. It is of great interest to me, as a historian of science, that the best writing on the subject before the 20th century was done by scientists themselves, many of whom fully appreciated the need to avoid what we call Whiggish interpretation. It says something very important about modern science that in our time this historical interest has largely evaporated from the groups actually doing science. A dissertation could be written on the significance of this transformation. Physicist James Clerk Maxwell was deeply and eloquently involved in assessing the evolution of his subject; much of naturalist Charles Darwin's work intimately involved the extraction of information from historical records; and geologist Charles Lyell, of course, forged his theories on a correlation between historical time and geological strata.

In our time, the perceived connection between doing scientific research and the evolution of science has eroded considerably. This led to a divergence within history of science as well. Let me illustrate this for the case of my own field, history of physics. For a couple of decades after the First World War, history of science was carried on in America by only a few individuals outside the sciences, most notably by George Sarton, the emigré Belgian who maintained but a tenuous relationship with Harvard University. Sarton's form of history, although still useful, is terribly out of date: it is more doxography than history, more a recitation of who thought what and when than it is anything like an analysis of trends in ideas [*Sarton*, 1952]. It almost goes without saying that matters beyond the purely internal development of ideas were not considered.

Then in the 1940's, arising largely out of the companion field of history of philosophy (which used to be a part of the philosophy curriculum), more detailed analytic study was devoted to understanding the meaning and influence of the ideas of science. This is primarily associated with Alexandre Koyré, who influenced a new school of internalist historians of science [*Koyré,* 1939, 1965, 1966]. These historians understood the scientific content of their subjects well and sought historical understanding from exegesis of the scientific ideas themselves.

The profession has recently begun to move away from this "internalist" stance. Yet in several centers, the University of California at Berkeley among them, the belief is still strong that to write anything like proper history of science, one must first understand the science in question.

In the past 10 or 20 years, history of science has moved even closer to methodologies employed in political, economic, social, and intellectual history. This has created stronger interest in the social and economic influences that act on the sciences through time; the institutional patterns as well as the philosophical presuppositions that affect the emerging sciences; sources of funding for scientific research; the sociology of scientific institutions and research strategies; in short, all the issues that come into play in history of nonscientific subjects. This is all to the good, for it puts the sciences where they belong historically: in the category of cultural accomplishments like art, music, and literature, each in its own way a product of its time and place.

In its most extreme form, this new social historiography of science dispenses altogether with need to understand the scientific material. At this, many scientists and historians draw the line. I recall the emphatic warning from Charles Gillispie, one of that middle generation of American historians of science, as he gave the George Sarton lecture to the American Association for the Advancement of Science in January 1980: history of science is threatened by scientifically illiterate practitioners who debase the pure metal of the history of scientific ideas.

What does all of this say for the real problem of deciding what documentation is important for future historians of geophysics? Serious interest in the history of geology and geophysics is growing in the United States. What should be done to foster that growth? What documentation should be saved in this age of the telephone, where the cultured letter of 2 generations ago has all but disappeared?

In discussing the documentation of science, I would like to draw a distinction between three sorts of records: "real-time records," those created at the time of the scientific investigation in question; "public records," those designed to let the world know of the work; and "past-time records," those created after the fact.

In the first category we put laboratory notebooks, memoranda, letters to colleagues, memos of telephone conversations, and the like. Among the public documents constructed to inform others of the work are published papers, as well as technical reports and lectures to communicate results to a larger audience. One particularly useful and revealing record of this second type (and one often overlooked) is the overhead transparency and the illustrative slide prepared for public presentation. In the third category, past-time records, we put reminiscences of and interviews with the principals, who have been asked, like proverbial grandparents, to tell once again how they won the war.

In general, the historical usefulness of these three sorts of documentation is inversely proportional to the distance in time between their creation and the events chronicled. Letters written to colleagues to summarize immediately exciting results or records of telephone conversations are more useful to historians than the published paper, whether in draft form or not. In turn, contemporary publications and the reaction to them by others, as exemplified by annotated reprints, are more useful than any retrospective account of the "golden years" of the field. This is only a generalization, so I must be slightly more specific.

The interview, which serves to flatter a founding father of the field, is frequently the easiest form of documentation for which to obtain funding. Thus there are many oral history projects afoot in such diverse fields as polymer chemistry, military lasers, solid state physics, and innovations in electronics. These efforts consume a sizable proportion of available funds. Properly interpreted as "the view held at the time of the interview of the evolution of events in the past," the interview transcript can be useful. Even so, it rarely justifies the high costs of professional preparation, travel, transcription, editing, and production. Moreover, improperly intepreted as primary documentation of past events, these past-time interviews can be insidiously misleading. A recent multivolume, self-proclaimed "definitive" history of quantum physics from a major publisher is rendered historically almost valueless by its pervasive reliance on hearsay reminiscence [e.g., *Mehra and Rechenberg,* 1982]. Support for interview projects has benefited historical research primarily by providing interviewers the opportunity to canvass important scientists for collections of real-time correspondence that can be cataloged, preserved, and used.

Published papers, of course, constitute the backbone of any historical reconstruction; and an understanding of the preprint/reprint communication system in modern science is essential to tracing influences. To the practicing scientist who uses those reprints, the collection is of great value. To the historian, however, the reprint collection is rarely if ever valuable in and of itself. A catalog of reprints held by this or that scientist will be useful, as would a catalog of the books owned or used by that person, but the documents themselves are usually of more use to the scientist's research team than to the historian. Thus most archival repositories will not store collections of reprints. The exception to this rule is reprints with annotations, which, because of their real-time value, should be treated as primary manuscript material.

In sum then, the differences in historical perspective between scientists and historians are understandable and perhaps inevitable. Many scientists view history as a convenient repository of useful and interesting facts and as a means to chart the course that led to today's views. The historian, if he does his work properly, sees the infinite multiplicity of possible paths that might be trod at a given point in time or, to return to our primal forest metaphor, he or she takes account of both the hardier trees and those that will fall. The "inevitability" of the path followed to today's scientific views appears linear and compelling only in retrospect. It is neither linear nor compelling to the historian whose perspective on the events is chronological, not retrospective.

For this reason, the primary documentation that will most efficiently assist the historian to whom falls the responsibility, desired or not, of having the last word on science, is the real-time rather than the past-time document: the letter, the telephone call, the annotated criticism of another's work, the drafts that chart the struggle to express clearly the scientific result for public consumption. Next in importance are the published accounts themselves, the lecture presentations and graphic aids generated for that purpose. For general information on the social environment within which science develops and for leads to the existence of additional documentation, the historian can also turn with caution to retrospective accounts and interviews with important persons in the field. Yet as Einstein wisely told an aspiring historian: If you wish to know the truth of a scientist's work, pay more attention to what he does than to what he says.

REFERENCES

Butterfield, H., *The Whig Interpretation of History,* Bell, London, 1931.

Butterfield, H., *Man on His Past: The Study of Historical Scholarship,* Cambridge University Press, London, 1955.

Sarton, G., *A History of Science,* Harvard University Press, Cambridge, Mass., 1952.

Koyré, A., *Etudes Galiléennes,* Hermann, Paris, 1939.

Koyré, A., *Newtonian Studies,* Harvard University Press, Cambridge, Mass., 1965.

Koyré, A., *Etudes d'Histoire de la Pensée Scientifique,* Presses Universitaires, Paris, 1966.

Mehra, J., and H. Rechenberg, *The Historical Development of Quantum Theory,* 4 volumes, Springer-Verlag, New York, 1982.

B. Wheaton, Office for History of Science and Technology, University of California, Berkeley, CA 94720.

Some Early Attempts at Theory Formation in Fluid Mechanics

SIMON INCE

Department of Hydrology and Water Resources, University of Arizona, Tucson, Arizona

Despite similarities in the axiomatic structure of theories in mathematics and natural sciences, their objectives are different. Mathematics is devoid of factual or empirical content and need not, and does not, assert anything about the physical universe. The theories in the natural sciences, no matter how well packaged in complex and sophisticated mathematics, are subject to observational and/or experimental verification. Some attempts at theory formation in the history of fluid mechanics illustrate the axiomatic structure of the theories and show the reasons for their failure or success. The basic theoretical structure of physical hydrology, resting on the foundations of Newtonian physics, is deterministic. Mathematical random-process theory is a very powerful technique in the management of many hydrological issues.

INTRODUCTION

The goal of any branch of knowledge is to obtain a theory within the framework of which the body of knowledge can be interpreted, explained, forecast, and events predicted quantitatively with a high degree of probability. The fact that mathematics is often referred to as the queen of sciences is due to the absolute certainty of its results.

For a long time the idea was prevalent in wide circles that if mathematics could be used as the language of natural science, or empirical knowledge formulated in mathematical terms and patterned according to the methodology of mathematics, the certainty of the results of empirical science could also be guaranteed. Western man's confidence in mathematics was so great that, in the nineteenth century, it was believed that the universe could be described by an infinite system of self-solving differential equations.

Then, in the twentieth century, Bertrand Russell shook the foundations of the entire system of sciences by calling mathematics "the only science where one never knows what one is talking about, nor whether what is said is true." The shock treatment liberated the patient from his delusions, which meant that, philosophically, the provisional nature of empirical science was recognized and differentiated from mathematics. It was realized that no proposition in empirical science—no matter how well-packaged in sophisticated mathematics—can attain the certainty of mathematics.

What is the nature of this mathematical certainty, and what is its significance in relation to the structure of physical theory?

Mathematical theory consists in the logical deduction of a proposition from other propositions previously established. This procedure presupposes an arbitrary origin where some propositions are accepted without proof; they are the axioms or postulates. Once the postulates for a theory have been laid down, each further proposition of the theory must be proven exclusively by logical deduction from the postulates; in this process no appeal is allowed to self-evidence, to the characteristics of the physical universe, or to our experiences concerning the behavior of rigid bodies in physical space, etc. The purely deductive character of mathematical proof forms the basis of mathematical certainly. In mathe-

matics, no assertion is made that the axioms have physical or factual content. For this reason a mathematical derivation or deduction is absolutely certain because it is devoid of factual or empirical content.

Historically speaking, however, Euclidean geometry, for example, had its origin in the generalization and systematization of empirical discoveries in connection with the measurement of areas and volumes, the practice of surveying and the development of astronomy. Thus understood, geometry has factual content and may be called physical geometry.

The physical interpretation transforms a given pure geometrical theory into a physical theory of the structure of physical space. Whether this theory is correct in interpreting nature, is not the concern of mathematics but of empirical science. It can only be proven by suitable experimentation and observation. It might seem that an easy way to test the validity of a theory is to test the axioms or postulates. However, in all theories of natural sciences, it is neither necessary nor in general possible, to submit the basic axioms to direct experimental tests. The testing of any scientific theory has to proceed indirectly by testing the deduced theorems. If enough relevant experimental evidence is found supporting the theorems and therefore the theory, it acquires a certain degree of reliability and may be accepted "until further notice." But, however great the degree of confirmation, the possibility always exists that new disconfirming evidence will be found. Herein lies the provisional character of all theories in empirical science. The great importance of mathematics for the empirical sciences lies in the fact that while it does not assert anything about empirical fact, it provides an indispensable and efficient machinery for deducing, from abstract concepts, such as the laws of Newtonian mechanics, concrete consequences which can be tested.

It has become customary to call the sciences which have a high degree of confirmation "exact sciences or hard sciences"; other sciences with lower degrees of confirmation "soft sciences." In fact we should only distinguish natural sciences and social sciences, both empirical, and mathematics. Only mathematics affords us abstract certainty, while all sciences—no matter how much sophisticated mathematics they contain in their theoretical structure—are subject to experimental verification.

Now, what happens if repeated experimental evidence disconfirms the theory? Do we have to reject the theory?

Not necessarily. We can introduce an additional postulate or a corollary which brings the theory in line with the experimental data. This process can be continued until the theory is so loaded with additional hypotheses that it becomes very cumbersome. In that case, a search is warranted for a theory with a new set of axioms, which is more compact, and therefore more elegant.

What happens to the old theories? Should they be relegated to the junkheap of history? Certainly not. Beside forming an integral part of mankind's intellectual heritage and therefore worthy of conservation and study, many of the superseded theories maintain their validity and usefulness within well defined albeit narrower boundaries, and within these limitations, can indeed be utilized very efficiently. Newtonian mechanics is a good example. The theory of mechanics of fluids, which is ultimately based on the laws of Newtonian mechanics, provides an interesting example of the checkered history of theory formation in this field.

Some Theories of Fluid Mechanics

Aristotle's (384–322 B.C.) concept of "horror vacuii" or "nature's abhorrence of a vacuum" could be considered as one of the earliest theories of fluid motion. On the basis of this postulate, we are able to explain why liquid will not flow out of an inverted can with a single small hole punched into it; for if the liquid discharged from the hole, a vacuum would be created at the upper end of the can, which would be contrary to the postulate that nature will not tolerate a vacuum. On the basis of this theory we can predict that the same thing will occur during future experiments; we can also predict that if a second small hole is punched into the can, liquid will pour out of it, since now air can rush in and prevent the formation of a vacuum. This is a perfectly respectable and adequate theory for the phenomenon at hand. The short-coming of the theory is that it is qualitatively and quantitatively very limited and incapable of explaining and/or predicting many of the other observed phenomena of fluid flow.

Another early attempt to formulate a theory of hydrostatics was by Archimedes (287–212 B.C.). [For this and all other references, unless specifically mentioned, see *Rouse and Ince*, 1957]. Judging by the deductive method employed and the validity of the results achieved, Archimedean hydrostatics is an amazing monument in the history of fluid mechanics. He based his theory upon two postulates:

Postulate 1: We pose in principle that the nature of fluids is such that its parts being uniformly placed and continuous, that which is less pressed is displaced by the one which is pressed the more, and that each part is always pressed by the whole weight of the column perpendicularly above it, unless this fluid is enclosed some place or is compressed by something else.
Postulate 2: Let it be granted that bodies which are forced upwards in a fluid are forced upwards along a perpendicular which passes through their center of gravity.

Based on these two postulates, Archimedes derived, by purely mathematical deduction, many of the propositions of hydrostatics and equilibrium of floating bodies. Some twenty centuries later Lagrange commented on this: "This work is one of the most splendid monuments attesting to the genius of Archimedes, for it contains a theory of stability of floating bodies to which the moderns have added very little." Despite the limited scope of Archimedes' hydrostatic the-

ory, the results obtained are impressive. Even more noteworthy, however, is the method employed by Archimedes. It is a perfect example of the method of theory formation discussed in the introduction. There is nothing self-evident or obvious about the axioms, especially when viewed in the general philosophical and scientific atmosphere of the third century B.C. The theorems deduced by purely geometrical considerations, however, can be verified—even though there is no evidence that Archimedes did so himself—and bear out the validity of the postulates.

The next major contribution to hydrostatic theory was by Stevin (1548–1620). Stevin followed the method of Archimedes by setting down postulates and deriving propositions or theorems by logical deduction. His exposition is a good example of the axiomatic method, based on two postulates.

Postulate VI: That the upper surface of the water (what is ordinarily called the fleur d'eau) be plane and level, that is to say, parallel with the horizon.

The other postulate, given in terms of a theorem and proposition, reads:

Any designated body of water maintains whatever position is desired in water, (because if it were not so) . . . . . this water would be in perpetual motion, which is absurd.

As a corollary to the second postulate, Stevin stated that "a solid body parigrave to water holds itself in such position and place as is desired." Broadly interpreted, this implies that if any part of the water is replaced by a rigid body of the same density, the forces exerted on it by the rest of the water will remain unchanged.

On the basis of the two postulates, Stevin demonstrated, for example, that: "The bottom of a mass of water, parallel to the horizon, supports a weight, equal to the weight of a column of water of which the base is the aforesaid bottom and the height a line perpendicular to the horizon, between the bottom and the surface."

Thus, the so-called hydrostatic paradox was shown not be be a paradox at all, but a lawful proposition in a new theory of hydrostatics. In evaluating this theory of hydrostatics, one must still agree with Dijksterhuis that a very essential concept was missing from his reasoning: "Stevin does not know the idea of hydrostatic pressure acting at a point of the liquid equally in all directions; the consequence is that Stevin does not succeed in deducing the various subjects treated by him (Archimedes' principle, hydrostatic paradox, pressure upon an inclined wall) from a single point of view to be brought into relation with static conditions." It would be interesting, however, to perform a thought experiment to demonstrate how close Stevin came to this concept of pressure [*Conant*, 1951].

Consider the postulate of the impossibility of perpetual motion. In Figure 1 is shown a vessel containing a liquid, with a tube running through the sides of the vessel as indicated. If the pressure at A in one direction were greater than in the other, then the liquid would flow around the tube; but this would be perpetual motion, which is impossible by postulation. Hence the pressure in both directions must be the same. It is this concept of pressure which eluded Stevin.

Pascal (1623–1662) reformulated many of Stevin's arguments and demonstrated the principle of the instantaneous transmissibility of pressure. In the case of the hydraulic press, which he called "a machine for multiplying forces,"

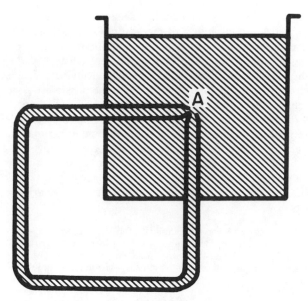

Fig. 1. Demonstration of the concept of pressure based on the impossibility of perpetual motion [*Conant*, 1951]

he introduced the notion of pressure as force per unit area, but there still was no clear statement about the concept of pressure acting equally in all directions. It remained for Euler (1707–1783) to formulate this concept in a clear form and thus to lay the foundations of a more ample and useful theory of hydrostatics. How fruitful a concept this is can perhaps best be judged from the fact that Euler used it also as one of the axioms for a theory of hydrodynamics. In a series of three papers, published in the Mémoires de L'Académie des Sciences de Berlin, 1755, Euler formulated a new theory of fluid mechanics.

The historical importance of these papers is not only that they created a new theory of hydrostatics and hydrodynamics, but in doing so introduced a new principle in mechanics, the continuum concept of matter. In many cases, the history of scientific thought is too intertwined to allow setting definite dates for scientific breakthroughs, except by tradition or for convenience. Euler was influenced, as he himself has admitted, by the ideas of pressure and continuum put forward by John Bernoulli (1667–1748), who first suggested the method of calculating the force acting on an infinitesimal element. "A true and genuine method," Euler called it. Around the same time, d'Alembert was tangling with ideas of internal pressure but was unable to free himself from the atomistic view of matter.

By 1749, Euler had reached the conclusion that further advances in mechanics were only possible by giving up the atomistic view of matter. Instead, he put forward the concept of a continuous medium, defined a particle to mean a point in that continuum, and postulated an internal pressure at a point with equal intensity in all directions. On this one postulate of pressure Euler erected, by logical deduction, a completely new, extremely broad and very simple theory of hydrostatics.

Now the question arises whether this theory is any better than its predecessors and if so, why? Furthermore, is this theory the final formulation of fluid statics? The answer to the first question is easy; it is better because it is simpler, more general, and it works. Up to now we have found no

observation or experiment which contradicts the theory, so until further notice, we accept it as a useful theory.

There is nothing to indicate, however, that this is the ultimate of all possible theories of hydrostatics. It is entirely within the realm of possibility that some day a better theory will be found.

It is customary to indicate the origin of theoretical fluid dynamics with the publication, in 1738, of Daniel Bernoulli's "Hydrodynamica." Leaving aside, for the time being, the legitimacy of this assumption, it is certain that until the beginning of the 18th century there was no broad theory of fluid motion. Daniel Bernoulli's "Hydrodynamica" was a landmark in the history of fluid mechanics, not only because it coined an imaginative and descriptive new name, but also because it attempted to build a wider theory based on the postulate of the conservation of the total energy of a body of fluid. The criticisms of the disciples of Euler are all valid: The "Hydrodynamica" was obscure, complicated and limited in scope, treating mainly some of the problems of applied hydraulics. Nevertheless, it was a theory as defined in the introduction of this paper.

When the scientific climate in a given period in history is fertile for the development of new conceptual schemes, cross-fertilization of ideas does frequently lead to the successful formulation of new theories. The first half of the 18th century was ripe for a theory of hydrodynamics. The efforts of Daniel Bernoulli, d'Alembert, Clairaut, John Bernoulli and others to establish a broader and better theory remained by and large fruitless; but the sparks of insight emanating from their work kindled Euler's imagination. In 1755, Euler's efforts culminated in the publication of a classical hydrodynamics of ideal fluids, which, in form, content and notation, remains essentially unchanged until today.

In Euler's hydrodynamics, the fundamental postulate was again the equality of pressure in all directions at a point in a continuum. In addition, he introduced Newton's momentum principle which he had earlier adapted to apply to an infinitesimal element in a rectangular coordinate system, fixed in space. The third postulate in Euler's theory of fluid motion was the principle of conservation of mass, known in hydrodynamics as the continuity equation. The history of this principle is more difficult to follow, but it is beyond qyestion that the first quantitative statement of the continuity equation is to be found in the writings of Leonardo da Vinci. It is written in simple language, about the flow in a river, expressed in forms of proportions and applicable to incompressible fluids: "A river in each part of its length in an equal time gives passage to an equal quantity of water, whatever the width, the depth, the slope, the roughness, the tortuosity."

In this form the continuity equation was used by the hydraulicians for practical purposes; d'Alembert and John Bernoulli recognized the principle of continuity as a fundamental notion in hydrodynamics, but credit for the clear and elegant formulation of the principle of mass conservation in a continuum must go to Euler. Euler treated the problem in its full generality by extending his analysis to embrace compressible fluids.

Now, once again, it is pertinent to ask why this theory is better than, say, Bernoulli's. It is better because it works better; that is, it explains and predicts a larger range of phenomena with a greater degree of reliability and with greater economy of intellectual effort.

Is this the final theory of hydrodynamics? Obviously not, since already there have been occasions when disconfirming evidence put into question the validity of the theory. D'Alembert's paradox—that the net thrust on a sphere in a flow field was calculated to be zero—was a severe blow to the prestige of Eulerian hydrodynamics, which we now call the theory of potential flow. To bring it in line with the experimental results, additional hypotheses had to be introduced. One such postulate was the free streamline concept, which, while still working with an ideal fluid, was successful in overcoming some of the more blatant departures of the theory from observation. Other important additional postulates were the concepts of viscosity and boundary layer, the introduction of which enlarged considerably the scope and the limits of validity of hydrodynamic theory. However, Eulerian hydrodynamics is still very effectively used in the theory of deep water waves and in the theory of flow through porous media.

Euler's success was largely due to his ability to break away from the conventional atomistic thinking of his contemporaries and to visualize a continuous medium. It would be absurd to maintain that this is the only valid way to hydromechanics. It is quite possible that an even better theory can be formulated on atomistic concepts. But, until then, and so long as it works, we provisionally believe in what we have.

The conceptual framework of physical hydrology rests on the foundations of Newtonian physics, and, as such, its theoretical structure is deterministic. Yet we find it necessary to use the mathematics of probability and random functions to overcome the uncertainties encountered in its operation. Does this mean that something is wrong with the conceptual framework, and that we should now try to move away from Newtonian physics and seek a better understanding by adapting the tenets of modern physics? Would there be a philosophical necessity and an operational advantage? I think not; and I have the feeling that physicists wrestling with the problems of the particle zoo would advise us against such a move at this time. Even though the possibility is not precluded that some day we might not find a better theoretical foundation, for the present and the near future the deterministic structure is adequate; the imperfections and uncertainties are not conceptual. For the practical and practicing hydrologist, to whom all hydrological processes such as rainfall, runoff, infiltration, etc. appear to be random, I recommend the point of view of Bras and Rodríguez-Iturbe:

> Randomness and the applicability of random-process theory may be inherent in the structure of the process or may result from the lack of knowledge or from the scale of observation. Many arguments, mainly philosophical, exist to refute or justify the above statement. The techniques and philosophy in this book have proved their usefulness to us. The nonbeliever hopefully will be impressed by the power of the various techniques and therefore accept them. [*Bras and Rodriguez-Iturbe*, 1984]

REFERENCES

Conant, J. B., *Science and Common Sense*, 371 pp., Yale University Press, New Haven, CT, 1951.

Bras, R. L., and I. Rodríguez-Iturbe, *Random Functions and Hydrology*, 559 pp., Addison-Wesley, Reading, MA, 1984.

Rouse, H., and S. Ince, *History of Hydraulics*, 264 pp., Iowa Institute of Hydraulic Research, Iowa City, IA, 1957.

S. Ince, Department of Hydrology and Water Resources, University of Arizona, Tucson, AZ   85721.

Medieval Saint Barbara Worship and Professional Traditions in Early Mining and Applied Earth Sciences

H.O. Pfannkuch

Department of Geology and Geophysics, University of Minnesota

From the early Middle Ages through the Renaissance and up to the Age of Enlightenment, the applied earth sciences were synonymous with, or largely revolving around mining and its traditions. The following is an essay to look at this historically important period of the early geo-sciences from the perspective of the worship of Saint Barbara, the patron saint of mining. Affiliation to her patronage was very strong because of the specific environmental conditions and dangers involved in mining, hence, St. Barbara served as a rallying point and focus around which professional attitudes and traditions developed in the early mineral industries. The legend of St. Barbara who suffered martyrdom from the hands of her own father, is presented in its historical context of the persecution of the early Christians under the Emperor Diocletian in the declining Roman Empire. Her veneration spread from the Netherlands in the 14th Century to Central and Western Europe. The connection with mining is traced back to 15th Century Bohemia and Saxony, from where it rapidly spread and solidly established itself in other mining regions of Central Europe. The importance of mining and its socio-economic context is documented in scientific works of Agricola, including hydrologic subjects, and by the rich collections of sacred and secular art, art objects, uniforms and paraphernalia produced and in use in the principal mining districts of Central Europe.

THE EARLY EARTH SCIENCES AND THEIR ROLE IN THE HISTORY OF SCIENCE

At the end of the Middle Ages and the beginning of the Renaissance, fundamental changes in the approach to natural sciences occurred. Field experience and observation of nature was added to, or replaced, scholastic theoretization and speculation based on the uncritical reliance on ancient sources and writings of the early natural philosophers. In the applied earth sciences, a great upsurge of popular and state interest in mining and its economic benefits led to the development of innovative technologies and economic and administrative structures. These served as models for the engineering approach in the mechanical arts, the institution of technical universities or professional schools, the dissemination of technical knowledge. The establishment of pre-capitalist forms of the means and organization of production, preceded by several centuries those used at the height of the industrial revolution. Development of the medieval mining industry in Central Europe is therefore not only of interest to the mining industries of today, but also to the applied earth sciences at large, and to history of science in general. In this article, we shall examine the history of mining technology

and applied earth science during this important period in time by focussing on the worship of St. Barbara (Figure 1), especially as it was practiced in the mineral industries. In particular, we shall look at the development of professional attitudes and traditions, the rise of mining technology, the dissemination of knowledge of the mining arts and earth sciences through early treatises, and the founding of technical teaching institutions in the 18th century.

The most important figure in this context is Georgius Agricola who studied and described phenomena of general geology, mineralogy and ore formation and the art of mining in his best known works between 1530 to 1556. Although not exclusively focussed on hydrology Agricola presents for his time the most complete and up-to-date state of knowledge about general and groundwater hydrology because of its great importance in the operation and dewatering of mines and ore generation by mineralized solutions. The only other extensive work dealing with groundwater dates from the first century A.D. by Vitruvius.

My thesis is that the mining profession, in choosing and settling on St. Barbara, who already was a very popular saint, as their exclusive patron, created a rallying point that would not have been possible with a diversity of other saints, or even local non-specific patrons as had been the case when the industry was in its early and locally fragmented state. This rallying around one saint created an atmosphere of solidarity which went across hierarchic levels within one mine, and extended horizontally to other mining operations locally and regionally throughout Central Europe. The intensity of her veneration is clearly linked to the environmental conditions and dangers inherent in many underground mining operations, past and present, where the individual miner cannot survive without complete reliance on his team.

It would be presumptuous to maintain that the solidarity created through St. Barbara's worship was the strongest or even the only factor without which the organizational and administrative changes, and the introduction of modern technology, in the medieval mining industries would not have occurred. But it seems that the veneration and the atmosphere of solidarity developed around it, at least contributed to a more rapid transformation of the early fragmented and small scale operations to actually quite modern forms of organization and economic structures that still mark the mining industry in Central Europe. As a supporting point and corroboration, I would like to point to the enormous wealth of art objects and artifacts, including ceremonial paraphernalia and mining lore, in Central Europe, which is unparalleled in other professions of the time, and which reflects to me, this inner coherence and solidarity of the early mining industry.

Fig. 1 Saint Barbara, engraving by the Master E.S., 15th Century. The attributes of the saint shown are: the crown as a symbol of sainthood or document of her high birth, in her right hand a peacock's feather, symbol of immortality, in her left a book, symbol of her erudition, the chalice and host in a niche symbol of a happy death, and the tower with the three windows in the background.

THE LEGEND OF ST. BARBARA

The Legenda Aurea or Golden Legend

We shall need to look at the general legend of St. Barbara, and concentrate on those aspects that are of particular interest to her becoming the patron saint of miners. Several versions of the legend exist, and many embellishments were added during the Middle Ages at the height of her general veneration. Some of the very early versions are Greek manuscripts, specifically one by the Byzantine Simon Metaphrastes from the 10th century. One of the most popular is the Latin version of the history of saints *Legenda Aurea*, the golden legend, written by Jacobus a Voragina, Archbishop of Genoa in the 13th century. This is the version on which many of the representations of the saint in medieval art are based, [*Daras*, 1870; *Peine*, 1896].

"When Maximianus was emperor, a rich noble heathen, Dioscurus, lived in Nicomedia. He had a beautiful daughter named Barbara. To keep her away from the temptations of the world, he confined her in a tower" [*Peine*, 1986]. Barbara was very intelligent and through her own reasoning concluded that the idols her parents venerated could not be

gods, and that some higher being would have had to create them. At this time it became known in Nicomedia that a wise man, Origen, of great intelligence and religious persuasion lived in Alexandria where he taught the Christian religion. Barbara wrote to him, presented her thoughts and asked him to counsel her. Origen responded by letter and sent a teacher, Valentinus, with religious books for her to study. She received him with great veneration and became his most ardent pupil. After instruction about the Holy Trinity, and the Holy Sacrament of baptism, she was secretly baptized by Valentinus in her tower.

Many suitors from among the nobles of the land asked her father that he select one of them as her husband. Barbara angrily refused. To placate her, Dioscurus hired artisans and artists to have a bathhouse built for her, then he left for an extended trip. In his absence, Barbara persuaded the masons to add a third window to the two on the south wall. After returning her father immediately noticed the third window and asked his daughter about it. Barbara answered that she had ordered it because the three windows give light to the entire world. "It is the three that illuminate the world and guide the course of the stars, namely the Father, the Son, and the Holy Ghost, and these are the Holy Trinity." Her father realized that she had become a Christian and drew his sword in rage to kill her. Barbara fled through the wall which opened miraculously to let her escape and hid in a large cavern in a rocky area on top of a mountain. Dioscurus and his henchmen searching for her asked two sheperds if they had seen Barbara. The first one, fearing for her, swore that he knew nothing. The other one, however, pointed his finger in the direction of her hiding place. Immediately his sheep turned into locusts and he himself into a marble statute. Dioscurus dragged Barbara by her hair to the Roman governor Marcianus to accuse his own daughter and to insist that she be punished in the most severe way. The governor impressed by her beauty, offered to spare her if she abjured, but Barbara remained steadfast. Enraged, the governor had her tortured and flogged with heavy whips until her flesh was torn and her body was covered with blood. Thrown back into the dungeon, Christ himself appeared to Barbara and in the deep of the night encouraged her not to fear the menace of the tyrant and to be steadfast under torture, then all her wounds disappeared. The next morning the governor saw that the marks of her torture had vanished, but still ordered to have her burnt with torches, beat on the head with hammers, and her breasts cut off with the sword. As she still suffered these tortures with courage he drove her naked through town flogging and whipping her. An angel descended at this moment to cover her with a white stole. Then Marcianus orderd her put to death and her irate father himself dragged her to the place of execution. On the way she implored the Lord to grant absolution to all those that are faced with sudden death without having had the possibility to confess if they implore her name. Her father beheaded her with his own sword. "Was no longer her father but her executioner," says an old German rendition from 1563 [*Wicelium*]. Immediately thereafter, lightning struck him and not even his ashes could be found. So far the golden legend, the basis for the veneration St. Barbara has received by various groups and professions.

Some later versions of the legend particularly interested in justifying her as the patron saint of miners place the story in the silver mining region of Laurion in Greece where Barbara was sheltered by sympathetic miners underground, but when she ascended the mine shaft her father caught her and decapitated her outside the mine [Koch, 1964].

The original version, however, also furnishes justification to relate her to mining, namely the miraculous opening of a rock to serve as a hiding place, and the death of Dioscurus by lightning was extended to death by artificial lightning bolts such as gun powder explosions used to blast ore and introduced in the late 16th century and early 17 century.

Geographic and Historical Context of the St. Barbara Legend

The city where Barbara lived is most often given as Nicomedia, in those days the capital of Bithynia in the northern part of Asia Minor near the Maramara Sea. Its present name is Ismid. Although it was a small place, it was the residence of the Roman Emperor Diocletian. Often manuscripts mention a town Heliopolis in Galatia, not too far from Nicomedia. In the Middle Ages, at the height of her veneration, a large number of cities throughout the Middle East and Europe claimed to be the place of her martyrdom [Peine, 1896].

Somewhat more ambiguity exists about the time of her death. The day of December 4th is universally accepted as St. Barbara's day, or miners day, but the exact year claimed for her death is open to question. The most likely period is towards the end of the reign of Maximian (286 to 310 AD), a co-emperor under Diocletian. Maximian is known in history to have been a more severe persecutor of Christians than Diocletian. He started one wave of persecution in Bithynia by razing the church in Nicomedia 303 AD. Other versions place her under the reign of Emperor Maximinus (235-238) who succeeded Alexander Severus, undoubtedly in order to make her correspondence with Origen (died in 254) more plausible. This period of the declining Roman Empire was rather tumultuous, with more than 20 emperors and co-emperors following each other in short succession between 234 and 286 AD. Of these several were named Maximian and Maximinus, and the different manuscripts in Latin and Greek, were somewhat loose about the exact spelling of the name.

The important point is that the origin of the St. Barbara legend is placed in an area and a period of time in history where great upheavals, political and religious, took place—these were difficult and uncertain times for Christians and non Christians alike, and it is logical that they sought help from wherever it would come—one source were patron saints who interceded for individuals under general, as well as more special circumstances. Besides the general attributes of sainthood and interceding St. Barbara early on was implored by those who faced sudden death without having time to confess and obtain absolution.

DEVELOPMENT OF ST. BARBARA WORSHIP

Geographic Diffusion of the St. Barbara Legend in Western and Central Europe.

The legend of St. Barbara originated in the 5th century: From Nicomedia, where miraculous healings were reported from near her grave site, the worship of St. Barbara and her veneration spread rapidly throughout the Middle East, especially to Constantinople where her remains were said to have been transported in 565, and where, around the year 900, a St. Barbara church was constructed. The Copts erected a chapel in honor of the saint in Cairo during the 7th century. In Edessa, now in Turkey, one of the first monasteries in her name was founded in 861, and somewhat later, another church in her honor was erected in the province of Capadocia also in Turkey. She became the patron saint of Syria and during the 10th century St. Barbara's day was one of the main holidays in Antioch.

Although she is mentioned in the compilation of saints, the *Martyrologium Romanum*, around 700 AD, the veneration of St. Barbara in western Europe was greatly facilitated by the exchanges with the near and Middle East that took place during the period of the Crusades from the end of the 11th century to the end of the 13th century. Around 1003 AD her reliquiae had supposedly been transferred from Constantinopel to San Marcos in Venice, but many other towns in Italy, especially Rome, claim to posses reliquiae of the saint.

The Saint Barbara adoration found a firm place in the church services especially in the Netherlands from where it rapidly spread through France, Germany, Bohemia, Hungary and Italy. By way of Spain and Portugal, St. Barbara was introduced into the new world [Koch, 1964].

General Patronages of St. Barbara

When, in the 14th century, the plague ravaged Europe, the frightened populace sought protection from the saints of heaven, since no help was found on earth. During this time people believed that a group of 14 saints had special powers of intercession; they were called the 14 intercessors, and they were ardently invoked. They are first mentioned in Munich during the year of the plague of 1348. St. Barbara was one of them. She also became part of the "four main virgin saints (*quatuor virgines capitalibus*) including besides her, St. Catherine, St. Margaret and St. Dorothy. They have a special place in the entourage of St. Mary and are often depicted around her in medieval paintings. On altar pieces and religious art, St. Barbara is often joined with St. Catherine [Koch, 1964].

As part of the intercessors and as part of the four capital virgins, St. Barbara was invoked to intercede for the dying, to allow them time to confess and receive the last sacraments before expiring. This makes her one of the eucharist saints and she was also called *mater confessionis* [Réau, 1958]. Within certain parishes in France, fraternal societies (Confreredries de la Bonne Mort) or corporations were formed in honor of St. Barbara. The earliest of these was established in Laval in 1481, and some of the richest were found in Bruxelles, Poitiers and Bourges. Numerous were the pious accounts of miracles she had performed to help the dying. Her other important patronage was to protect against lightning and the dreaded plague [de Lapparent, 1926].

In a more specific way, St. Barbara became the patron saint of various professions which extracted certain aspects from her legend to justify their relation to the saint. Because she protected from fire and lightning, she became, from the 15th century on, the patron of artillerists, whose thundering cannons throw artifical lightning bolts, and who are constantly exposed to accidental explosions and to sudden death in times of war. Even today, the store room for explosives, or formerly gunpower, on French warships is called "Sainte Barbe". Other professions having to deal with the dangers of fire, placed themselves under her protection: fire fighters,

Fig. 2. The legend of St. Barbara, oil on wood by the Master of the Saint Barbara Legend (Flemish School) end of the 15th Century. Right portion of the central panel of a triptyk. It depicts different episodes of the legend notably her baptism, her miraculous flight into a rock cavern, and her appearance before the judge. (With permission: Musées Royaux des Beaux-Arts de Belgique)

foundry workers and others who produce metals with fire. Because church bells were rung in times of great danger, she has also been claimed as patron of bell ringers and carillonneurs.

Besides these large groups and professions, numerous other minor professions or groups that have found some connection with the legend and claim her as their patron. Because of her interest in learning, she is also the patron of students, librarians and book publishers; of architects and masons, because of their involvement to build the bathhouse, and of prisoners because she was kept in a tower.

This great popularity explains the multitude and large number of representations of St. Barbara in the arts (Figure 2). Practically all major medieval and Renaissance artists have created images of her in painting, sculptures or print. With the advent of the printing press, popular representations found their way into many homes [*Peine*, 1986; *de Lapparent*, 1926].

ST. BARBARA AND HER VENERATION IN MINING

The Legend as Basis for St. Barbara's Status in Mining

The reason St. Barbara has become the preferred patron saint of miners must be connected to the particular environmental conditions in mines and the dangers connected with working underground, and it is certainly directly linked to her patronage for all those that face sudden death. Clearly other episodes from her legend reinforced this particular connection, such as her hiding in a cavern in a rock. Her patronage to protect against fire and lightning appear to be drawn from the manner of death of her executioner father.

Further embellishment of the legend to place her martyrdom in the silver mining region of Laurion in Greece must have been an *a posteriori* justification after she already had been accepted as the patron of miners. Exactly when and where her veneration originated specifically in the context of mining is not clear but it must have been connected either with the mining regions of Saxony, Bohemia, and Hungary, or those of Alpine Austria. One of the earliest specific associations of her with mining is the erection (1388 to 1585) of the Gothic St. Barbara Cathedral in the mining town of Kuta Hora in Bohemia. The cathedral is on the site of an even earlier St. Barbara Chapel [*Koch*, 1964].

Mining activities in Central Europe clearly antedate this time, but in the early stages other patrons may have preceded her. Quite often the role was given to the local saint, meaning that different localities even within one mining district would have different patrons. Sometimes other saints became patrons of the miners in a given area. The ore mining districts in Saxony and Silesia had St. Joachim and St. Anna, hence the mining towns of Joachimsthal and Annaberg. Even St. Nicholas was at one time a mining patron, as was St. Daniel in the Alpine mining regions.

As the veneration of St. Barbara became more and more exclusive to the mining profession, which started to develop and become an important socio-economic factor during the end of the Middle Ages, she was separated from the group of 14 intercessors and the four *virgines capitales* to lead a more independent existence directed more closely to the needs of the mining profession [*Koch*, 1964].

Introduction of St. Barbara to European Mining Regions

From the 13th century on, and especially since the rapid

rise and expansion of mining activities in the 14th and 15th centuries, St. Barbara is the undisputed patron saint of mining. Even in the mining districts of the southwestern United States, veneration of St. Barbara has developed and still persists in the form of "Santos" [*Eimon*, 1985]. It was introduced through the Spanish conquests in Latin America.

The principal mining regions in Central Europe from the 11th century to the 17th century are those of Silesia (e.g. city of Annaberg), Saxony around Freiberg, Bohemia with Kuta Hora and Joachimsthal, upper Hungary around Schemnitz, the alpine ore districts in Tyrol, and the Harz Mountains. Later in the 18th and 19th centuries, the coal mining regions of Upper Silesia, and of the Ruhr, Borinage and Saar came into being, and St. Barbara was readily accepted there also.

In the mining regions, numerous churches, chapels and altars within churches were dedicated to St. Barbara, many mines were named after her, and the effigy of St. Barbara turns up on coins such as the St. Barbara pennies coined in Annaberg [*Peine*, 1896]. Most of the mines had small chapels or altars for St. Barbara, where the miners would offer a prayer for protection before descending into the earth. Celebration of her feast day on December 4th was common practice, with church services, parades in elaborate uniforms and with flags and pennants of the different mines or mining associations, and libations afterwards. In most areas, no work was done on her day, for fear of attracting her ire.

My thesis is that St. Barbara, as the patron saint of mining, served as a rallying point around which a professional coherence and an *esprit de corps* could develop in the mining industry. Certainly St. Barbara worship was not the only or even the most important element in establishing this coherence, without which many of the structural changes and advances in the mining industries could not have been accomplished. Other factors had to do with the high status and preferential treatment accorded to the Central European miner; technical innovations and new ways of capitalization; the interest of the rulers in the mining industry, including their direct participation in the exploitation and their implacement of an administrative system that permitted control over the industry. For example, the rise of the Habsburg dynasty in Austria would not have been possible without the wealth generated from the alpine mining industry.

The regional and supra regional coherence in the mining industry was aided by the fact that by the end of the 14th century, St. Barbara essentially was the universally accepted patron. The situation would have been different had there remained a large fragmentation with local or regional saints. An additional positive point is the fact that St. Barbara was already a very popular saint in Western Europe in general; therefore her acceptance by the miners was greatly facilitated. Furthermore, specific elements in her legend were directly applicable to the miner's conditions of work and his particularly dangerous environment. Some of the other elements that contributed to the exceptional standing of the mining industry in Central Europe will be elucidated in the following discussion of mining in medieval and Renaissance Europe.

MINING AND RELATED HYDROLOGY IN MEDIEVAL EUROPE

Historical Development of Mining in Europe

In order to understand the importance of the mining industry in medieval Europe, some historical notes are in order. Britain had an important mining industry already in Roman times. As a matter of fact, part of the reasons for the Roman invasion was to obtain access and control over the Cornish tin mines. Interestingly enough its development and traditions evolved quite differently from Central Europe, although mining was one of the most important bases of its economy from early times through the industrial revolution. France on the other hand, never had any extremely rich and important ore deposits of the scarce metals, particularly silver, so important as the monetary base of early medieval Europe. Germany under Roman occupation had no mineral exploitation; as Tacitus remarks in his *Germania*: "there is no trace of metals, but then there have also not been any diggings" [quoted in: *Gimpel*, 1975]. This changed drastically with the find of the silver ore veins of the Rammelsberg in the Harz Mountains in 968. The mine and its associated beneficiation and smelting operation were in full swing in the 11th century. In 1136, the ores of Freiberg in Saxony were discovered after samples had been sent to Rammelsberg for assessment. German miners from these regions were very sought after, and their labor aided in the establishment of mining industries in Iglau (Bohemia) and Shemnitz and Kremnitz (Hungary). In the 12th century, German miners were invited to Transylvania and Serbia, then under the Ottoman rule. As a proof of that influence remains the fact that the basic mining vocabulary in Turkish is essentially German. In the 14th century the copper mine of Stora Kopparberget in Sweden and somewhat later the silver mines of Kongsberg in Norway were started, essentially with German miners [*Gimpel*, 1975].

Miners enjoyed exceptional privileges such as exemption from the usual taxes and tolls as well as from military service. Certain regions with rich ore deposits and thriving mining industries were given the privilege of free towns (Bergfreie Stadt) where all citizens enjoyed administrative advantages and greater freedom. Such cities were Freiberg, Goslar, Iglau, Kuttenberg (Kuta Hora) and Joachimsthal for example.

The rise of the medieval mining industry between the 11th and 13th centuries is linked to what *Jean Gimpel* [1975] calls the "first industrial revolution". It was characterized by an intense technological activity, and was extremely fruitful in new inventions both on the mechanical, agricultural and organizational level. It was marked by a population explosion. Free enterprise was favored; new forms of capitalization through stock companies and the division of labor were introduced. All these factors were either directly applied in the mining industries or originated with it. The search for new materials and minerals in greater quantities was vastly accelerated. Precious metals were in demand for obvious reasons by a larger and more prosperous population and as the base for the monetary system, but also iron was required to meet the needs of this first industrial revolution. Innovations in the methods and technology of warfare drastically increased the demand for metals—base metals and iron. Large forces of mercenary soldiers had to be armed, new techniques of fortification placed their own demand on metal building parts, and the more effective and protective fortifications engendered more and heavier weapons for the assault, such as cannons (bronze) and ammunition (first iron cannonballs from 1370). Besides internal warfare the crusades were great consumers of men and materials. Richard I ordered 50,000 horseshoes made in 60 iron works in the forest of Dean for his first crusade. New and more efficient exploitation of water power allowed for higher and more efficient output from mechanized hammer works, and the greater availability and lower unit prices created in turn greater demands for the metals [*Gimpel*, 1975].

The direct repercussions of this higher demand on the mining industry were the need for larger unit operations and deeper mines. This required larger and larger machines and mechanical equipment at a scale unheard of in other industries and only paralleled by the war machinery. Other industries also experienced a phenomenal rise, but the increase in output was obtained mainly by increasing the number of production units, which operated more or less at the same scale as before the technological and industrial revolution. Richard I had his horseshoes made in 60 smith shops of about equal size and efficiency, not in three or in one single gigantic plant. In the mining industry the scale of operations could not be handled by simply adding more small operations. The easily accessible ores had been mined and greater depths had to be attained for which new machines for material handling and hoisting had to be introduced. Going to deeper mines meant that vertical shafts had to be constructed. These posed problems for the dewatering of the mine workings which formerly had been drained by slightly inclined addits permitting free flow out of the hillside. Dewatering could no longer be handled by simple lifting and hoisting but had to be done by continuous lifting schemes via bucket wheels, or later by pumps. Note that even in the industrial revolution of the 18th-19th century, the first steam engines were constructed especially for the dewatering of mines by pumping. As mines became deeper, natural air circulation became a problem and machines for mine ventilation albeit on a primitive scale had to be invented, implemented, and driven by various forms of energy [*Suhling*, 1980].

Going to greater depths increased the cost and the risk of mineral exploration. These costs and risks as well as the cost for the mining machinery could no longer be shouldered by one or a few individuals, therefore stock companies were founded, forerunners of present day shareholder corporations, which were able to generate the capital necessary to sink and equip a mine and to operate it while at the same time spreading the risk of running out of ore over a larger number of shareholders. On the other hand large fortunes were amassed by the new and rising class of bourgeois merchants as well as by smaller speculators. Some of the larger firms based in southern Germany, such as the Fugger, Welser, Pammgartner and others, were able to grant large credits from their mining profits to secular and ecclesiastic princes and thereby to indirectly exercise great influence on political decisions and matters of state. Mining as an economic and engineering activity became a subject of great popular imagination which is expressed in the large number of popular and technical treatises in mining of the times [*Suhling*, 1980].

Organizational Innovations in Mining

Parallel to the technical and socio-economic innovations, a new system of mine administration and hierachic organization was introduced in central Europe, especially Germany. They had far reaching implications for information transfer,

education and the foundation of professional schools in the arts of mining and metallurgy which were to become the precursors of todays technical universities.

Since early times the mining industry had its own legal system with jurisdiction over matters of mining and exploration. This was separate from the common courts of law in the land, and it was more or less directly under the ruler of the land. This was, in part, a necessity since civil courts would generally lack the technical understanding of the mining process; a specially trained court intimately familiar with the mining arts would be more efficient. The jurors were selected among miners, shareholders and mine officials. On the other hand this system allowed bypassing civil procedures in matters such as access to land for exploration and exploitation, and litigation about claims and pollution, and have them tried before a court inherently sympathetic to the interests of the mining industry. It was also tacitly or actively supported by the rulers in whose interest it was to have as few impediments as possible to the development of the mining industry, a source of direct or indirect benefits to the state treasury [*Heilfurth*, 1981].

In addition to the judicial system, the state needed a class of civil servants that combined the technical and the administrative skills necessary either to run the state owned mines or to control and assure compliance with the mining laws and regulations in the privately owned mines. The administrative structure was very hierarchic and detailed to the last degree. The rank and position of a given member was expressed in colorful uniforms, insignia and paraphernalia, not unlike military hierarchies. Control over mines was assured by the police power invested in the civil servants to lead investigations, to fine or even close down mines not in compliance. In order to assure compliance with the state laws and current and accepted practice of mining methods, most of the management and technical personnel in the higher echelons in privately owned mines went through the same educational process and passed through the same in-service training as the civil servant. As a matter of fact, many engineers after having obtained civil service status slipped over to private industry, not unlike present day IRS agents who join large corporations to guide them through the complexities of the tax laws with the knowledge of the insider. The training of these highly specialized functionaries made it necessary to establish a common technical literature on the subject of mining and to assure the proper and efficient education of the upper echelons in institutions of higher learning. At the miner's level a system of apprenticeship and practical instruction was in practice.

Mining Publications and Professional Schools

The early diffusion and popularization of mining arts was in general not carried out by practitioners of the craft, who often were quite secretive about their store of empirical knowledge, but by educated laymen with a broad range of interests and a humanistically influenced pedagogical motivation. They explored the rich empirical knowledge for works of instruction to the neophyte and continuing education of miners, but also for general scientific interests dealing with mineralogical or pharmaceutical studies, and for the enlightenment of the general public. The source for this information was based on the experience and philosophy of mining in Central Europe, particularly Germany. One of the first texts was written by the physician and mayor of Freiberg, Ulrich Rülein von Calw about 1500 *Ein nützlich bergbaubüchleyn*—(useful little book on mining), many others followed; the most important and extensive one is Georg Agricola's posthumously edited *De re metallica libri XII* [1556] of which an admirable English translation by Herbert and Lou Hoover exists. In Agricola's preface to the Minister of Interior of the King of Saxony he says about the content of the work: ''I shall indicate the methods by which one can find the ores, how one has to mine them, prepare them and smelter them, and on the whole the craft of preparing and separation of metals and solid mixtures. I shall also explain the mining machineries and much more.'' For more than 200 years after its edition Agricola's encyclopedic monograph of mining practices remained the most regarded standard work both inside and outside of Germany.

Agricola is a true representation of the multifaceted renaissance man, interested in many aspects of nature. He had studied humanities in Italy, then medicine and became a practicing physician in the mining regions of Saxony, notably in St. Joachimsthal where his interest in the mining industry originated and culminated in the authorship not only of the *de re metallica*, but many other treatises on technical and earth science subjects [*Heilfurth*, 1981].

His works as those of others which were based on observation and empiricism in the earth sciences became the stock and foundation for teaching at the newly instituted academies of mining science (Bergakademien) or professional mining schools that were created in the 18th century to meet the demand for trained mining engineers and officials. The curriculum in these academies was broad and founded on the inclusion of basic sciences such as mathematics, mechanics and mineralogy in clear recognition of their applicability to advanced and scientific methods in mining and metallurgy. This philosophy and basic approach makes these academies precursors of present day technical universities or Institutes of Technology.

Many institutions dispute the honor of having been the first mining academy to be founded, often the different interpretations of the dates is due to the fact that lower institutions at the level of educating mine foremen and managers confuse the issue. In general most of the traditional academies were founded in the middle and towards the end of the 18th century, such as Freiberg in Saxony, academic home of Werner, Clausthal Zellefeld in the Harz, Leoben in Austria, Metz in France, Schemnitz in Hungary and Kongsberg in Norway. The only full university that introduced a curriculum and courses in mining was Prague, Czechoslovakia [*Heilfurth*, 1981].

The Role of Hydrology in Agricola's Work

Interest in water as it moves on and within the earth was based on practical and more theoretical considerations. Up to the 18 century water was the principal factor in limiting the depth to which underground workings could penetrate. It is therefore not surprising that Agricola dedicates a large portion of the *de re metallica* to an explanation of the origin of mine waters, both from surface inflow as well as subsurface infiltration, and to an exhaustive description of counter measures and the technology of removing and hauling mine waters. He addresses methods of deviation of surface waters from mine workings, of proper design of mine drainage and

Fig. 3. Water bailing works, woodcut from Book 6, de re metallica, 1556.

upkeep of drainage channels, the construction of mine sumps and auxiliary shafts for water collection and hauling in Book 5 [*Agricola* 1556].

Book 6 deals with a detailed description of the available equipment to collect water and to lift it. He describes lifting where water and ore are winched intermittently with buckets and water bags. This was for shallow and relatively dry mines. Other technology consisted of elaborate machines that hoisted water by drawing chains of dippers through the sump, by suction pumps, or by rag and drain pumps. In general, the largest machine on a mine working was the one for hauling water since the feasibility and the existence of the mine was predicated upon the timely removal of the mine waters. Figure 3 gives an indication of the scale of these operations, a complicated hoisting structure for large water-bags with reversible water driven wheels, 36 feet in diameter. Other authors such as *Balthasar Rössler* [1700] who had worked about a century after Agricola gave examples of economic feasibility studies and cost factors for pumping and mine dewatering. Rössler also seems to have remarked on the time lag between precipitation events and water accumulation into the mine. He therefore attributed mine waters to infiltration through joints and fissures.

Agricola [1556] further discusses how recognizing the nature of spring waters by taste can lead to the discovery of minerals. He also clearly understood the importance of surface water resources for power to drive the hoisting machinery and washing operations and for the general welfare of the mining operations. And in the first book of *de re metallica* he discusses environmental problems caused by mining such as the pollution of streams and deforestation.

Of far greater importance to earth sciences and geohydrology are two of Agricola's earlier works; *de ortu et causis subterraneorum lilbri V* [1546a] (about the origin and causes of subterraneous phenomena) and *de natura eorum qua effluunt ex terra libri IV* [1546b] (about the nature of effluents from the earth) in which his extraordinary attention to water and its manifestations becomes obvious. This stems from his peripatetic view of the four basic elements: water, earth, fire, air, which by their mixing give rise to all material substances. Although the aristolelian world view no longer can serve as a basis for explaining rock formation, these two works of Agricola nevertheless give evidence of his keen observation of nature, and clarity in critically reviewing ancient theories as far as possible within the framework of the then existent scientific and philosophic ideas. He had an astonishingly clear view about water and a modern approach to its description and classification. This is done according to quality, taste, color and provenance and occurrence such as in springs, wells, rain, snow melt, oceans, lakes and swamps. He clearly states that well water is groundwater made mobile through human intervention, understands the relationship between depth to water and climate. He even has some grasp about well hydraulics: "when a well is dug all water near it is drawn down to the lower spot be it flowing from the sea or be it collecting from rain falls" [*Agricola*, 1546a]. Agricola's encyclopaedic knowledge extends to concepts of the hydrologic cycle, base flow, groundwater temperatures and flow in karst terranes. On the other hand, he is still beholden to aristolelian views that groundwater exists in lakes beneath the earth and that ocean waters recirculating through the ground are purified to form freshwater.

Agricola's interest in water stems from his public health concerns—he was a physician and elected official as mayor of Joachimsthal—and from his interst in ore formation, and other geologic processes linked to water such as erosion and sedimentation. Although his ore formation theory based on the peripatetic view is outdated, his observation and description of ore forming minerals, their attributes and classification follows a modern approach. With his peripatetic theory that ores and rocks were generated by an appropriate mixture of the elements water and earth and application of fire (heat) to form liquids emplaced into veins and partings he was at least ahead of the alchemist's fantasies which he heartily criticized during his professional career.

Although water in inself was not the prime interest of Agricola's work he realized its importance in mining, geologic and mineralogic processes, and public health concerns. In his letter to Meurer [*Agricola*, 1546c] he appends a dictionary of earth science and mining terms from Latin to German in which there are no less than 27 definitions of different waters. Far be it from trying to make Agricola into a hydrologist, nevertheless, it needs to be stressed that the sections and chapters in his scientific work on water and hydrology are the first coherent and serious treatment of the subject matter since the early works of Vitruvius from the first century A.D., and only 14 years after his death a treatise on finding groundwater is published by Jaques Besson: *The Art and Science of Finding the Waters and Springs Hidden Underground Other Than by the Vulgar Means Employed by Farmers and Architects*. It was edited in French in Orleans by Eloy Gibier in 1569. It lacks the clarity and style of Agricola's works.

Expressions of Mining Professionalism in the Arts and Artifacts

One expression of the status of the miner and the mining industry in the late Middle Ages and through the 18th century is the large number of paraphernalia, ceremonial and art objects used in the traditions that had evolved around mining and its lore. No other profession of this time or any other has such a large and extensive fund of artifacts which reinforce the collective identity of the members of the profession.

The secular paraphernalia revolve around the uniforms and parades and utensils and decorative objects of art. The uniforms worn by miners were originally work clothes developed basically from utilitarian and protective clothing adapted to the particular mining environment and the specialized tools in use (Figure 4). One persistent element of the miner's uniform is the so called arse leather (Arschleder) which protected his behind when crawling and sliding through the narrow confines of the mine workings. With the increased importance of the hierarchic structure of the mine officials and the division of labor, uniforms and insignia served to identify an individual's position in the hierarchy and his work function. Miners involved in hauling and hoisting would have different uniforms than those working at the face, for example. The uniforms became more elaborate as one ascended the organizational ladder and became quite fantastic in the Baroque. Common mining tools such as axes, pry irons, hammer and gad were transformed into elaborate and flashy ceremonial tools to accompany the uniform.

Besides the hierarchic function the uniforms also served as display pieces of the full regalia in mining parades— organized for holidays such as St. Barbara's feast day, or special occasions such as the reception of foreign dignitaries, weddings and births in the ruling families. Because of the splendor and variety of the uniforms these parades were spectacular, involving large number of paraders. They are commemorated in prints of the times and in the fabrication of painted tin figurines much like elaborate toy soldier which were used to recreate the pageantry of the parades for those who had not seen them or for the memory of the prince — at least a more peaceful application than tin soldiers.

Another large area that demonstrates this feeling of cohesion around mining is the large number of household utensils and decorative items that are linked to mining and the use of mining motives by those directly involved. Also the general population's interest and imagination must have been stirred not only by the wealth produced by the mining industries, but also by the somewhat mystical conditions of danger and darkness under which the miners worked.

Large collections of silver tankards, artfully decorated with figurines from mining crews, tin steins and cups inscribed with mining motives and painted glasses (Halloren-

Fig. 4. Oberberghauptmann ("Director of bureau of Mines") in parade uniform with ceremonial axe, ca 1700 Electorate of Saxony, engraving by A. Weigel, 1721.

gläser) attest not only to the wealth of artistic and craftsman-like expression in the mining milieu, but undoubtedly also to the predelection of miners for serious drinking.

More decorative items include candelsticks held by figurines in mining uniforms, center pieces made of rare crystals or ore specimens embellished with silver figurines and machines to simulate mines and mining activities. Mining scenes and single figurines in uniform were produced by some of the best known porcelain manufactures (Saxe) which had a considerable output of mining motives in the 18th century. Locally many carved and cast figurines of miners in varying uniforms were created.

In the sacred arts, magnificent hymn books exist such as the Kanzionale of Kuta Hora (Kuttenberg). Stained glass renderings of mining motives and miners working are found in church windows (Freiburg Cathedral), altars and chapels throughout the mining regions of central Europe.

ST. BARBARA — A RALLYING POINT FOR MINERS

The development of the mining industry and the applied earth sciences in the Middle Ages had as a profound effect on technology and its development as had the more abstract and pure earth and planetary sciences of the times on the concepts of cosmology and the pure sciences. This extraordinary development and its impact on society with its *supra*

regional importance can only be explained by the special situation of the mining industry, its vertical and horizontal coherence and sense of unity and the openness of the industry to new methods, machinery and organizational forms. Many of the contributing factors to this condition were externally applied such as the pressures of increasing demand for metals in an expanding protoindustrial society, the exigencies of sovereign princes to control and to benefit from the mining industries in their state by improving administrative forms and essentially creating a loyal cast of mining officials, and by creating a favored position of miners through tax exemptions and other privileges. Internal factors were the high professional image that the mining profession projected, its general esteem, and its sense of coherence as a profession rather than based on geographical location or ethnic/political adherence. St. Barbara worship, as developed in and for the mining industry, certainly was one of the internal factors that contributed to the coherence and was an expression of the *esprit de corps*—on which so many of the achievements of the industry depended.

Acknowledgments.   Much of the material on which this article is based was obtained or inspected during a trip of the author to Europe during the summer of 1985. Curators and librarians in the following museums, collections or libraries have been extremely helpful in locating and discussing important materials. The organizations that deserve special thanks and acknowledgement are in the order of the itinerary: Maison de la Géologie, Ecole Nationale Supérieure des Mines, Musée de l'Armée, Librairie Jules Verne, all in Paris; Erzbischhöfliches Diözesanmuseum, Cologne; Bergbau Bücherei der Bergbau Forschung, Essen; Deutsches Bergbau Museum, Bochum; Staatliche Kunstsammlungen, Kassel, all in Germany; Bergverksmuseet, Kongsberg, Norway; Société des Bollandistes, Bruxelles, and Musée de la Mine, Bois-du-Luc, Belgium.

REFERENCES

Agricola, G., *de ortu et causis subterraneorum libri V*, pp. 81, Frobenius, Basel 1546 a, German translation by G. Fraustadt in, Georgius Agricola-Schriften Zur Geologie und Mineralogie I, pp. 81-187, VEB Verlag, Berlin, 1956.

Agricola, G., *de natura eorum quae effluunt ex terra libri IV*, pp. 87-164, Frobenius, Basel 1546 b, German translation by G. Fraustadt in Georgius Agricola-Schriften zur Geologie und Mineralogie I, pp. 226-319, VEB Verlag, Berlin 1956.

Agricola, G., *epistula ad Meurerum*, 1546 c, German translation by G. Fraustadt in, Georgius Agricola-Schriften zur Geologie und Mineralogie I, pp. 7-42, VEB Verlag, Berlin 1956.

Agricola, G., *de re metallica libri XII*, pp. 538, Frobenius, Basel 1556, English translation by H.C. Hoover and L.H. Hoover, pp. 640, The Mining Magazine, London, 1912.

Besson, J., *L'art et science de trouver les eaux et fontaines cachées sous terre, autrement que par les moyens vulgaires des agriculteurs et architectes*, pp. , Eloy Gibier, Orleans, 1569.

Daras, E., *Vie des Saints pour Tous les Jours de l'Année*, pp. 480-490, tome IV, Gaumet ct Cic, Paris, no date. (Approx. 1870).

Eimon, P., Legendary Saint Barbara still honored as the patron saint of mining, *Mining Engineering, 37*, 1281-1283, 1985.

Gimpel, J., *La Revolution Industrielle du Moyen Age*, 244 pp., Editions du Seuil, Paris, 1975.

Heilfurth, G., *Der Bergbau und seine Kultur*, pp. 321. Atlantis Verlag, Zürich, 1981.

Koch, M., Sancta Barbara-Schutzheilige der Hüttenleute?, *Stahl und Eisen, 84*, 157-165, 1964.

de Lapparent, le Cte., *Sainte Barbe*, 64 pp, Henri Laurens, Paris, 1926.

Peine, S., *St. Barbara, die Schutzheilige der Bergleute und der Artillerie, und ihre Darstellung in der Kunst*, 38 pp, Gustav Fock, Leipzig, 1896.

Réau, L., *Inconographie de l'Art Chrétien*, pp. 169-177, Presses Universitaires de France, Paris, 1958.

Rössler, B., *Hell polierter Bergbauspiegel*, pp. 167, J.J. Winkler, Dresden, 1700; facsimile edition by Verlag Glückauf, Essen, 1980.

Suhling, L., Bergbau und Hüttenwesen in Mitteleuropa zur Agricola-Zeit, in *Georg Agricola: Zwölf Bücher vom Berg und Hüttenwesen*, edited by George-Agricola Gesellschaft, pp. 573-584, Deutscher Taschenbuch Verlag, 2nd edition, München, 1980.

Wicelium, G., *Chorus Sanctorum Omnium*, pp. 803-806, Quentels und Calenium Erben, Cologne, 1563.

H. O. Pfannkuch, Department of Geology and Geophysics, University of Minnesota, Minneapolis, MN 55455.

A History of Paleoflood Hydrology in the United States, 1800–1970

JOHN E. COSTA

U.S. Geological Survey, Cascades Volcano Observatory, Vancouver, Washington

The origins of paleoflood hydrology in the United States can be traced back to the beginning of the 19th century, when windgaps and watergaps in the Applachians were believed to have been eroded by extraordinary floods as large lakes that were ponded behind the ridges rapidly drained. Sediment evidence for extraordinary floods was evoked several decades later when glacial sediments in New England were interpreted as deposits from the great Biblical deluge, and estimates of the depth and velocity of the great flood were attempted. The popularization of the glacial origins of drift by Agassiz by 1840 resulted in strong beliefs in uniformitarianism and waning interests in paleoflood investigations. The documentation of the origins of the channeled scablands in eastern Washington by catastrophic glacial outbreak floods, begun by Bretz in the early 1920s, led to renewed interest in paleoflood hydrology. Subsequent efforts to reconstruct hydraulic variables of past floods used conventional open channel flow equations applied to other enormous Pleistocene floods. The elevation of sediments was used as a paleostage estimator in the 1880s, and botanical techniques for estimating paleoflood frequency and magnitude were well documented by the mid-1960s. Since 1970, an exponential expansion has occurred in the recognition and use of paleoflood hydrology in the United States.

INTRODUCTION

Paleoflood hydrology is the study of the movements of water and sediment in channels before the time of continuous hydrologic records or direct measurements. Elapsed time since the floods of interest can range from several years to thousands of years. The most commonly used indirect evidence includes sediment deposits, landforms, and vegetation. The past 2 decades have produced a renewed interest in and appreciation for paleoflood hydrology techniques and investigations. Examples of this interest include recent books, such as *Background to Palaeohydrology* [*Gregory*, 1983], a daylong symposium on paleoflood hydrology at the 1984 AGU Fall Meeting in San Francisco, Calif. [*Eos*, November 6, 1985, pp. 890–891, 893–894], and the creation of a National Research Council subcommittee on paleoflood hydrology [*V. R. Baker*, University of Arizona, Tucson, personal communication, 1986]. The purposes of this paper are to document the history of paleoflood hydrology in the United States from ca 1800 to 1970 and to remind readers in general about existing technology that can help extend floodflow data beyond the period of streamflow-gaging records.

Traditionally, hydrologists and engineers rely on historical records of stage and discharge and use these data in models or statistical analyses to predict the magnitude and frequency of future floods. Unfortunately, records are often not available at desired locations, or the period of record is too short for useful extrapolation. Unquestionably, a single outstanding flood can have a profound effect on conventional engineering hydrology methods. For example, Plum Creek drains about 780 km² in the Great Plains south of Denver, Colo. In the 17 years of gaging station data prior to 1965, the largest flood was 108 m³ s⁻¹ in 1954, and the magnitude of the 100-yr flood was estimated to be 195 m³ s⁻¹. In June 1965, a catastrophic rainstorm on the headwaters of Plum Creek produced a flood of 4361 m³ s⁻¹. As a consequence

of that single flood, the 100-year flood estimate is now 940 m³ s⁻¹. Great uncertainty persists about the frequency and interpretation of these large-magnitude high-outlier floods. The relatively short flood history in most places in the United States created research opportunities for those who were not engineers but were interested in floods, such as geologists, botanists, and geomorphologists. They applied stratigraphic principles and absolute dating techniques with conventional engineering hydraulic principles or developed new methods that used sediments and vegetation to ascertain the magnitude and frequency of prehistoric floods. Paleoflood hydrology can produce estimates of magnitude as well as frequency of large flood flows of the past that are well beyond the record that can be obtained by conventional engineering hydrology methods [*Kochel and Baker*, 1982], thus decreasing some of the uncertainty of conventional analysis.

Geologists have been the primary developers and users of paleoflood techniques, primarily because of their familiarity with the interpretation of sediment deposits and landforms and their use of dating methods, such as radiocarbon dating. Consequently, incorporation of the sedimentologic, geomorphic, and vegetation records to extend flow histories has not been fully recognized or appreciated by many hydrologists, even though much of the pioneering work in paleoflood hydrology has been widely available in the published literature for many years.

HISTORY OF PALEOFLOOD HYDROLOGY

Probably the earliest attempts at paleoflood hydrology in the United States were qualitative descriptions of the origins of wind- and watergaps in the Applachian Mountains. At the beginning of the 19th century, it was believed that wind- and watergaps were breaches in barriers or dams that had ponded ancient oceans or large lakes on their north sides [*Thompson*, 1800; *Mitchill*, 1818]. The existence of wind- and watergaps and the speculations about the origins of these breaches in the Applachians formed the basis for the belief in the past occurrence of extraordinary floods through the gaps. Probably the earliest attempt at quantitative paleo-flood hydrology in the United States involved estimates by 19th-century geologists of the depth and velocity of the Biblical deluge. *Jackson* [1839] established that diluvial waters were more than 1500 m deep on the basis of observations of erosional and depositional features (now known to be glacial in origin) on Mount Katahdin, Maine. Calculations by *von Buch* [1811] from elevation differences and boulder deposits in the Jura Mountains, Switzerland, indicated that the deluge floodwaters attained velocities from 170 to 5930 m s^{-1}.

The popularization of the glacial origin of drift by *Agassiz* [1838] in Europe had an important influence on American paleoflood hydrology. Large floods were no longer believed necessary to explain much of the topography and surficial geology in the northeastern United States, and so interest in catastrophic flooding shifted to specific locations where more rigorous scientific fieldwork led to conclusions about the occurrence of extraordinary floods. The new glacial theory did not end paleoflood investigations, but glaciers replaced Noah's flood as the source of large quantities of water.

In 1882, J. D. Dana proposed that the melting of Quaternary glaciers in New England produced an enormous flood in the Connecticut River valley that was responsible for the formation of several high terraces along the valley [*Dana, 1882a,b*]. Dana believed that long periods of sustained high flow would allow aggradation of terrace deposits up to the level of the maximum flood stage. He believed that high terraces at tributary junctures at an average elevation of 43 m along the Connecticut valley were a record of the maximum stage of this large flood [*Dana, 1882a*, p. 95]:

> . . . but if the conditions in the drainage area of the Connecticut Valley were those of a flooded river with simultaneously flooded tributaries, the so-called "delta terraces," or terraces at the mouths of tributaries, may mark the height of maximum flood in the main river.

Dana plotted the slope of the high terraces and demonstrated that the slope paralleled the Connecticut River; he measured valley widths at the tops of the high terraces and computed a mean flood velocity by using an equation for large rivers that was obtained from an early Mississippi River report:

$$v = [(225 \, R \, S^{1/2})^{1/4} - 0.0388]^2$$

where v is mean velocity, R is hydraulic radius, and S is mean river slope. Dana's reconstructed hydraulic variables for his hypothetical Connecticut River valley flood were a slope of 0.000625, a mean depth of 43 m, a mean width of 1220 m, and a mean velocity of 5.2 m s^{-1}. Although Dana's interpretations of the Connecticut valley terraces was incorrect, his methods for reconstructing the flood characteristics were remarkably insightful and not appreciably different from some modern paleoflood hydrology techniques.

In 1922, J. E. Stewart of the U.S. Geological Survey determined historic flood peaks in the Skagit River basin, Washington, after damaging floods occurred in 1921. Stewart prepared an unpublished report in 1923; most of his results are included in *U.S. Geological Survey Water Supply Paper 1527*, "Floods in the Skagit River Basin, Washington" [*Stewart and Bodhaine, 1961*]. He determined the stages (and thus discharges) of the two largest historical floods on the Skagit River, which occurred in about 1815 and 1856, from water stains on trees and canyon walls, flood-deposited sand and gravel bars, and flood sediments lodged in the bark of old cedar trees and deposited in cracks in canyon walls. He dated the 1815 flood from Indian legends and the 1856 flood from the ages of young fir trees growing on a flood-deposited sandbar. Yet it was fortuitous information about old large floods, provided by Indian elders, that led Stewart to investigate for paleoflood evidence of these earlier floods.

Stewart observed that sediments that backfilled tributary gulches (slackwater sediment) were at an elevation consistent with his other high-water mark data, and he incorporated this information into his stage estimates. Slackwater sediments have been used extensively in the last decade as paleostage indicators for floods that occurred as far back as thousands of years [*Patton et al., 1979*]. Stewart's investigations of this geomorphic and sedimentologic evidence extended the flood peak record back 100 years and indicated the occurrence in about 1815 of a flood that was nearly twice the existing flood of record on the Skagit River. An early, detailed description of the stratigraphy and sedimentology of similar flood deposits is provided by *McKee* [1938], who studied such deposits from Colorado River floods in the Grand Canyon.

Unquestionably, the greatest catalyst to fuel paleoflood hydrology in the United States was the scientific controversy created by the staunch insistance by J Harlen Bretz in the early 1920s that a gigantic flood had carved and deposited the remarkable topography of eastern Washington. *Bretz* [1923] proposed that an area of 40,000 km^2 in eastern Washington (known as the channeled scablands) was formed by a single catastrophic flood. The source of the flood was the failure of a glacial dam that had impounded a large lake near Missoula, Mont., sometime between 16,000 and 12,000 yr ago. The lake was 7770 km^2 in area and had a volume of 2.0×10^{12} m^3 of water, about half the size of Lake Michigan. When the ice dam failed, the rapidly draining water became known as the Lake Missoula Flood, or the Spokane Flood. Despite enormous skepticism and criticism, time has proven Bretz essentially right [*Baker, 1978*], but the number of floods produced by failure of the ice dams remains a point of debate [*Waitt, 1985; Baker and Bunker, 1985*].

Because this gigantic flood or floods occurred 16,000–12,000 yr ago, conventional engineering analysis of the flood (depth, velocity, inundated areas) required extensive sedimentologic and geomorphic evidence, which engineers are untrained to provide. This allowed geologists the opportunity to contribute to this and other catastrophic Pleistocene flood investigations.

Bretz [1925a,b] estimated the discharge of the Missoula Flood at Wallula Gap, Wash., by using erosional evidence on uplands for estimates of depth and the Chezy formula:

$$v = C \, (RS)^{1/2}$$

where v is average velocity, C is a "smoothness" coefficient, R is hydraulic radius, and S is energy slope. Hydraulic computations were made by D. F. Higgins, an engineering colleague of Bretz at the University of Chicago. Higgins chose the value C "to indicate a maximum of impedance from irregularites of sides and from eddies and crosscurrents generated by turns in the course of the valley," [*Bretz, 1925a,b*]. Velocities were estimated to be 6.4–9.1 m

s^{-1}, and discharge was estimated to be 1,873,000 m³ s⁻¹. Bretz noted that this discharge estimate probably erred toward the low side.

Pardee [1942] also estimated the discharge of the Lake Missoula flood near its source in Eddy Narrows, Mont., by applying the Manning and Chezy equations. Hydraulic computations were made for him by W. W. Rubey and W. B. Langbein of the U.S. Geological Survey. From the field evidence reported by Pardee, Rubey and Langbein selected values of $C = 100$ and $n = 0.029$ (where n is Manning's roughness coefficient) for flood flows that were hundreds of meters deep. Estimated flood discharge was 10,946,000 m³ s⁻¹ [*Pardee*, 1942].

The most accurate and comprehensive paleoflood study of this remarkable flood was completed by *Baker* [1973], who used the slope-area method to calculate a discharge of 21.3×10^6 m³ s⁻¹ for the Missoula flood. The most consistent high-water marks used in this study were eroded channels in loess at minor divide crossings. High-water marks were interpreted as the elevation that lies between the floor elevation of an eroded divide crossing and the elevation of the lowest nearby loess divide that was not modified by passage of floodwater.

Following disastrous flooding in the Ohio River valley in January and February 1937, M. M. Leighton, the chief of the Illinois Geological Survey, suggested to the U.S. Geological Survey that the flooding was of sufficient magnitude that it must have left a distinctive depositional record in the valley. The Ohio River flood deposits of 1937 were investigated by *Mansfield* [1938]. He documented that the 1937 flood deposits had buried glacial till and loess that had not heretofore been inundated by floodwaters. This implied that the magnitude of the 1937 Ohio River flood had not been exceeded since the glacial sediments were deposited several thousand years ago.

Following two catastrophic floods in the Connecticut River valley in 1936 and 1938, R. H. Jahns, working under the direction of G. R. Mansfield, began work in the Connecticut valley in cooperation with the State of Massachusetts. It was hoped that this study would lead to a determination of the periodicity of such extraordinary floods in the Connecticut River valley. The resulting report, *U.S. Geological Survey Water Supply Paper 996*, "Geological Factors of the Connecticut Valley, Massachusetts, as Related to Recent Floods," is a benchmark work in paleoflood hydrology [*Jahns*, 1947]. Relatively coarse sediments from the floods covered low terraces along the Connecticut River. From this stratigraphic evidence, Jahns concluded that the terraces were flooded in 1936 for the first time since they had ceased to be active floodplain surfaces, which was estimated to have been 2500–6000 yr ago.

In a study of the effects of a large flood in 1949 on the Little River valley, Va., J. T. Hack and J. C. Goodlett [*Hack and Goodlett*, 1960] concluded that no storm producing comparable damage had occurred prior to 1949 within the lifespan of the trees now standing. Many old hemlock stands in the floodplains of nearby undamaged areas indicated that extraordinary floods had not occurred within the last 150 yr.

The most substantial contribution of the use of vegetation to deduce quantitative information on floods and floodplain deposition was that of R. S. Sigafoos, who used examples from the Potomac River floodplain. *Sigafoos* [1964] determined that trees growing on floodplains are commonly scarred, broken, or toppled by floodwaters but rarely killed. New wood will grow over scars, and the number of annual rings that have grown since scarring of the tree will be an accurate measure of the number of years that have passed since the flood occurred. Also, when trees are inclined or knocked down by floodwaters, new sprouts grow vertically, and their annual rings can be used to determine the length of time that has elapsed since the flood damaged the vegetation. Sigafoos determined that if a tree survives partial burial by flood sediments, new wood formed in the buried part of the trunk is more like root wood than stem wood. From this observation, he could measure the year and amount of sedimentation of a particular flood. Sigafoos' remarkable contribution was the establishment of botanical techniques (tree-ring dating) that can be used to reconstruct paleoflood history along any channel bordered by woody vegetation, with or without flow records, for hundreds of years back, depending on the ages of trees along the channel.

Scars on trees are a particularly useful indication of floodwater levels. The height of scars on floodplain trees do not necessarily reflect the maximum stage of floodwaters, but in some cases they serve as an approximate indication. *Harrison and Reid* [1967] constructed a flood-frequency curve for the Turtle River, N.D., with tree scar data for stage estimates. Their results compared very well with nearby streamflow-gaging station records.

Everitt [1968] used cottonwood trees to establish the age relationships of floodplain surfaces along the Little Missouri River in western North Dakota. He documented that a higher floodplain surface was not a postglacial terrace that formed from isostatic rebound following retreat of the last ice sheet, as was believed formerly. Cottonwood trees on the lower surface were no older than 15 yr; cottonwood trees on the upper surface were no younger than 35 yr. Using this botanic evidence as his guide, Everitt documented that a large flood in 1947 had caused extensive channel widening, destruction of all cottonwood trees on the channel floor, and formation of a pronounced erosional scarp that was 1.5–3 m high. Cottonwood trees were the clue to the history of the valley sediments and landforms produced by the flood in 1947.

Following the disastrous Christmas flooding in northern California in December 1964, J. H. Stewart and V. C. LaMarche investigated the valley of Coffee Creek, Calif., which was severely modified by the flooding [*Stewart and LaMarche*, 1967]. They determined that many trees toppled in the flood were from 200 to more than 400 yr old. These trees had survived all previous floods in at least the last 200 yr. Previously undisturbed alluvial fan deposits along the valley sides were extensively eroded. These sediments were as old as 1700 ¹⁴C yr. Bouldery natural levee deposits were a prominent depositional feature produced by the flood. Older levee deposits were widespread on the valley bottom of Coffee Creek, and the highest old deposits were as much as 0.6 m above the high-water lines of the 1964 flood. This indicates that floods larger than the flood of 1964 had occurred in the valley, if it can be assumed that there had not be extensive valley degradation.

In mid-June 1965, intense rains caused extraordinary flooding in the South Platte River basin in eastern Colorado. Bijou Creek, a tributary to the South Platte River, was severely flooded, and the extensive sand deposits from the flood were investigated in detail by *McKee et al.* [1967].

H. F. Matthai of the U.S. Geological Survey supplied hydraulic and scour data for the project and suggested additional locations that had extensive flood deposits for investigation. McKee et al. documented that floodplain sand deposits were hundreds of meters wide and as much as 3.7 m thick. Thinly bedded horizontal strata, formed in the upper flow regime, constituted 90–95% of all deposits. Extensive horizontal bedding, in association with climbing ripple laminations and convolute structures, was determined to be diagnostic of blanket sand deposits formed by flash floods. H. E. Malde investigated the catastrophic flood caused by the overflow and lowering of Pleistocene Lake Bonneville at Red Rocks Pass near Preston, Idaho [*Malde, 1968*], about 14,000 yr ago [*Scott et al., 1980*]. C. T. Jenkins (U.S. Geological Survey) computed a flood peak of 0.42×10^6 m³ s⁻¹ at a canyon neck south of Boise, Idaho, for Malde, by assuming that the canyon acted as a gigantic streamflow measuring device (venturi flume) and that the flood was at critical depth [*Malde, 1968, p. 12*]. Flood discharges also were estimated at nine locations along the Snake River canyon in southern Idaho by using Manning's equation and $n = 0.03$.

In 1968, P. W. Birkeland estimated the mean velocity and tractive force necessary to transport glacial outwash boulders in the Truckee River in California and Nevada [*Birkeland, 1968*]. While this was not the first attempt to reconstruct hydraulic parameters from boulder sizes, it was one of the first reports solely devoted to such paleohydraulic reconstructions. Paleoflood velocities and tractive forces were estimated by the Manning equation to be about 9.1 m s⁻¹ and 958–1437 N m⁻², respectively, for a flood transporting $12.2 \times 6.1 \times 3.0$–m boulders in a flow 12.2–24.4 m deep at a slope of 0.007. Values of n were chosen to be 0.06–0.08.

This history of paleoflood hydrology ends at 1970 because this date marks a threshold in paleoflood interest and methodology. Beginning with the flooding caused by Hurricane Camille in 1969 and ending with the Buffalo Creek, W.Va., Rapid City, S.D, and Hurricane Agnes floods in 1972, in which nearly 500 lives were lost, major federal laws such as the Flood Disaster Prevention Act (Public Law 93–234) focused renewed multidisciplinary efforts in flood studies, including paleoflood hydrology. Since 1970 there has been an exponential increase in the types and number of paleoflood investigations. Because the primary purpose of this report is historical background, 1970 was a logical point at which to end it. For more information about post-1970 ways to estimate paleoflood magnitude, the papers by *Kochel and Baker* [1982], *Foley et al.* [1984], and *Williams* [1984] are recommended. A summary of contemporary approaches to estimate paleoflood frequency can be found in the work of *Costa* [1978].

Conclusions

The development of paleoflood hydrology has been an excellent example of the interdisciplinary cooperation of several specialized sciences. Hydrologists and engineers provided the preliminary computations, which were based on energy equations from open channel hydraulics or sediment transport, that were used by geologists in attempting to reconstruct flow characteristics of large Pleistocene floods. Geomorphic, botanic, and sedimentologic evidence was then recognized as helpful for extending flood frequency esti-

mates beyond the period of record, as well as for estimating the magnitude of past large flows. Paleoflood hydrology has not yet been developed to its greatest potential, but it will become more and more of an integral part of water resources investigations [*Greis, 1983*]. Therefore the origins of this important subject need to be documented as well as possible.

Acknowledgments. I would like to thank R. F. Hadley, V. R. Schneider, J. M. Stewart, C. R. Hupp, R. C. Kochel, D. E. Hillier, V. R. Baker, and W. H. Kirby for their helpful reviews of the manuscript.

References

Agassiz, L., Upon glaciers, moraines, and erratic blocks, *Edinburg New Philos. J., 24*, 364, 1838.

Baker, V. R., Paleohydrology and sedimentology of Lake Missoula flooding in eastern Washington, *Geol. Soc. Am. Spec. Pap. 144*, 79 pp., 1973.

Baker, V. R., The Spokane flood controversy and the Martian outflow channels, *Science, 202*, 1247, 1978.

Baker, V. R., and R. C. Bunker, Cataclysmic late Pleistocene flooding from Glacial Lake Missoula: A review, *Q. Sci. Rev., 4*, 1, 1985.

Birkeland, P. W., Mean velocities and bounder transport during Tahoe age floods of the Truckee River, California-Nevada, *Geol. Soc. Am. Bull., 79*, 137, 1968.

Bretz, J H., The channeled scablands of the Columbia Plateau, *J. Geol., 31*, 617, 1923.

Bretz, J H., The Spokane flood beyond the channeled scablands (part 1), *J. Geol., 33*, 97, 1925a.

Bretz, J H., The Spokane flood beyond the channeled scablands (part 2), *J. Geol., 33*, 236, 1925b.

Costa, J. E., Holocene stratigraphy in flood frequency analysis, *Water Resour. Res., 14*, 626, 1978.

Dana, J. D., The flood of the Connecticut River Valley from the melting of the Quaternary glacier (part 1), *Am. J. Sci., 123*, 87, 1882a.

Dana, J. D., The flood of the Connecticut River Valley from the melting of the Quaternary glacier (part 2), *Am. J. Sci., 123*, 179, 1882b.

Everitt, B. L., Use of the cottonwood in an investigation of the recent history of a flood plain, *Am. J. Sci., 266*, 417, 1968.

Foley, M. G., J. M. Doesburg, and D. A. Zimmerman, Paleohydrologic techniques with environmental applications for siting hazardous waste facilities, in *Sedimentology of Gravels and Conglomerates*, edited by E. H. Koster and R. J. Steel, pp. 99–108, *Can. Soc. Pet. Geol. Mem. 10*, Calgary, Canada, 1984.

Gregory, K. J. (Ed.), *Background to Palaeohydrology*, 486 pp., John Wiley, New York, 1983.

Greis, N. P., Flood frequency analysis: A review of 1979–1982, *Rev. Geophys. Space Phys., 21*, 699, 1983.

Hack, J. T., and J. C. Goodlett, Geomorphology and forest ecology of a mountain region in the central Appalachians, *U.S. Geol. Surv. Prof. Pap. 347*, 66 pp., 1960.

Harrison, S. S., and J. R. Reid, A flood-frequency curve based on tree-scar data, *Proc. N.D. Acad. Sci., 21*, 23, 1967.

Jackson, C. T., Reports on the geology of the state of Maine, and on the public lands belonging to Maine and Massachusetts, *Am. J. Sci., 36*, 143, 1839.

Jahns, R. H., Geologic features of the Connecticut Valley, Massachusetts, as related to recent floods, *U.S. Geol. Surv. Water Supply Pap. 996*, 158 pp., 1947.

Kochel, R. C., and V. R. Baker, Paleoflood hydrology, *Science, 215*, 353, 1982.

Malde, H. E., The catastrophic late Pleistocene Bonneville flood in the Snake River plain, Idaho, *U.S. Geol. Surv. Prof. Pap. 596*, 52 pp., 1968.

Mansfield, G. R., Flood deposits of the Ohio river, January–February, 1937, in Grover, N.C., *U.S. Geol. Surv. Water Supply Pap. 838*, 693, 1938.

McKee, E. D., Original structures in Colorado River flood deposits of Grand Canyon, *J. Sediment. Petrol., 8*, 77, 1938.

McKee, E. D., E. J. Crosby, and H. L. Berryhill, Flood deposits, Bijou Creek, Colorado, June 1965, *J. Sediment. Petrol., 37*, 829, 1967.

Mitchill, S. L., Observations on the geology of North America, in *Essay on the Theory of the Earth,* by G. Curier, pp. 321–431, New York, 1818.

Pardee, J. T., Unusual currents in glacial Lake Missoula, Montana, *Geol. Soc. Am. Bull., 53,* 1569, 1942.

Patton, P. C., V. R. Baker, and R. C. Kochel, Slack water deposits: A geomorphic technique for the interpretation of fluvial paleohydrology, in *Adjustments of the Fluvial System,* edited by D. D. Rhodes and G. P. Williams, pp. 225–253, Kendall-Hunt, Dubuque, Iowa, 1979.

Scott, W. E., W. D. McCoy, R. R. Shroba, and R. D. Miller, New interpretations of the Late Quaternary history of Lake Bonneville, western United States (abstract), *Am. Q. Assoc. Abstr. Progr., 6,* 168, 1980.

Sigafoos, R. S., Botanical evidence of floods and flood plain deposition, *U.S. Geol. Surv. Prof. Pap. 485-A,* 35 pp., 1964.

Stewart, J. E., and G. L. Bodhaine, Floods in the Skagit River basin, Washington, *U.S. Geol. Surv. Water Supply Pap. 1527,* 66 pp., 1961.

Stewart, J. H., and V. C. LaMarche, Erosion and deposition produced by the flood of December 1964 on Coffee Creek, Trinity County, California, *U.S. Geol. Surv. Prof. Pap. 422-K,* 22 pp., 1967.

Thompson, C., Observations, appendix 1 in *Notes on the State of Virginia,* by T. Jefferson, Baltimore, Md., 1800.

von Buch, V. H. Uber die ursachen der verbreitung grofser Alpengeschiebe, *Akad. Wiss. Abh.,* 161, 1811.

Waitt, R. B., Case for periodic, colossal jokulhlaups from Pleistocene glacial Lake Missoula, *Geol. Soc. Am. Bull., 96,* 1271, 1985.

Williams, G. P., Paleohydrologic equations for rivers, in *Developments and Applications of Geomorphology,* edited by J. E. Costa and P. J. Fleisher, pp. 343–367, Springer-Verlag, New York, 1984.

J. E. Costa, U.S. Geological Survey, Cascades Volcano Observatory, Vancouver, WA   98661.

Measuring the Rivers of the Past: A History of Fluvial Paleohydrology

PETER C. PATTON

Department of Earth and Environmental Sciences, Wesleyan University, Middletown, Connecticut, 06457

Fluvial paleohydrology, the study of the long-term hydrologic behavior of ancient and modern rivers, has historically been approached in two ways. The first approach concerns the hydrologic conditions that existed during the formation of ancestral streams. The evolution of this paleohydrologic approach is directly linked to the evolution of theories concerning the origin of the fluvial landscape. Hydrologic reconstructions are based on the morphology and sedimentology of paleochannels and the analogy to modern rivers. The reconstructions result in estimates of relatively high frequency stream discharge, such as bankfull discharge. These data, with other paleoenvironmental indices, assist in the definition of the paleoclimate at the time of channel formation and the magnitude of past hydrologic fluctuations.

A second paleohydrologic approach concerns discrete hydrologic events, usually high-magnitude floods. Paleoflood hydrology involves attempts to reconstruct the magnitude and frequency of rare great floods from stratigraphic evidence. The study of paleoflood hydrology can be traced to the pioneering work of J Harlen Bretz who made the first comprehensive analysis of a paleoflood, the Late Pleistocene catastrophic flood of the Channeled Scabland in eastern Washington. Paleoflood data can be related to modern rivers in order to construct long flood frequency records that can provide insight into the frequency of extreme hydrologic events within a climate or range of climates.

INTRODUCTION

Paleohydrology can be defined as the study of past hydrologic regimes and hydrologic processes that operated before the collection of systematic records [*Schumm*, 1965]. Paleohydrologic studies identify phenomena that are the products of specific hydrologic processes and which contain information about those processes. By analysis of similar contemporary processes transfer functions are developed that allow the reconstruction of past hydrologic conditions.

When broadly defined as above, the study of paleohydrology applies to the entire hydrosphere. Thus, reconstruction of past glacier mass budgets and ice sheet dynamics [*Pierce*, 1979], paleolimnology investigations [*Butzer et al.*, 1973] or analysis of long-term ground water flow [*Kafri and Arad*, 1978] can all be considered studies of paleohydrology. For the purpose of this review I wish to focus on one specific aspect of paleohydrology that is concerned with the changing hydrology of streams over long time periods.

The study of fluvial paleohydrology can be subdivided into two general areas. One approach to fluvial paleohydrology provides estimates of the average runoff and sediment yield of a basin under past climatic conditions [*Schumm*, 1965]. Paleohydrologic estimates of past discharge and sediment load are made from the study of paleochannels preserved in alluvial fill deposits. These paleohydrologic reconstructions are based on quantitative relationships that equate the morphology and sedimentology of stream channels to the formative hydrologic processes [*Schumm*, 1968; *Baker and Penteado-Orellana*, 1977]. These paleohydrologic reconstructions can be used to estimate past climatic conditions based on relationships between climate and hydrology. Thus, estimates of mean annual runoff can be used to predict mean annual precipitation [*Langbein and Schumm*, 1958]. The study of paleochannels not only allows estimates of past hydrologic conditions but also provides information on stream channel evolution over long time periods. Paleohy-

drologic reconstructions based on these methods yield information on changing hydrologic conditions over time periods of thousands of years.

A second approach to fluvial paleohydrology is concerned with the identification of individual hydrologic events. Recently this approach has focused on determining the frequency and magnitude of rare large floods, an aspect of fluvial paleohydrology that has been referred to as paleoflood hydrology [*Costa*, this volume]. Many paleoflood reconstructions are concerned with prehistoric floods, but the techniques of paleoflood hydrology have also been extended to the study of floods which have occurred in historic time in drainage basins that are not only ungaged but are too remote for even eyewitness accounts [*Baker et al.*, 1985]. In this way paleoflood hydrology has added to the data base on flood magnitude and frequency.

PALEOCHANNELS AND PAST RIVER REGIMES

Paleodischarge Estimates from Underfit Streams

The recognition that past river regimes differed significantly from those of today can be traced to work on stream patterns in the late 19th century. Specifically, *William Morris Davis* [1896] identified streams that had meanders of smaller radius of curvature and wavelength than the meandering valley which enclosed them. Davis used the term underfit stream to describe these shrunken rivers and advanced several hypotheses to explain the reduction in discharge since the time of valley formation. In some cases, stream capture and divide migration which reduced drainage area were responsible for the decreased discharge [*Davis*, 1896, 1913]. The map of the River Bar illustrates an example of extreme underfitness caused by stream capture (Figure 1). But, in other valleys where underfit streams exist there is no evidence of recent capture. For these settings *Lehmann* [1915] made the interesting suggestion that increased subsurface flow, the result of underflow in permeable floodplains and valley alluvium that accumulated as the valley enlarged,

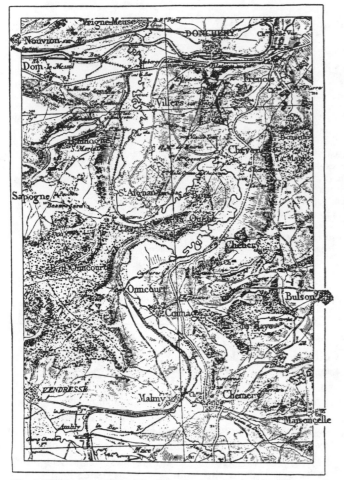

Fig. 1. The lower valley of the River Bar, France, a classic example of a manifestly underfit stream [from *Davis*, 1896]. The small stream meanders can be seen best in the center of the map where the Bar flows about the larger valley meander.

robbed the streams of discharge and so created the underfit pattern. Although bed seepage may be important in ephemeral stream channels and in streams draining karst terrain, it is not likely to be significant on the humid temperate streams of Europe that Lehmann considered. In spite of the flawed mechanism for discharge reduction, Davis avidly supported Lehmann's theory and in fact published the idea in his essay on underfit streams [*Davis*, 1913] before Lehmann published in 1915 [*Lehmann*, 1915]. Although climate change was commonly mentioned as a possible cause of reduced stream discharge, which would lead to underfitness, the lack of recognized underfit streams on a regional scale was cited as negative evidence that supported the other two hypotheses.

The recognition of underfit meandering streams implied a direct relationship between meander size and discharge, a relationship that has since been quantified [*Inglis*, 1938; *Friedkin*, 1945; *Leopold and Wolman*, 1957; *Dury*, 1964]. An early attempt to quantify this relationship is the work of *Jefferson* [1902] who identified the nearly constant ratio of meanderbelt width to stream width for alluvial streams of all sizes, a result later confirmed by *Bates* [1939]. His work is one of the first quantitative illustrations of the relations among river pattern characteristics (Figure 2). He reasoned that the increase in meanderbelt width with stream width reflected increased river discharge, and though he had only four measurements of stream discharge to correspond to his

meander data, he predicted the constant increase in stream discharge with meander size. Finally, he noted that rivers actively incising into bedrock had meander geometries that did not correspond to those for alluvial streams. The meander belt width for incised rivers was nearly twice as great for an equivalent size stream, and Jefferson thereby recognized the distinction between alluvial meanders and valley or bedrock meanders that G. H. Dury would elaborate upon 60 years later.

The observation that past river patterns were preserved in the landscape, that ancestral rivers had discharges different from those of today, and that quantitative measures of channel pattern could be related to river size and discharge provided the fundamental concepts for later work on paleohydrologic reconstructions based on channel pattern dimensions.

G. H. Dury has made the most extensive research on underfit streams and their paleohydrologic significance [*Dury*, 1954, 1964, 1965, 1976]. Dury, in a series of papers beginning in 1954, demonstrated that many underfit streams did not evolve through processes of capture or diversion, but instead reflected decreases in discharge caused by climate change. His estimates of the paleodischarges of the ancestral rivers were largely dependent on the empirical relationship between the meander wavelength of alluvial channels and bankfull discharge, a discharge that he assumed had a universal constant frequency of 1.5 years (Figure 3). Thus, the ratio of past valley meander wavelength to present day meander wavelength for underfit streams was a measure of the discharge reduction of a relatively high-frequency bankfull flood. His data on stream and valley meanders from a wide variety of fluvial environments indicated that this ratio varied between 5:1 to 10:1 (Figure 4). Based on the power function relationship between discharge and meander wavelength this ratio would translate to a 25 to 100 fold increase in bankfull discharge [*Dury*, 1965]. Adjusting this ratio for changes in slope associated with stream pattern change and for changes in roughness caused by changes in bed material, Dury estimated that discharges responsible for creating the preexisting valley meanders were typically 20 times that of present, but as great as 50 or 60 times for some extreme examples of "manifestly" underfit streams. Valley meander formation was ascribed to increased storminess during the

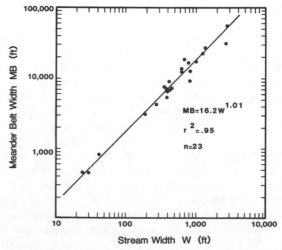

Fig. 2. Relationship between stream width and meander belt width [data from *Jefferson*, 1902].

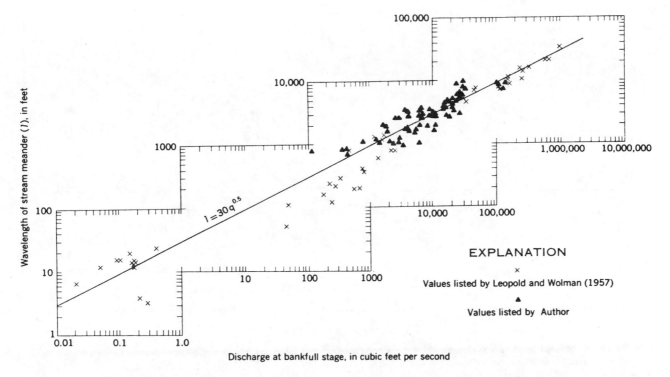

Fig. 3. Relation between meander wavelength and discharge at bankfull stage [from *Dury*, 1965].

latest glacial period and subsequent periods of reduced runoff were the result of increasing aridity during the present interglacial.

Over the past 20 years additional information on the formation of valley meanders has made the analysis of past runoff using only the meander wavelength criterion more equivocal. For example, studies of erosion in bedrock channels indicate that much of the work involved in creating valley meanders is accomplished during less frequent high magnitude floods, on the order of the 10 to 50 year flood or perhaps during still more rare flood events [*Tinkler*, 1971; *Patton and Baker*, 1977]. Also, although bankfull discharge can have a well-defined recurrence interval in some environments, such as the Appalachian Piedmont [*Wolman*, 1955]; in other environments the frequency of bankfull discharge is both variable and significantly greater than the 1.5 year flood proposed by Dury. *Williams* [1978] carefully reviewed the different methods of determining bankfull stage and bankfull discharge. He concluded that the frequency of bankfull discharge based on the annual peak series varied from about .25 years to 32 years for 36 stream cross-sections where bankfull discharge could be precisely determined and compared with long-term gaging records [*Williams*, 1978]. Thus a reconstruction of bankfull discharge from the meander wavelength criterion might represent a less frequent runoff event than suggested by Dury.

Another complicating factor is the effect of change in grain size of the sediment load which can cause major changes in channel pattern without a significant change in the magnitude of bankfull discharge [*Schumm*, 1968]. For example, a decrease in meander wavelength to produce an underfit stream pattern might be caused by a decrease in coarse bedload and a relative increase in suspended load creating a lower gradient, shorter wavelength, channel pattern [*Schumm*, 1968].

Finally, *Kehew* [1982] has reinvestigated the large glacial

outflow channels in southern Canada and in the midwestern U. S. cited as classic examples of stream underfitness. He has demonstrated that many of the large scale valley meander forms were eroded as bedrock inner channels during a few large glacial outbreak floods through these spillways [*Kehew*, 1982]. Therefore the meander forms were created during a few large floods [*Kehew*, 1982] and do not represent a meander form created under a rainfall-runoff regime 50 to 100 times wetter than today. Thus, the multiple causality of underfit streams and the the lack of a well defined relationship between a single frequency flow and channel pattern make tenuous the interpretation of past discharge regimes from meander wavelength alone.

Alluvial Fills, Paleochannels, and River Metamorphosis

A more comprehensive analysis of channel pattern related to paleohydrology is the study of preserved paleochannels and alluvial terrace deposits. By extrapolation from modern studies that equate river form and sedimentology to process, paleohydrologic reconstructions can be accomplished. The study of alluvial fills and their paleohydrologic implications has been one of the fundamental goals of researchers who study the evolution of fluvial landscapes. In fact, as *Gregory* [1983] notes, *Leopold and Miller* [1954] introduced the term paleohydrology to describe their estimate of the sediment yields for the ancestral streams which deposited a sequence of Quaternary alluvial terraces in Wyoming.

The most elementary inference in the reconstruction of past hydrologic conditions is that ancestral rivers created the terrace deposits adjacent to the modern stream, a concept whose general acceptance dates to about 1870. The debate over the origin of river terraces can be traced to the early 19th century where it is intertwined with the larger debate over the diluvial origin of the landscape.

The evolution of thought on river terraces can be outlined by the debate over the origin of the terraces in the Connecti-

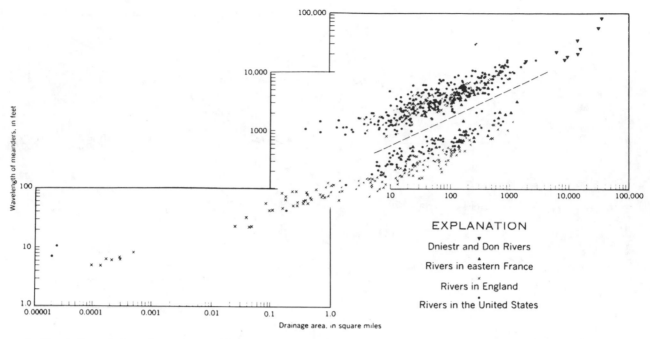

Fig. 4. Massed plots of wavelength against drainage area. Upper band, wavelength of valley meanders; lower band, wavelength of stream meanders [from *Dury*, 1965].

cut River valley of New England. Edward Hitchcock first studied the terraces in the Connecticut River valley in the early 19th century [*Hitchcock*, 1835]. He recognized that the terrace deposits were younger than the diluvium, sediment which he first attributed to Noah's flood [*Hitchcock*, 1835] and later to the deposits of "an ocean crowded with great icebergs, derived from corresponding glaciers, which ocean has been gradually withdrawn" [*Hitchcock*, 1850a, p. 88]. He noted that the lowest terrace or alluvial meadow was a product of the modern river which frequently overflowed its banks and covered this surface with sediment. Approximately 30 to 40 ft (9 to 12 m) above this meadow was a second terrace which he reasoned was an erosional remnant of an earlier meadow created by processes similar to those he observed acting on the modern river. Still higher, at an elevation 40 to 50 ft (12 to 15 m) above this second terrace he recognized a high terrace which formed the great plain of the Connecticut valley. The highest terrace was not considered fluvial in origin, but instead he called these high level terraces "sea beaches" which he attributed to marine submergence following the diluvial period [*Hitchcock*, 1850a, 1850b, 1852]. Hitchcock's theory of marine flooding creating high level terraces remained in the literature for over a quarter of a century both as a model for other investigators who reported evidence of submergence based on the position of terrace remnants [*Lesley*, 1878; *White*, 1887] and as a theory of great enough importance to attract the critical review of the leading geologists of the day [*Dana*, 1882].

Dana's [1871, 1875, 1882] model of alluvial terrace formation was equally unique. He constructed a longitudinal profile of the modern Connecticut River and its highest terrace (Figure 5) and noted that the terrace profile sloped downstream similar to the modern stream profile [*Dana*, 1882]. He reasoned that marine submergence would not produce such a profile and instead suggested that fluvial processes had created the terraces. The specific fluvial process that he proposed was a catastrophic flood generated

by the melting of the continental glacier. He interpreted the surfaces of the terrace remnants as deposits that had built up beneath the flood waters as flood bars and that the deposits of terraces in back-flooded tributaries approximated the maximum stage of this flood. The modern alluvial meadow or floodplain of the river represented the post flood excavation of the bed of this ancestral stream. Dana estimated the magnitude of this flood based on the reconstructed flood profile from the height of terraces in back-flooded tributaries and the dimensions of the valley cross-section. The flood had an estimated mean depth of 185 ft (56 m) in New Hampshire decreasing to 125 ft (38 m) in Connecticut, an average cross-sectional area of 560,000 ft^2 (170,700 m^2) and an average velocity of 15 to 23 ft/s (4.5 to 7 m/s) depending on the mean depth, hydraulic radius and slope of the water surface at specific cross-sections. Dana did not calculate the discharge for this flood, but his hydrologic reconstruction would have resulted in a peak flow of at least 8.4 million cfs (240,000 cms), equal to the Amazon River's discharge during flood. Dana did, however, recognize that his velocity figures were too great to explain the predominately fine-grained sedimentology of the terrace deposits. He considered the possibility that sections of the river were dammed and the effect of marine submergence in reducing the gradient of the flood's surface. Although Dana's interpretation of the origin of the terraces was wrong, the methods used in his paleohydrologic reconstruction are not significantly different from those used today, and his work stands as one of the first attempts to explain the origin of terraces as the product of past river regimes.

At the same time, *Warren Upham* [1877, 1891], working in the Connecticut Valley in New Hampshire, suggested that river terraces in glaciated environments resulted from deposition by sediment laden glacial streams. Glacial streams caused aggradation of the valleys and subsequent climate changes resulted in stream downcutting. Upham's views were supported by study of proglacial fluvial terraces along

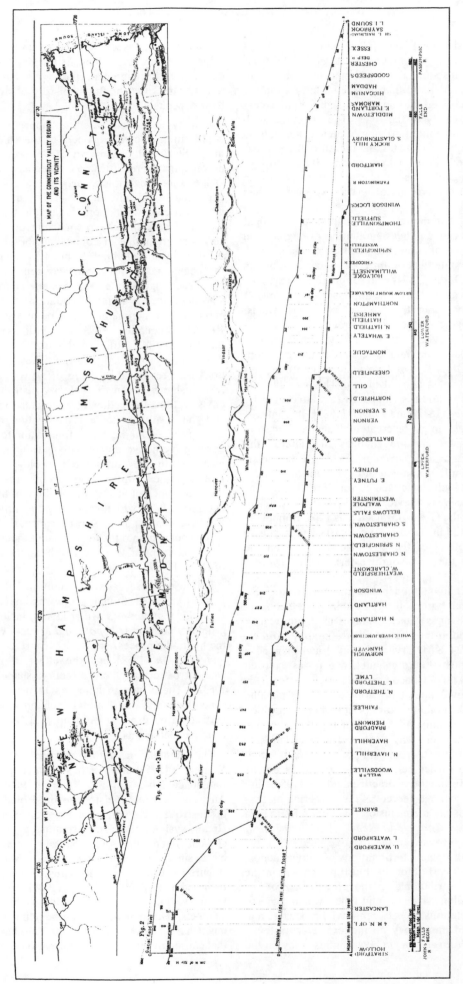

Fig. 5. Map and long profile of the Connecticut River Valley illustrating the elevation of the flood from the melting of the glacier [from Dana, 1882]. The upper solid line profile in figure 3 represents the elevation of the flood. The lower solid line profile is the modern low water level. Downstream of Holyoke, MA, the modern flood level is shown for comparison with the glacial flood.

the Ohio and Mississippi Rivers [*Chamberlain and Salisbury*, 1891] and in the upper Indus valley [*Drew*, 1873]. *Drew* [1873] specifically discounted the submergence theory of terrace formation and stated that high level terraces in the Indus valley were created by a supply of sediment in excess of the transport capacity of the river. The increased sediment supply was attributed to more intense mechanical weathering during glacial climates and therefore the terraces recorded past periods of glacial conditions. By the turn of the century the significance of glacial meltwater stream deposition in creating river terraces was well established [*Davis*, 1902].

The recognition that non-glacial climate changes might affect streams and cause either aggradation or degradation and result in terrace formation evolved at the end of the 19th century. One early statement of this concept can be found in the report of *R. E. Dodge* [1894] who summarized the results of his study in the advanced course in physical geography at Harvard University under the tutelage of W. M. Davis. *Dodge* [1894] recognized "normal" terraces as the necessary result of the Davisian cycle of landform evolution whereby lateral planation and stream downcutting, enhanced by periods of rising base level and tectonic uplift, left behind remnants of past alluvial plains. This non-climatic model of terrace formation is similar to that advocated by *Gilbert* [1877], *Miller* [1882] and *Powell* [1883]. In contrast, "subnormal terraces" might be created by aggradation from glacial streams or by climatic changes that altered the rainfall-runoff regime and sediment load of the river. Dodge's observation that non-glacial environments had undergone significant hydrologic change was directly attributed to the recent discovery of evidence for past high stands of the pluvial lakes in the Great Basin such as Lake Bonneville [*Gilbert*, 1890]. In addition, other geologists had begun to speculate on the effect of the post-glacial aridity on the stream systems in the arid southwestern U. S. [*Dutton*, 1882].

Investigations of alluvial fill deposits in the western U. S., far beyond the glacial border, firmly established the concept that past climate changes caused changes in stream regime which were reflected in the alluvial fill stratigraphy [*Antevs*, 1952]. Thus, in 1924 Kirk Bryan identified and mapped a paleochannel, the post-Bonito channel, which was exposed in the latest alluvial fill of Chaco Canyon [*Bryan*, 1954]. This paleochannel was evidence of previous periods of channel incision similar to the contemporary period of erosion which was identified as beginning at the end of the 19th century. This latest erosional event was attributed to poor land-use practices in the southwest, specifically overgrazing [*Dodge*, 1902]. Because the earlier period of erosion could not be explained by harmful land-use practices, *Bryan* [1954] suggested that climate change served as the triggering mechanism for arroyo incision, a conclusion that continues to be a point of debate (see *Cooke and Reeves* [1976] and *Graf* [1983] for a thorough review of the "arroyo problem").

Modern paleohydrologic interpretations of alluvial deposits are rooted in this early thought, but rapid growth in the science is directly attributable to the growth of process-oriented geomorphology since the mid 1940's which began to quantify the interrelationship between fluvial processes and channel pattern and morpology on modern river systems. Among others, *J. Hoover Mackin* [1948] in his essay on the graded river stressed the need to understand the relationships between alluvial deposits forming today and the slope, discharge, and channel morphology of modern streams so as to better interpret the fluvial history of stream channels and their deposits.

Equally important was the incorporation of the large contribution of civil engineers to the study of river adjustment. Specifically, *Kennedy* [1895] who demonstrated the power function relationship between velocity and depth for stable non-silting, non-scouring canals in India. Kennedy's expression is significant because it included a coefficient which varied as a function of the grain size and erodibility of the canal bed, thereby recognizing the importance of the sediment grain size in controlling the critical velocity and depth of a stable channel. Kennedy's equation, which marks the beginning of the regime concept for designing stable channel configurations, was expanded upon by *Lacey* [1930] who developed a series of equations to predict the width, depth, wetted perimeter and slope of a stable channel. Like Kennedy's equation, however, one important variable was the Lacey silt factor which summarized the grain size distribution of the bed material. These important contributions were reviewed by *Lane* [1937] who also described the relationship between the velocity distribution in a channel cross-section, the sediment characteristics of the channel, and the resulting stable cross-section morphology. This work provided an important foundation for later attempts to develop predictive empirical equations relating channel dimensions to the formative hydrologic process. Perhaps Lane's greatest contribution was his prescient discussion of the importance of fluvial morphology to hydraulic engineering [*Lane*, 1955] which presents a theoretical framework for the incorporation of the short-term changes predicted by the regime concept into the longer time framework of the graded stream concept of *Mackin* [1948] and the geographical cycle of *Davis* [1899].

Following these early contributions, the rapid growth of process oriented fluvial geomorphology, summarized by *Leopold, Wolman and Miller* [1964], included the hydraulic geometry concept [*Leopold and Maddock*, 1953]; studies of the hydraulic processes that control river patterns [*Leopold and Wolman*, 1957] and the effect of sediment type on channel pattern and cross-section shape [*Schumm*, 1960, 1963a]. These new insights led to new classifications and generalizations about alluvial channels [*Schumm*, 1963b] that could be used to estimate past hydrologic conditions from paleochannels.

The culmination of this approach to paleohydrology is *Schumm's* [1968] analysis of the paleochannels of the Murrumbidgee River on the Riverine Plain of southeastern Australia. The late Pleistocene and Holocene paleochannels of the Riverine Plain reveal a transition from a braided stream system, the Prior streams, to a large meandering stream system, the Ancestral Murrumbidgee, to a smaller more sinuous, meandering modern Murrumbidgee River (Figure 6). From the dimensions of the paleochannels and their sedimentology, *Schumm* [1968] reconstructed the water and sediment discharge conditions that formed the paleochannels. He speculated on the climatic conditions that might have been responsible for the changes in hydrology that caused the channel transformations, and introduced two

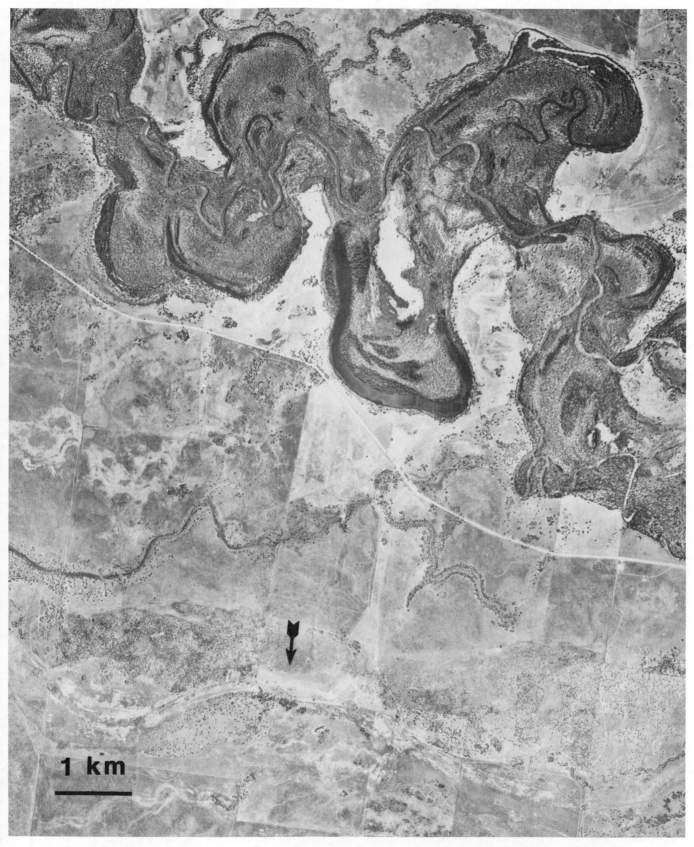

Fig. 6. The Murrumbidgee River and Riverine Plain with paleochannels of the braided prior stream (arrow) and large meandering channel of the ancestral river. Modern Murrumbidgee is an underfit stream within the valley eroded by the ancestral river [from Schumm, 1968].

proportionalities that can be used to predict river "metamorphosis" [Schumm, 1969]. The first proportionality:

$$Q_w \; \alpha \frac{L \; w \; d}{S} \tag{1}$$

relates high frequency bankfull discharge (Q_w) directly to the width (w) and depth (d) of the channel as predicted by the hydraulic geometry relationships [Leopold and Maddock, 1953] and to meander wavelength (L) as shown by Dury [1964]. Slope (S) is inversely proportional to discharge, for with constant sediment discharge, an increase in discharge should result in scour and a decreasing stream gradient. The second proportionality:

$$Q_s \; \alpha \frac{w \; S \; L}{d \; P} \tag{2}$$

indicates the increase in channel width, slope and wavelength with increases in bed sediment discharge (Q_s) and the corresponding decrease in channel depth and sinuosity (P) with a relative decrease in suspended sediment load [Schumm, 1960]. Because these relationships can be quantified, the absolute shift in hydrologic conditions that caused the river channel changes can be estimated. However, one caution that must be emphasized is that the relationships developed by Schumm were based on a limited sample of modern rivers, primarily those draining the semiarid Great Plains of the western U. S. [Etheridge and Schumm, 1978]. More data on the relationships between channel patterns and formative variables from a broader range of hydrologic environments will undoubtedly improve the accuracy of paleohydrologic estimates [Etheridge and Schumm, 1978; Osterkamp and Hedman, 1982]. With these limitations in mind, careful paleohydrologic reconstructions have demonstrated the potential utility of Schumm's approach to interpret both Quaternary fluvial adjustments [Baker and Penteado-Orellana, 1977] and the hydrologic character of streams preserved in the rock-stratigraphic record [Gardner, 1983].

PALEOFLOOD HYDROLOGY

The goal of paleoflood hydrology is to reconstruct the magnitude and frequency of rare great floods from indirect evidence of the hydraulic characteristics of the flow and from stratigraphic evidence of the timing of the runoff event. For example, paleoflood magnitudes have been estimated on the basis of the force necessary to transport large boulders found in flood sediments. The reader is referred to Costa [this volume] and Williams [1983] for a comprehensive review of this approach. Another approach is the reconstruction of flood elevations from indirect evidence of water surface elevation, such as the elevation of flood sediment found in backwater environments, the slackwater deposits of Bretz [Bretz et al., 1956].

Indirect evidence of the frequency of individual prehistoric flood events can be obtained by a number of methods including botanical studies of floodplain vegetation [Sigafoos, 1964, Helley and LaMarche, 1973]; analysis of the degree of soil development on floodplain alluvium [Cain and Beatty, 1968], on flood bars [Bretz et al., 1956; Baker, 1973;

Patton and Baker, 1978], and on geomorphic surfaces truncated by floods [Costa, 1978a, 1978b]; radiocarbon dating of buried organic debris within flood deposits and within organic rich floodplain soils [Helley and LaMarche, 1973; Patton and Baker, 1977; Costa, 1978a]; and from radiocarbon dated archeological sites interstratified with flood deposits [Kochel and Baker, 1982; Patton and Dibble, 1982]. Recent interest and development of paleoflood methodology stems from its potential for developing unusually long flood frequency records.

J Harlen Bretz and the Channeled Scabland

There are many starting points for a history of paleoflood hydrology; but many, such as Dana's [1882] paleoflood reconstruction in the Connecticut Valley, are false starts. In contrast, J Harlen Bretz's interpretation of the flood scoured landscape of the Channeled Scabland in eastern Washington, first published in 1923, is a landmark study in the field of paleoflood hydrology [Bretz, 1923a, 1923b]. It would be a landmark simply because the geologic field evidence which he used to build the case for catastrophic flooding on the Columbia Plateau represents the first comprehensive analysis of a paleoflood. But his contribution is more remarkable because of the extreme controversy that it generated [Baker, 1978] and because he could not identify the source of the water needed for the cataclysmic "Spokane Flood". Thus, Bretz's flood hypothesis was based on a firm belief in the field evidence and was developed in the total absence of any hydrologic data against which he could compare his observations of flood phenomena.

Today, it is an accepted fact that the Channeled Scabland of eastern Washington, an anastamosing network of channels eroded into the flood basalts of the Columbia Plateau (Figure 7), was created by catastrophic outbreak floods from Lake Missoula during the Quaternary [Bretz, 1969]. But, when Bretz published his first paper on the flood origin of the scabland topography in 1923 his evidence for a catastrophic flood origin was based entirely on observation of the morphology and interrelationships of the erosional and depositional features in the scablands. The scarified surface of the scabland channels with their irregular butte and basin topography, longitudinal grooves, and inner channels or rock basins which end at cataracts, all suggested to him erosion on a tremendous scale. While many of these scabland channels follow the lines of the preglacial drainage, he recognized other conspicuous channels that cross the divides of the earlier drainage. One spectacular divide crossing is the southern diversion of the Palouse River which resulted in the erosion of the modern Palouse Canyon to its new junction with the Snake River.

The margins of these dry channels, or coulees, have steeply eroded scarps cut into the loess mantle of the plateau and along the margins of these scarps the preglacial drainage enters the scabland channels as hanging valleys. He noted that loess hills rimmed by channels formed islands within the scabland tracts and that these loess islands had sharp erosional prows on their upstream ends. In numerous instances small watergaps cut across the loess islands and truncate the preglacial drainage on their surface, a further indication of a large divide crossing flood event.

Along the course of the scabland channelways he ob-

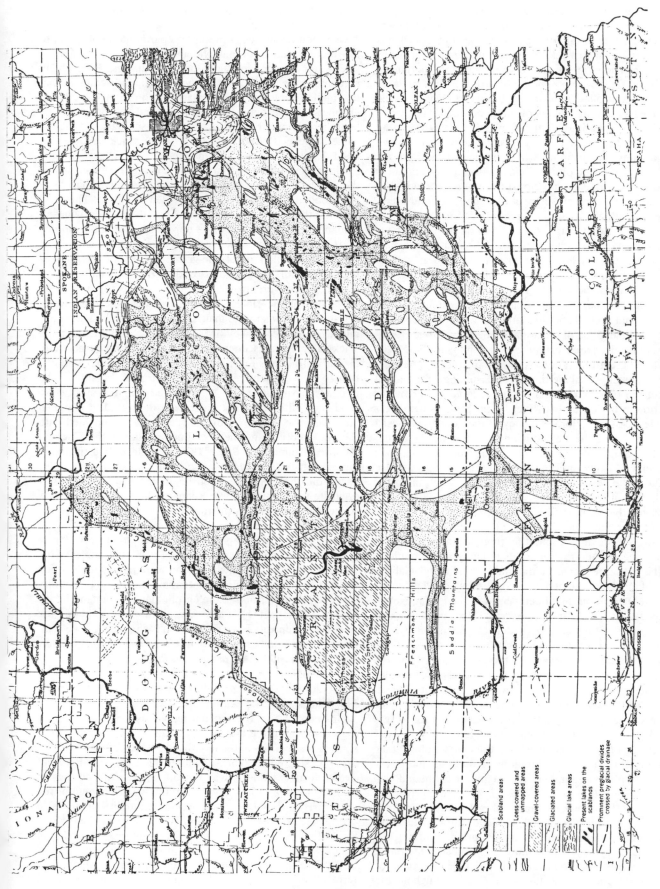

Fig .7. Geomorphic map of the Channel Scabland of eastern Washington [from Bretz, 1923b]. The anastamosing channel complex that trends northeast to southwest on the eastern side of the scablands is the Cheney Palouse tract referred to in the text. The confluence of the Columbia and Snake Rivers at Pasco, just upstream of Wallula Gap, is located at the center of the bottom margin.

served immense gravel deposits preserved only where protected by an upstream obstacle. Many bars occur downstream of resistant basalt buttes or in the lee of loess islands while others occur in backflooded tributaries and at major channel expansions. In backwater areas along the margins of the scabland tract where ponding occurred and in the large structurally controlled depositional basins he recognized the fine-grained slackwater facies of the flood deposits.

Bretz's investigation of these phenomena led him to propose that the scablands could only have been formed during a catastrophic flood, which he named the Spokane Flood for its supposed origin along the front of the continental ice sheet near present day Spokane. Not only could Bretz not identify the source of water for this immense flood event, but attempts at paleohydrologic reconstructions only resulted in greater skepticism that such a flood could have occurred. Bretz had a colleague at the University of Chicago calculate the velocity and discharge of the flood at Wallula Gap, a constriction downstream of the confluence of the Snake and Columbia Rivers (Figure 7). The estimate was made using the Chezy equation and Bretz's estimate of the cross-sectional area of the flow and the water surface slope based on the elevation of erosional topography [Bretz, 1925]. The resulting discharge estimate of 1.9 million cfs (53,800 cms) was so great that it could not be explained by the most extreme rates of glacial melting, even assuming a continental ice sheet ten times larger than that available for meltwater production in the Columbia River basin. Still, though Bretz acknowledged this major deficiency of the flood hypothesis, he reiterated that the field evidence in the scablands demanded a catastrophic flood. The source of the "Spokane Flood" eluded Bretz until Pardee documented the existence of glacial Lake Missoula and the evidence which indicated that it had rapidly drained [Bretz, 1930].

Bretz concluded his 1923 paper [Bretz, 1923b] with a statement that puts the Spokane Flood hypothesis in the context of the prevailing scientific thought on the origin of the landscape and the role of floods in landscape evolution:

"If the battle between the diluvialists and the glacialists, out of which has emerged our conception of Pleistocene continental glaciation, had been staged in the Pacific Northwest instead of the Atlantic Northeast, it seems likely that the surrender of the idea of a debacle might have been delayed a decade or so. Fully 3,000 square miles of the Columbia plateau were swept by the glacial flood, and the loess and silt cover removed. More than 2,000 square miles of this area were left as bare, eroded, rock-cut channel floors, now the scablands, and nearly 1,000 square miles carry gravel deposits derived from the eroded basalt. It was a debacle which swept the Columbia Plateau."

The types of field evidence and the methodology that Bretz utilized in support of his flood hypothesis and in his reconstruction of the number and magnitude of the individual flood events [Bretz et al., 1956; Bretz, 1969] provide a starting point for modern studies of paleofloods. In fact, Baker [1973] utilized the various evidences of the elevation of high water throughout the scablands, originally described by Bretz, and by applying a more sophisticated hydraulic analysis to these data produced the first detailed paleohydrologic reconstruction of the last great flood throughout the scabland. Ongoing investigations using still more sophisticated unsteady flow models are further refining the character of these flow events [Hanson and Craig, 1985].

Slackwater Deposits and Paleoflood Reconstructions

One sedimentary deposit that has particular application to the reconstruction of paleofloods is the interpretation of slackwater deposits in backflooded tributaries. Bretz [1929] recognized the significance of the fine-grained sediment that had infilled tributary valleys marginal to the main scabland channels. These deposits also blanketed the floors of the large depositional basins such as the Pasco basin where the name Touchet Beds was applied to the thick sequence of flood deposits that had accumulated.

Along the eastern margin of the Cheney Palouse tract of the scablands, Bretz identified 41 valleys which had been backflooded and filled with fine-grained sediment. The flood origin of the tributary deposits was based on several lines of evidence. First, the slackwater deposits began at the mouths of tributaries where the scabland topography ends. The terrace accumulations of fine-grained sediment are thickest near the mouth of the tributary and become thinner upstream eventually converging with the floor of the tributary. The elevations of the slackwater terraces coincide with water surface elevations in the main channels which he had determined from other field evidence. Finally, the grain size of the slackwater deposits decreases upstream, the internal sedimentary structures indicate upstream flow and the composition of the sediment requires a source from outside of the drainage basin. Bretz [1929] reasoned that the slackwater sands and silts could not have been deposited in marginal lakes because the elevations of the terraces coincided with the water-surface gradient of flooding down the Cheney-Palouse channelway. Bretz [1929] also described upstream dipping slackwater deposits on the Snake River above Lewiston-Clarkson, the deposits in the Tucannon Valley opposite the Palouse-Snake River confluence, and the thick sequences deposited in the the Walla Walla basin and in the Yakima River basin.

Bretz [1929] was impressed with the flood record preserved in the slackwater deposits. He later wrote that the mechanics of slackwater deposition were poorly understood but that the deposits offered potentially the best opportunity for precisely determining the chronology of scabland floods [Bretz, 1969, p. 151]. Since Bretz's first description, the slackwater deposits have remained a focus for the investigation into the number and timing of scabland floods [Baker, 1973; Bunker, 1982; Atwater, 1984; Baker and Bunker, 1985; Waitt, 1985].

In addition to Bretz's [1929] observations of Missoula Flood slackwater deposition, other workers have noted that such deposits are formed during floods on modern river systems. One of the first observations of the flood origin of slackwater deposits in the mouths of tributaries was made by Tarr [1892]. While working along the Colorado River of Texas he noted that it was not uncommon to find logs in trees up to 50 ft (15 m) above the low water channel of the stream. He recognized the extreme variablility of runoff in central Texas streams and identified two alluvial plains along the Colorado River, a low floodplain covered by moderate floods and a second "upper flood plain terrace" up to 40 or 50 ft (12 to 15 m) above the channel. The "upper flood plain terrace" was attributed to deposition during large floods and at this level there were bars deposited in the mouths of tributary streams, presumably created by damming of the tributary runoff during floods. Tarr noted that these tributary deposits were similar to those described by *Dana* [1882] for the great flood in the Connecticut Valley. It is ironic that while Dana's flood bars are in reality glacial delta deposits, the deposits that Tarr recognized are in fact of flood origin [*Baker*, 1977; *Patton et al.*, 1979]

Stewart [*Stewart and Bodhaine*, 1961] in 1922 used slackwater deposits to reconstruct flood magnitudes on the Skagit River in Washington. He determined the stages of floods that had occurred about 1815 and 1856 on the Skagit River from water marks on trees and canyon walls and from the height of sediment lodged in the bark of trees and deposited in crevices in the canyon sides. He observed that the sediment which backfilled tributary gulches was at an elevation consistent with his other high-water-mark data, and he incorporated this information into his stage estimates.

Jahns [1947] was able to identify stratigraphic layers in slackwater silts preserved in a small gully cut into a terrace adjacent to the Connecticut River. He related the deposition of the individual layers to the 1927, 1936, and 1938 floods, and used the elevation of the deposits and their stratigraphic relationships to infer the relative frequency of those floods. Sediment from the 1936 flood occurred at the highest elevation and covered the low terrace (Terrace III in Jahn's report) of the Connecticut River. Because the flood sediment buried a fine-grained sedimentary sequence typical of an open floodplain environment, he reasoned that the 1936 flood must have been the largest flood to occur since Terrace III had formed. He estimated that Terrace III was the active river floodplain level approximately 2500 to 6000 years B. P.

McKee [1938] noted the occurrence of small terraces at the mouths of Travertine Canyon and Separation Canyon, tributaries of the Colorado River in the Grand Canyon of Arizona. These terraces, which are found above the floodplain or "beach" of the river are formed by surges of sediment-laden flood water into the tributary from the main stem. *McKee* [1938] described these slackwater deposits because he was interested in the climbing ripple stratification preserved in the sediment. His sketch of these deposits indicates that the flood deposits which comprise the terraces are up to 25 ft (8 m) above the low flow elevation of the channel. Recent investigation of slackwater deposits in the narow canyons of the Colorado Plateau province is illustrating the potential of these deposits for paleoflood analysis [*O'Connor et al.*, 1984].

Since *Baker's* [1973] reinvestigation of the slackwater deposits in the channeled scabland, their use in paleohydrologic reconstructions has increased rapidly. Research in central and west Texas has identified sequences of flood deposits that allow the reconstruction of long-term flood histories at a single site as well as the reconstruction of a single flood through a drainage basin [*Patton et al.*, 1979; *Kochel and Baker*, 1982; *Kochel et al.*, 1982; *Patton and Dibble*, 1982]. Investigations in the arid interior of Australia have demonstrated the ability to reconstruct and discriminate between historic floods in a basin where few standard hydrologic records exist [*Baker et al.*, 1985]. Finally, ongoing investigations in the southwest U. S. have shown that paleohydrologic data from slackwater deposits can be incorporated into standard water surface profile models to develop realistic discharge estimates and to extend the flood frequency record to time periods of up to 1,000 years [*Ely and Baker*, 1985]. Although there are important limitations to the interpretation of slackwater deposits [see the discus-sion in *Kochel et al.*, 1982], continued investigation of overbank flood sedimentation in slackwater depositional settings offers the greatest potential for paleoflood hydrology.

FUTURE DIRECTIONS IN FLUVIAL PALEOHYDROLOGY

The approaches to paleohydrology outlined in this review will continue to be a significant focus of study for unraveling the response of fluvial systems to both long and short term changes in hydrologic conditions. I would like to end this review with several suggestions for areas where future research will improve our ability to make these important reconstructions. First, improved understanding of the relationship between channel form and hydrologic-sedimentologic processes is necessary to further refine the paleohydrologic interpretations based on the analysis of paleochannels. Although the fluvial system is complex and although it can be difficult to make unequivocal linkages between process and form, the fluvial record is often the only record preserved in an otherwise erosional landscape [*Baker and Penteado-Orellana*, 1977]. Also, paleohydrologic interpretations are not limited to the Quaternary and improved understanding of modern geomorphic systems has direct application to the entire stratigraphic record. In this regard certain fluvial environments, such as the tropical, the periglacial and the hyper-arid river systems have been inadequately studied by comparison to the stream systems which occur in humid-temperate to arid region climates. This undoubtedly biases the interpretations made of ancestral stream systems and research efforts should be made to improve our understanding of these less studied environments.

Paleoflood hydrology is emerging from a period of rapid growth and interest. But again, studies of paleofloods have focused on streams in arid, semiarid and humid-temperate environments. There is a clear need to collect additional data on the hydrodynamics and sedimentology of rare large floods in other climatic regimes, particularly as these environments are the least understood hydrologic systems. In addition to this need for a broadened perspective, two areas of research offer great potential. One is the application of hydraulic modeling of paleoflood data to improve the reliability of the discharge estimates. The second is the incorporation of paleoflood data with conventional gaging station data and synthetic streamflow data to generate realistic long-term records of flood runoff.

Acknowledgments. Thoughtful reviews by V. R. Baker, S. A. Schumm and an anonymous reviewer have contributed to the preparation of this manuscript. S. A. Schumm graciously provided the aerial photograph of the Murrumbidgee channels used in Figure 6.

REFERENCES

Antevs, E., Arroyo-cutting and filling, *J. Geol.*, *60*, 375-385, 1952.

Atwater, B. F., Periodic floods from glacial Lake Missoula into the Sanpoil arm of glacial Lake Columbia, northeastern Washington, *Geology*, *12*, 464-467, 1984.

Baker, V. R., Paleohydrology and sedimentology of Lake Missoula flooding in eastern Washington, *Geol. Soc. Am. Spec. Pap. 144*, 1973.

Baker, V. R., Stream-channel response to floods with examples from central Texas, *Geol. Soc. Am. Bull.*, *88*, 1057-1071, 1977.

Baker, V. R., The Spokane flood controversey and the Martian outflow channels, *Science*, *202*, 1249-1256, 1978.

Baker, V. R., and R. C. Bunker, Cataclysmic Late Pleistocene flooding from Glacial Lake Missoula: a review, *Quat. Sci. Rev.*, *4*, 1-41, 1985.

Baker, V. R., and M. M. Penteado-Orellana, Adjustment to Quaternary climatic change by the Colorado River in central Texas, *J. Geol.*, *85*, 395-422, 1977.

Baker, V. R., G. Pickup, and H. A. Polach, Radiocarbon dating of flood events, Katherine Gorge, Northern Territory, Australia, *Geology*, *13*, 344-347, 1985.

Bates, R. E., Geomorphic history of the Kickapoo Region, Wisconsin, *Geol. Soc. Am. Bull.*, *50*, 819-880, 1939.

Bretz, J H., Glacial drainage on the Columbia Plateau, *Geol. Soc. Am. Bull.*, *34*, 573-608, 1923a.

Bretz, J H., The Channeled Scabland of the Columbia Plateau, *J. Geol.*, *31*, 617-649, 1923b.

Bretz, J H., The Spokane flood beyond the Channeled Scabland, *J. Geol.*, *33*, 97-115, p. 236-259, 1925.

Bretz, J H., Valley deposits immediately east of the Channeled Scabland of Washington, *J. Geol.*, *37*, 393-427, 505-541, 1929.

Bretz, J H., Lake Missoula and the Spokane flood, *Geol. Soc. Am. Bull.*, *41*, 92-93, 1930.

Bretz, J H., The Lake Missoula floods and the Channeled Scabland, *J. Geol.*, *77*, 505-543, 1969.

Bretz, J H., H. T. U. Smith, and G. E. Neff, Channeled Scabland of Washington; new data and interpretations, *Geol. Soc. Am. Bull.*, *67*, 957-1049, 1956.

Bryan, K., The geology of Chaco Canyon New Mexico in relation to the life and remains of the prehistoric peoples of Pueblo Bonito, *Smithsonian Misc. Collections*, *122*, 1-65, 1954.

Bunker, R. C., Evidence of multiple late-Wisconsin floods from glacial Lake Missoula in Badger Coulee, Washington, *Quaternary Res.*, *18*, 17-31, 1982.

Butzer, K. W., G. F. Fock, R. Stuckenrath, and A. Zilch, Paleohydrology of Late Pleistocene lake, Alexandersfontein, Kimberly, South Africa, *Nature*, *243*, 328-330, 1973.

Cain, J. M., and M. T. Beatty, The use of soil maps in the delineation of flood plains, *Water Resour. Res.*, *4*, 173-182, 1968.

Chamberlin, T. C., and C. M. Salisbury, On the relationship of the Pleistocene to the pre-Pleistocene formations of the Mississippi Basin south of the limit of glaciation, *Am. J. Sci.*, *141*, 359-377, 1891.

Cooke, R. U., and R. W. Reeves, *Arroyos and Environmental Change in the American South-West*, 213 pp., Oxford University Press, London, 1976.

Costa, J. E., Holocene stratigraphy in flood frequency analysis, *Water Resour. Res.*, *14*, 626-632, 1978a.

Costa, J. E., Colorado Big Thompson flood: geologic evidence of a rare hydrologic event, *Geology*, *6*, 617-620, 1978b.

Costa, J. E., Paleohydrologic reconstruction of flash-flood peaks from boulder deposits in the Colorado Front Range, *Geol. Soc. Am. Bull.*, *94*, 986-1004, 1983.

Costa, J. E., A history of paleoflood hydrology in the United States, 1800-1970, this volume.

Dana, J. D., On the geology of the New Haven region, with special reference to the origin of some of its topographical features, *Conn. Acad. Sci. Trans.*, *2*, 45-112, 1871.

Dana, J. D., On southern New England during the melting of the great glacier, *Am. J. Sci.*, *110*, 168-183, 1875.

Dana, J. D., The flood of the Connecticut River valley from the melting of the Quaternary glacier, *Am. J. Sci.*, *123*, 87-97, 179-202, and *124*, 98-104, 1882.

Davis, W. M., The Seine, the Meuse, and the Moselle, *Nat. Geog. Mag.*, *7*, 228-238, 1896.

Davis, W. M., The geographical cycle, *Geog. Jour.*, *14*, 481-504, 1899.

Davis, W. M., River terraces in New England, *Bull. Mus. Comp. Zool.*, *38*, 281-346, 1902.

Davis, W. M., Meandering valleys and underfit rivers, *Annals Assoc. Am. Geog.*, *3*, 3-28, 1913.

Dodge, R. E., The geographical development of alluvial river terraces, *Boston Soc. Nat. Hist. Proc.*, *26*, 257-273, 1894.

Dodge, R. E., Arroyo formation, *Science*, *15*, 746, 1902.

Drew, F., Alluvial and lacustrine deposits and glacial records of the upper Indus basin, *Quart. J. Geol. Soc. London*, *29*, 441-471, 1873.

Dury, G. H., Contribution to a general theory of meandering valleys, *Am. J. Sci.*, *252*, 193-224, 1954.

Dury, G. H., Principles of underfit streams, *U.S. Geol. Surv. Prof. Pap. 452-A*, 1964.

Dury, G. H., Theoretical implications of underfit streams, *U.S. Geol. Surv. Prof. Pap. 452-C*, 1965.

Dury, G. H., Discharge predicition present and former, from channel dimensions, *J. Hydrology*, *30*, 219-245, 1976.

Dutton, C.E., *Tertiary History of the Grand Canon District with Atlas*, 264 pp., U.S. Geol. Surv. Monograph II, 1882.

Ely, L. L., and V. R. Baker, Reconstructing paleoflood hydrology with slackwater deposits: Verde River, Arizona, *Phys. Geog.*, *5*, 103-126, 1985

Etheridge, F. G., and S. A. Schumm, Reconstructing paleochannel morphologic and flow characteristics: methodology, limitations, and assessment, in *Fluvial Sedimentology*, edited by A. D. Miall, pp. 703-721, Memoir 5, Canadian Soc. of Petrol. Geol., Calgary, Alberta, 1978.

Friedkin, J. F., A laboratory study of the meandering of alluvial rivers, *U.S. Waterways Exp. Sta.*, 40 pp., U.S. Army Corps Eng., Vicksburg, MS, 1945.

Gardner, T. W., Paleohydrology and paleomorphology of a Carboniferous meandering, fluvial sandstone, *J. Sediment. Petrol.*, *53*, 991-1005, 1983.

Gilbert, G. K., *Report on the geology of the Henry Mountains*, 160 pp., U.S. Govt. Printing Office, Washington, D.C., 1877.

Gilbert, G. K., *Lake Bonneville*, 438 pp., U.S. Geol. Survey Monograph I, 1890.

Graf, W. L., The arroyo problem - palaeohydrology and palaeohydraulics in the short term, in *Background to Palaeohydrology, A Perspective*, edited by K. J. Gregory, pp. 279-302, J. Wiley & Sons, New York, 1983.

Gregory, K. J., Introduction, in *Background to Palaeohydrology, A perspective*, edited by K. J. Gregory, p. 3-23, J. Wiley & Sons, New York, 1983.

Hanson, J. P., and R. G. Craig, Modelling Missoula floods in the Pasco Basin, Washington (abstract), *Geol. Soc. Am. Abst. Prog.*, *17*, 603, 1985.

Helley, E. J., and V. C. LaMarche, Historic flood information for northern California streams from geological and botanical evidence, *U.S. Geol. Surv. Prof. Pap. 485-E*, 1973.

Hitchcock, E., *Report on the geology, mineralogy, botany and zoology of Massachussetts*, J. S. and C. Adams, Amherst, MA, 1835.

Hitchcock, E., On terraces and ancient sea beaches especially those on the Connecticut River, and its tributaries in New England, *Rept. Brit. Assoc. Adv. Sci.*, *20*, 87-88, 1850a.

Hitchcock, E., On the river terraces of the Connecticut Valley, and on the erosions of the earth surface, *Am. Assoc. Adv. Sci. Proc.*, *2*, 148-156, 1850b.

Hitchcock, E., On the terraces and sea beaches that have formed since the drift period, especially those along the Connecticut River, *Am. Assoc. Adv. Sci. Proc.*, *6*, 264-269, 1852.

Inglis, C. C., Relationship between meander belts, distance between meanders, width and discharge of rivers, *Res. Pap. 4*, annual report, Central Irrigation and Hydrodynamic Research Station, Poona, India, 1938.

Jahns, R. H., Geologic features of the Connecticut Valley, Massachusetts, as related to recent floods, *U.S. Geol. Surv. Water Supply Pap. 996*, 1947.

Jefferson, M., Limiting width of meander belts, *Nat. Geog. Mag.*, *13*, 373-384, 1902.

Kafri, U., and A. Arad, Paleohydrology and migration of the ground-water divide in regions of tectonic instability in Israel, *Geol. Soc. Am. Bull.*, *89*, 1723-1732, 1978.

Kehew, A. E., Catastrophic flood hypothesis for the origin of the Souris spillway, Saskatchewan and North Dakota, *Geol. Soc. Am. Bull.*, *93*, 1051-1058, 1982.

Kennedy, R. G., 1895, The prevention of silting in irrigation canals, *Proc. Inst. Civil Eng. London*, *119*, 281-290, 1895.

Kochel, R. C., and V. R. Baker, Paleoflood hydrology, *Science*, *215*, 353-361, 1982.

Kochel, R. C., V. R. Baker, and P. C. Patton, Paleohydrology of southwestern Texas, *Water Resour. Res.*, *18*, 1165-1183, 1982.

Lacey, G., Stable channels in alluvium, *Proc. Inst. Civil Eng. London*, *229*, 259-384, 1930.

Lane, E. W., Stable channels in erodible material, *Am. Soc. Civ. Eng. Trans.*, *102*, 123-142, 1937.

Lane, E. W., The importance of fluvial morphology in hydraulic engineering, *Am. Soc. Civ. Eng. Proc., 81*, 745-1 - 745-15, 1955.

Langbein, W. B., and S. A. Schumm, Yield of sediment in relation to mean annual precipitation, *Am. Geophys. Union Trans., 39*, 1076-1084, 1958.

Lehmann, O., Tal-und Flusswindungen und die Lehre vom Geographischer Zyklns, *Zeitschr. Gesell. Erdkunde*, 92-111, 171-179, 1915

Leopold, L. B., and T. Maddock Jr., The hydraulic geometry of stream channels and some physiographic implications, *U.S. Geol. Surv. Prof. Pap. 252*, 1953.

Leopold, L. B., and J. P. Miller, Postglacial chronology for alluvial valleys in Wyoming, *U.S. Geol. Surv. Water Supply Pap. 1261*, 61-85, 1954.

Leopold, L. B., and M. G. Wolman, River channel patterns - braided, meandering, and straight, *U.S. Geol. Surv. Prof. Pap. 282-B*, 39-84, 1957.

Leopold, L. B., M. G. Wolman, and J. P. Miller, *Fluvial Processes in Geomorphology*, 522 pp., W. H. Freeman, San Francisco, 1964.

Lesley, J. P., On terrace levels in Pennsylvania, *Am. J. Sci., 116*, 68-69, 1878.

Mackin, J. H., Concept of the graded river, *Geol. Soc. Am. Bull., 59*, 463-511, 1948.

McKee, E., Original structures in Colorado River flood deposits of Grand Canyon, *J. Sediment. Petrol., 8*, 77-83, 1938.

Miller, H., River terracing, its methods and their results, *Proc. Roy. Phil. Soc. Edinbourgh, 112*, 263-305, 1882.

O'Connor, J. E., R. H. Webb, and V. R. Baker, The relationship of pool and riffle pattern development to large magnitude flow hydraulics within a canyonland stream system (abstract), *Geol. Soc. Am. Abst. Programs, 16*, 612, 1984.

Osterkamp, W. R., and E. R. Hedman, Perennial-streamflow characteristics related to channel geometry and sediment in the Missouri River basin, *U.S. Geol. Surv. Prof. Pap. 1242*, 1982.

Patton, P. C., and V. R. Baker, Geomorphic response of central Texas stream channels to catastrophic rainfall and runoff, in *Geomorphology of Arid Regions, Publ. in Geomorph.*, edited by D. O. Doehring, pp. 189-217, State University of New York, Binghamton, 1977.

Patton, P. C., and V. R. Baker, New evidence for pre-Wisconsin flooding in the channeled scabland of eastern Washington, *Geology, 6*, 567-571, 1978.

Patton, P. C., and D. S. Dibble, Archeologic and geomorphic evidence for the paleohydrologic record of the Pecos river in west Texas, *Am. J. Sci., 82*, 97-121, 1982.

Patton, P. C., V. R. Baker, and R. C. Kochel, Slackwater deposits: A geomorphic technique for the interpretation of fluvial paleohydrology, in *Adjustments of the Fluvial System*, edited by D. D. Rhodes and G. Williams, pp. 225-252, Kendall-Hunt, Dubuque, Iowa, 1979.

Pierce, K. L., History and dynamics of glaciation in the northern Yellowstone National Park area, *U.S. Geol. Surv. Prof. Pap. 729-F*, 1979.

Powell, J. W., On terraces, *Science, 2*, 321, 1883.

Schumm, S. A., The shape of alluvial channels in relation to sediment type, *U.S. Geol. Surv. Prof. Pap. 352-B*, 1960.

Schumm, S. A., Sinuosity of alluvial rivers on the Great Plains, *Geol. Soc. Am. Bull., 74*, 1089-1100, 1963a.

Schumm, S. A., A tentative classification of alluvial river channels, *U.S. Geol. Surv. Circ. 477*, 1963b.

Schumm, S. A., Quaternary paleohydrology, in *The Quaternary of the United States*, edited by H. E. Wright and D. G. Frey, pp. 783-794, Princeton University Press, Princeton, New Jersey, 1965.

Schumm, S. A., River adjustments to altered hydrologic regimen - Murrumbidgee River and paleochannels, Australia, *U.S. Geol. Surv. Prof. Pap. 598*, 1968.

Schumm, S. A., River metamorphosis, *J. Hyd. Div. Proc. Am. Soc. Civil Eng.*, HY 1, 255-273, 1969.

Sigafoos, R. R., Botanical evidence of floods and floodplain deposition, *U.S. Geol. Surv. Prof. Pap. 485-A*, 1964.

Stewart, J. E., and G. L. Bodhaine, Floods in the Skagit River basin, Washington, *U.S. Geol. Surv. Water Supply Pap. 1527*, 1961.

Tarr, R. S., A hint with respect to the origin of terraces in glaciated regions, *Am. J. Sci., 144*, 59-61, 1892.

Tinkler, K. J., Active valley meanders in south-central Texas and their wider implicaions, *Geol. Soc. Am. Bull., 82*, 1783-1800, 1971.

Upham, W., The northern part of the Connecticut Valley in the Champlain and terrace periods, *Am. J. Sci., 114*, 459-470, 1877.

Upham, W., A review of the Quaternary era with special reference to the deposits of flooded rivers, *Am. J. Sci., 141*, 33-52, 1891.

Waitt, R. B. Jr., Case for periodic, colossal jokulhlaups from Pleistocene Lake Missoula, *Geol. Soc. Am. Bull., 96*, 1271-1286, 1985.

Williams, G. P., Bankfull discharge of rivers, *Water Resour. Res., 14*, 1141-1154, 1978.

Williams, G. P., Paleohydrological methods and some examples from Swedish fluvial environments, I. cobble and boulder deposits, *Geografiska Annaler, 65*, 227-243, 1983.

White, I. C., Rounded boulders at high altitudes along some Appalachian rivers, *Am. J. Sci., 134*, 374-381, 1887.

Wolman, M. G., The natural channel of Brandywine Creek Pennsylvania, *U.S. Geol. Surv. Prof. Pap. 271*, 1955.

P. C. Patton, Department of Earth and Environmental Sciences, Wesleyan University, Middletown, CT 06457.

Discovery of the Aquifers of the New Jersey Coastal Plain in the Nineteenth Century

C. M. EPSTEIN

Faculty of Natural Sciences & Mathematics, Stockton State College, Pomona, New Jersey 08240

The New Jersey coastal plain aquifers were discovered before 1900 through the efforts of local authorities, well drillers, and the New Jersey State Geological Survey as a result of the search for new, safe water supplies for its rapidly expanding population. George Cook, the survey's director, began the accumulation of the more than one thousand 19th-century well logs and began to correlate the water-bearing horizons of New Jersey. Lewis Woolman largely completed Cook's efforts by identifying most of the known aquifers and correlating them across the coastal plain. G. N. Knapp, H. Poland and survey director H. B. Kummel applied modern hydrogeologic nomenclature to Woolman's identification. The hazards to ground water quality had also been identified before 1900. Surface contaminant infiltration, salt water intrusion, and naturally non-potable ground water had been recognized by George Cook while well drawdown interference with neighboring wells and ground water diversion rights were recognized by another survey director John Smock.

SOCIAL HISTORICAL BACKGROUND

The aquifers of the New Jersey coastal plain were discovered in the second half of the nineteenth century as part of a search for new sources of water supply. The population of the coastal plain counties had tripled from 1850 to 1910 according to the United States census. The need for water by industry and agriculture and for domestic use by towns and resorts grew in the wake of this population expansion. New water sources were necessary to support this growth but springs and streams were easily contaminated and often too far from where their water was needed. Wells were subject to contamination from the surface and from salt water intrusion and the water was commonly too highly mineralized. Yet in spite of these obstacles, coastal plain development depended on adequate ground water supplies. The discovery of these ground water resources was worked out by the New Jersey State Geological Survey from 1863 to 1909.

New Jersey had three geological surveys in the nineteenth century. The third survey, established by the legislature in 1863, solved the water supply problem of the time. Its' success was due to a combination of factors. First, director George Cook had dedicated his career to the utilization of scientific knowledge for the public good and guided the survey's activities accordingly. Second, Cook was an experienced lobbyist and worked well with the state legislature-[*Sidar*, 1976]. Third, the survey was overseen by a Board of Managers made up of some of the state's most prominent citizens. This board not only guided the survey's activities but served as a powerful political lobby for its efforts. Fourth, the survey undertook activities that were beneficial to many segments of the population. Their work supported the efforts of farmers, municipalities, natural resource developers, and citizens plagued by floods, forest fires, droughts and unsafe water supplies. Finally the survey enlisted the support of more than forty-six well drillers who supplied the survey with their well logs. These drillers voluntarily provided this information and had access to the body of information accumulated by the survey on the location of water-bearing sediments throughout the state.

There were many obstacles inhibiting the use of ground water as a source of water supply. Initially, the survey believed ground water to be an unsafe and inadequate source of water supply. The existence and location of water-bearing sediments were not known. Moreover, correlating these units, once they were discovered, to other parts of the coastal plain could not be done because of the poor understanding of coastal plain stratigraphy and structure. Finally, the hazards to which ground water was subject had to be recognized and protective measures enacted.

The history of coastal plain aquifer development is recorded in the "Annual Reports of the State Geologist" published from 1863 to 1910. These reports name drillers, cite well locations, well depths, water-bearing sediments tapped, and the use to which the water was put. These reports also record the development of aquifer nomenclature, the hazards encountered during drilling and production, and the sequence of hydrogeologic discoveries that led to the discovery and development of the aquifers of the New Jersey coastal plain.

WATER CONTAMINATION & POPULATION GROWTH (1863–1878)

Certain aspects of the hydrogeologic setting of the New Jersey coastal plain were already established by the time George Cook became director of the third state geological survey in 1863. Henry D. Rogers had recognized that five stratigraphic units cropped out on the coastal plain. The strike of these was southwest to northeast. Rogers also recognized that these units dipped to the southeast toward the Atlantic Ocean [*Rogers*, 1840]. The age of several of the units was known to be of the Cretaceous Period based on their fossil content [*Cook*, 1857]. Cook, who previously had been a member of the second state geological survey, was in charge of surveying the coastal plain and had published the first well logs known in New Jersey. By the time Cook became the director of the third geological survey of New Jersey, he was quite familiar with the general geology of the New Jersey coastal plain.

Cook's first efforts dealing with the question of water supply occurred in 1868 with the publication of his first report article on "Water Supply". Here he not only described the origin of ground water but also the cause of ground water contamination. Cook maintained that the growth of towns led inevitably to the infiltration of surface filth resulting in well contamination and water-bourne disease. He established a water testing laboratory at the survey to help protect the state's water supply [Cook, 1868].

Cook was opposed to the use of ground water as a reliable water source. His past experience led him to believe that water from inland wells was often too highly mineralized for drinking or industrial use while wells along the shore were too easily contaminated with saltwater [Cook, 1874]. This bias was demonstrated when the survey undertook its first water resource survey in 1875 for the developing resort of Atlantic City. Cook recommended that wealthier residents use cisterns while municipal supplies be transported by means of a pipe line from Absecon Creek on the mainland [Cook, 1875].

In 1878 a typhoid epidemic struck New Jersey. Such epidemics had been recorded in the state since the 1860's. This epidemic struck the State Reform School at Jamesburg, killing two of its students [Cook, 1878]. Further, Cook's own daughter died during this epidemic [Sidar, 1876]. New, safe water supplies had to be found for the sake of public health.

GROUND WATER REAPPRAISAL (1879–1881)

The years from 1874 to 1881 marked a shift in survey policy. Cook was still cautious but several developments led him to reconsider his views on the efficacy of ground water as a water supply source. A successful production well had been completed in Charleston, South Carolina that reached a depth of 1970 feet. In addition, several wells had been successfully completed in New Jersey. Cook attempted his first stratigraphic correlation of the few water-bearing sediments known at that time and to assess their depth beneath the surface. His over-simplified analysis used twenty-one newly published well logs and assumed constant bed thickness and uniform dip for most units. Cook followed what he called the "Red Sand" from its outcrop downdip to the shore. From his projections, he predicted that the depth to bedrock beneath Atlantic City would occur at 1500 feet [Cook, 1879]. This was too shallow by a factor of four. Later, additional well logs and stratigraphic studies would show the existence of unconformities, downdip increases in thickness and facies changes that made stratigraphic correlation of the water-bearing strata more difficult.

In the following year, Cook, reviewing the comparative cost of transported surface water and deep artesian wells, found wells to be cost-effective for the barrier island communities [Cook, 1880].

COMMITMENT TO GROUND WATER DEVELOPMENT (1882–1888)

Cook was now committed to the development of the coastal plain's ground water resources. He wrote a seventy-five page review article on water supply in 1882 in which he discussed the history of water-bourne epidemics in the coastal plain region and thoroughly analyzed the "Report of the Rivers Pollution Commissioners on the domestic water supply of Great Britain" which recommended artesian wells as a safe source of water. (However, only five of New

TABLE 1. Number of Well Logs Published & Maximum Depth Reached in Nineteenth Century Coastal Plain Wells

Time Interval	Outer Coastal Plain		Inner Coastal Plain	
	Number of Wells	Maximum Depth (Ft)	Number of Wells	Maximum Depth (Ft)
1900–04	71	2306	102	710
1895–99	51	940	188	730
1890–94	45	931	89	776
1885–89	21	1400	17	475
1880–84	6	475	7	481
1870–79	7	118	20	356
1850–69	8	335	—	—

Jersey's thirty-two municipal water supplies used artesian wells.) In addition, new artesian wells had been completed in the coastal plain. This demonstrated the feasibility of artesian wells for tapping ground water resources [Cook, 1882].

The number of new wells reported by the survey and the depths to which they were drilled increased greatly in the 1880's. The number of wells nearly doubled from the first half of the decade to the last while the maximum well depth increased from almost five hundred feet to more than one thousand feet (see Table 1). Cook was now in a position to attempt his second hydrogeologic correlation of the water-bearing strata of the coastal plain. He divided southern New Jersey into three northeast-southwest trending belts based on characteristic lithologies of the formations cropping out at the surface. The western belt is composed of Cretaceous sands and clays. It crops out parallel to the Delaware River below Trenton and northeastward across central New Jersey to the southern shore of Raritan Bay. The middle belt, just east of the western belt, is composed of Cretaceous "green-sand marls". The eastern belt, occupying approximately two-thirds of the coastal plain, is composed of Miocene sandy clays and overlying Post-Miocene sands. Cook's second correlation was more sophisticated than his first in that he utilized the thirteen then-recognized stratigraphic units of the coastal plain in the construction of his cross section from Philadelphia to Atlantic City (see Figure 1). He used twelve wells in this cross section to correlate the water-bearing strata. He assumed generally uniform dips and thicknesses but depicted one unconformity beneath the Cretaceous and another above the Miocene units [Cook, 1885].

In spite of all this new information, Cook still felt that he needed more stratigraphic control along the coast. He requested that those seeking water on the barrier islands risk the expense of drilling deep wells [Cook, 1885]. This request was met in 1888 when a thousand foot well was drilled in Atlantic City [Cook, 1889]. Unfortunately, Cook died the following year without being able to utilize this new information. In any event, the ground water resources of the coastal plain were clearly being developed. It would be the efforts of Lewis Woolman, under the survey directorship of J. C. Smock, that provided the next and more definitive analysis of the coastal plain aquifers.

IDENTIFICATION OF THE "MIOCENE", OUTER COASTAL PLAIN AQUIFERS (1889–1893)

John Smock, assistant geologist to George Cook, was now survey director and progress on the development of the ground water resources of the coastal plain accelerated. New well logs poured into the survey office providing new

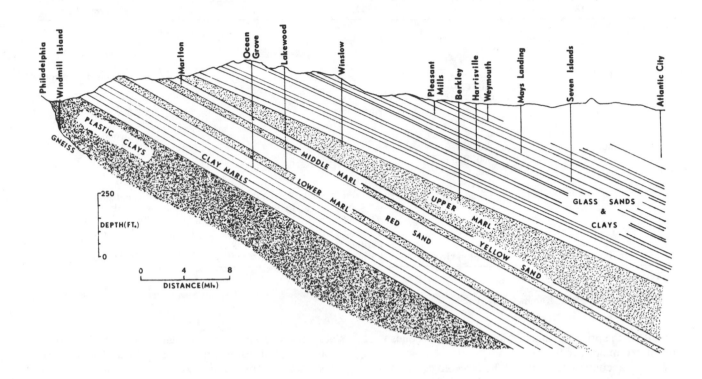

Fig. 1. Hydrogeologic cross section from Philadelphia, Pennsylvania to Atlantic City, New Jersey modified from that made by *George Cook* [1885].

information on unmapped parts of the coastal plain and also on strata occurring at greater depths than known previously. The number of well logs reported by the survey for the outer coastal plain (Cook's eastern sandy clay belt) doubled while that for the inner coastal plain (Cook's combined western clay and middle greensand marl belts) quadrupled. The maximum depths penetrated in the outer coastal plain remained near one thousand feet but those in the inner coastal plain increased from less than five hundred feet to more than seven hundred feet (see Table 1).

The appointment of Lewis Woolman to analyze the artesian wells of southern New Jersey was the most significant event of this phase of coastal plain water resource development. Woolman's research, published under an entirely new heading "Artesian Wells", occupied more and more pages of the survey's annual reports. His first step was to examine the new wells drilled in Atlantic City. He published a detailed stratigraphic column of the sediments beneath Atlantic City using fossils for identification and dating of strata. He used this column as his "type section" from which other outer coastal plain well logs were correlated. He initially identified five water-bearing units and the "Great Diatom Clay" confining bed in the Atlantic City area [*Woolman*, 1890].

His second step was to extend his Atlantic City findings to the rest of the coastal plain. He identified three more water-bearing units utilizing new well logs, correlating them by means of their fossil content and their stratigraphic relation

to the "Great Diatom Clay" [*Woolman*, 1891, 1892, 1893]. Ironically, one of the most important aquifers of the outer coastal plain, the Atlantic City 800 Foot Sand of the Kirkwood Formation, was the last to be identified [*Woolman*, 1893]. (The state's most important unit, the Potomac-Raritan-Magothy aquifer, was indentified on the inner coastal plain in the same year.) Woolman's attention now turned to the horizons of the inner coastal plain.

IDENTIFICATION OF THE "CRETACEOUS" INNER COASTAL PLAIN AQUIFERS (1894–1902)

Woolman initially recognized two water-bearing units in the inner coastal plain [*Woolman*, 1894]. However this soon rose to five which he named, in upward stratigraphic order, the Raritan Group, the Sewell, the Cropwell, the Marlton, and the Lindenwold (see Table 2) [*Woolman*, 1897].

The identification of the inner coastal plain water-bearing units marked the greatest innovation of this phase. However, Woolman also refined his outer coastal plain analysis during this period. First he identified several "post-Miocene" water-bearing units [*Woolman*, 1893]. Next he correlated the water-bearing units of Cape May county with those of the outer coastal plain [*Woolman*, 1894, 1900, 1902]. Finally he assessed the water production potential of the outer coastal plain water-bearing strata by distinguishing them as being principal or minor water-bearing units [*Woolman*, 1897]. He considered the Atlantic City 700 Foot Sand, the Atlantic City 800 Foot Sand, and the Atlantic City 950 Foot

TABLE 2.   Development of Water-Bearing Unit Nomenclature

Year Aquifer Name First Published					Current U.S. Geological Survey Name
1889[a]	1893[a]	1897[a]	1903[b]	1909[c]	
328'					
406'			Cohansey		
429'					Kirkwood-Cohansey
554'					
—	650'				Rio Grande (Kirkwood)
—	700–20'	Atl. City 700' Sand			
—	760'		Kirkwood		Atlantic City 800' Sand (Kirkwood)
—	800'	Atl. City 800' Sand			
950'		Atl. City 950' Sand			
—		Lindenwold			Piney Point
—	"sand"		#9 Sand	Vincentown	Vincentown
—			#7 Sand	Redbank	Redbank
—		Marlton	#5 Sand	Mt. Laurel-Wenonah	Mt. Laurel-Wenonah
—		Cropwell	#3 Sand	Englishtown	Englishtown
—		Sewell	Raritan		
—	Potomac Gravel	Raritan Group	Raritan	Raritan-Magothy	Potomac-Raritan-Magothy

[a] Terminology of L. Woolman
[b] Terminology of G. N. Knapp
[c] Terminology of H. B. Kummel & H. Poland

Sand to be the principal units while the remaining ones were considered minor producers.

Woolman constructed several hydrogeologic cross sections of both parts of the coastal plain based on new well logs submitted by well drillers to the survey. He correlated the various hydrogeologic units across the entire coastal plain using the elevations of contacts instead of correlation based on constant formation dips projected over large areas. His first cross sections involved limited distances and small numbers of well logs [Woolman, 1894]. However his later, most ambitious cross section, depicting the strata from Philadelphia east to Atco, a distance of twenty miles, used approximately 150 well logs [Woolman, 1898].

Lewis Woolman identified most of the aquifers of the New Jersey coastal plain and correlated them across the state before the turn of the twentieth century. But two other events mark this phase of coastal water resource history.

Survey director John Smock raised a prophetic issue previously unappreciated. The city of Camden had recently changed its water supply from the Delaware River to a group of 98 closely spaced wells. Smock felt that the wells might interfere with the one another. Moreover, ground water might be drawn from distant regions, depriving them of their own supply. He summed up this issue when he suggested that ground water diversion rights would become as important as surface water diversion rights [Smock, 1898].

By now, the number of wells logs sent to the survey had surpassed the 1200 mark. All this information had to be codified into a usable, retrievable form. It fell to a survey employee Laurel Lee to do this. In 1901, she recopied all the logs onto cards uniting them under a common format [Kummel, 1902]. Her efforts mark the beginning of the well permit files housed in the Division of Water Resources in Trenton that are still in use.

INSTALLATION OF MODERN HYDROGEOLOGIC TERMINOLOGY (1903–1909)

The period from 1903 to 1909 marked a transition for the state survey. John Smock resigned in 1900 and Woolman wrote a final artesian well article in 1902. The last annual report was published in 1910. Water resource research would be published, in the future, in bulletins issued by the State Department of Conservation & Development and in publications of the U.S. Geological Survey. Nevertheless, one further significant development in the study of coastal plain water resources occurred in this period.

G. N. Knapp, reviewing the water-bearing strata of the coastal plain, substituted numbers for the names Woolman had assigned to the water-bearing units of the inner coastal plain. But more significantly, Knapp introduced the name Kirkwood for the three principal outer coastal plain horizons and Cohansey for the minor ones overlying them [G. N. Knapp, 1904]. The introduction of many of the remaining modern aquifer names appeared in the last annual report when survey director H. B. Kummel and Howard Poland used the aquifer names currently used for the water-bearing strata named by Lewis Woolman in the 1890's [H. B. Kummel & H. Poland, 1910] (see Table 2).

CONCLUSIONS

The discovery of the aquifers of the New Jersey coastal plain involved many people. More than forty-six well drillers contributed more than 1200 well logs to the state geological survey by the turn of the century. Lewis Woolman, an employee of the survey, identified most of the aquifers known today. Two survey directors, George Cook and John Smock, recognized the problems associated with ground water development. Specifically, Cook noted the dangers of surface contaminant infiltration, salt water intrusion, and naturally occurring highly mineralized ground water to the use of ground water. Smock noted the effect of drawdown on nearby wells and the problem of ground water diversion rights. Finally survey director, H. B. Kummel, and two additional survey employees, G. N. Knapp and H. Poland, provided the names by which we know many of the aquifers of the New Jersey coastal plain today. But aside from the renaming, the discovery of the New Jersey coastal plain aquifers had been largely completed before the turn of the twentieth century.

Acknowledgments. The author wishes to thank Arthur Hunnewell and Carol Graff of the Division of Water Resources of the New Jersey Department of Environmental Protection for access to state well permit files and for helpful comments offered during the course of this study. In addition, the author acknowledges the financial support provided by the Research and Professional Development Committee of Stockton State College.

REFERENCES

Cook, G. H., *Report of the Geology And Agricultural Resources of the Southern Division of the State*, N. J. Geological Survey, Trenton, N. J., 25p., 1857.

Cook, G. H., *Geology of New Jersey*, N. J. Geological Survey, Trenton, N. J., 701–710, 1868.

Cook, G. H., *Annual Report of the State Geologist for the Year 1874*, N. J. Geological Survey, Trenton, N. J., 60–64, 1874.

Cook, G. H., *Annual Report of the State Geologist for the Year 1875*, N. J. Geological Survey, Trenton, N. J., 24–34, 1875.

Cook, G. H., *Annual Report of the State Geologist for the Year 1878*, N. J. Geological Survey, Trenton, N. J., 90–97, 1878.

Cook, G. H., *Annual Report of the State Geologist for the Year 1879*, N. J. Geological Survey, Trenton, N. J., 123–125, 1879.

Cook, G. H., *Annual Report of the State Geologist for the Year 1880*, N. J. Geological Survey, Trenton, N. J., 161–173, 1880.

Cook, G. H., *Annual Report of the State Geologist for the Year 1882*, N. J. Geological Survey, Trenton, N. J., 96–171, 1882.

Cook, G. H., *Annual Report of the State Geologist for the Year 1885*, N. J. Geological Survey, Trenton, N. J., 109–140, 1885.

Cook, G. H., *Annual Report of the State Geologist for the Year 1888*, N. J. Geological Survey, Trenton, N. J., 71–77, 1889.

Knapp, G. N., Underground Waters of New Jersey, in *Annual Report of the State Geologist for the Year 1903*, N. J. Geological Survey, Trenton, N. J., 73–93, 1904.

Kummel, H. B., *Annual Report of the State Geologist for the Year 1901*, N. J. Geological Survey, Trenton, N. J., xix–xx, 1902.

Kummel, H. B. and H. M. Poland, Records of Wells in New Jersey, 1905–1909, in *Annual Report of the State Geologist for the Year 1909*, N. J. Geological Survey, Trenton, N. J., 69–100, 1910.

Rogers, H. D., Description of the Geology of the State of New Jersey being a Final Report, C. Sherman & Co., Philadelphia, Pa., 301p., 1840.

Sidar, J. W., *George Hammell Cook: A Life in Agriculture and Geology*, Rutgers University Press, New Brunswick, New Jersey, 282p., 1976.

Smock, J. C., *Annual Report of the State Geologist for the Year 1897*, N. J. Geological Survey, Trenton, N. J., xxi–xxii, 1898.

Woolman, L., Artesian Wells, Atlantic City, N. J., in *Annual Report of the State Geologist for the Year 1889*, N. J. Geological Survey, Trenton, N. J., 89–99, 1890.

Woolman, L., Artesian Wells and Water Bearing Horizons of Southern New Jersey, in *Annual Report of the State Geologist for the Year 1890*, N. J. Geological Survey, Trenton, N. J., 269–283, 1891.

Woolman, L. Artesian Wells of Southern New Jersey, in *Annual Report of the State Geologist for the Year 1892*, N. J. Geological Survey, Trenton, N. J., 274–311, 1893.

Woolman, L., Artesian Wells and Water Horizons in Southern New Jersey, with Economical, Geological, and Paleontological Notes, in *Annual Report of the State Geologist for the Year 1893*, Geological Survey, Trenton, N. J., 389–421, 1894.

Woolman, L., Artesian Wells in Southern New Jersey, in *Annual Report of the State Geologist for the Year 1894*, N. J. Geological Survey, Trenton, N. J., 153–222, 1895.

Woolman, L., Artesian Wells in New Jersey, in *Annual Report of the State Geologist for the Year 1898*, N. J. Geological Survey, Trenton, N. J., 59–144, 1899.

Woolman, L., Artesian Wells in New Jersey, in *Annual Report of the State Geologist for the Year 1900*, N. J. Geological Survey, Trenton, N. J., 103–171, 1901.

C. M. Epstein, Department of Natural Sciences and Mathematics, Stockton State College, Pomona, NY 08240.

Early Twentieth-Century Investigations of the Radioactivity of Waters in North America

EDWARD R. LANDA

U.S. Geological Survey, 432 National Center, Reston, Virginia 22092

In the spring of 1903, J. J. Thomson, Cavendish Professor of Physics at Cambridge University, visited the Yale campus. This visit sparked the first investigations of the radioactivity of surface and ground waters in North America. During the next two decades there would be many more studies, the impetus for this work coming from both scientific interests in the phenomenon of radioactivity, and medical and commercial interests in the alleged therapeutic value of radioactive substances in water. As one might expect in a fledgling field, much attention was of necessity devoted to measurement methodology, and the experimental approaches were often very innovative. Attempts were made at correlating radioactivity with lithology and readily measureable water properties such as temperature and total dissolved solids, generally with little success. The studies did shed light on some important hydrogeochemical properties of the naturally occurring radionuclides including the differing mobilities of the chemically distinct members of the uranium decay series and the coprecipitation behavior of radium.

The phenomenon of radioactivity was discovered in 1896 and soon attracted much attention among the physics and chemistry communities. On May 4, 1903, J. J. Thomson, Cavendish Professor of Experimental Physics at Cambridge University read a paper entitled "On the Existence of a Radio-Active Gas in the Cambridge Tapwater" at a meeting of the Cambridge Philosophical Society. The report detailed experiments in which large volumes of gas were separated from well water boiled in the copper kettles of a local brewery. Through the cooperation of James Dewar, known for the Dewar flask, the gas, largely hydrocarbons, was liquefied. A radioactive component of the gas was also frozen out. Thomson [1903c] did not identify the gas but indicated that in some respects it differed from radon. Eight days later, Thomson, most noted as the discoverer of the electron, was at Yale to begin a series of lectures on electricity and matter. (Thomson was the first lecturer chosen for the University's Silliman Memorial Lectureship, established by a nephew of Benjamin Silliman, founder of the American Journal of Science, in honor of Benjamin Silliman's sister-in-law Hespa Ely Silliman. Other lecturers in the next 30 years would include Ernest Rutherford, Walter Nernst, William Osler, and Niels Bohr.) During these lectures [Thomson, 1904] he mentioned his recent hydrologic investigations, and at his request Yale physics professors Henry A. Bumstead and Lynde P. Wheeler sought to ascertain if a similar gas existed in the ground waters of the New Haven area. They subsequently examined a spring water estimated to be coming from a depth of about 1500 feet, and water from a surface-fed New Haven reservoir, and reported their findings in the October 1903 issue of the American Journal of Science. The gases driven off by boiling these two waters were both radioactive, and on the basis of decay measurements, the gas was identified as radon.

As the presence of radioactivity in water became known, some came to attribute the alleged curative powers of mineral waters to their radioactive constituents and this,

besides the scientific interest, became a further impetus for study. A 1927 report on the radioactivity of thermal waters of Castle Hot Springs, Arizona, by T. F. Buehrer [1927] of the University of Arizona, published in the American Journal of Science notes: "The interest in this problem was enhanced in part by authentic reports that the Apache Indians used these waters and ascribed remarkable curative properties to them as far back as a century ago." In 1904, the Department of the Interior sponsored a study by New Haven chemist Bertram Boltwood [1905] of the radioactivity of waters at the Hot Springs Reservation in Arkansas. In 1906, the U.S. Geological Survey sponsored studies by chemists Herman Schlundt of the University of Missouri and Richard B. Moore of Butler University on the radioactivity of thermal waters at Yellowstone National Park [Schlundt and Moore, 1909]. Federal and State sponsorship of studies of the radioactivity of waters at Saratoga Springs, New York by Richard Moore, who had moved to the U.S. Bureau of Mines [Moore and Whittmore, 1914], at Banff and other mineral springs in Canada by physicist John Satterly of the University of Toronto [Satterly and Elworthy, 1917], in Colorado by physicist O. C. Lester of the University of Colorado [George et al., 1920], and in Illinois by Clarence Scholl [1916], a graduate student in chemistry at the University of Illinois, followed during the next decade. In the reports of the Colorado Geological Survey [George et al., 1920] and the Canada Department of Mines [Satterly and Elworthy, 1917] describing these geochemical investigations, one also finds chapters on the therapeutics of radioactive waters and comparisons with the radioactivity of noted mineral springs in Europe. While never explicitly stated, the potential for commercial development of these domestic mineral water resources was clearly in mind. A belief in the physiological effects of radon extended directly into the hydrologic realm in the mid-1930's, when it was suggested that radon emanating from subterranean waters triggered subtle muscular contractions in persons on the surface, and that this was the mechanism by which water dowsers located ground-water supplies [Humphris and Williams, 1937, p. 35].

While governmental sponsorship of these studies was

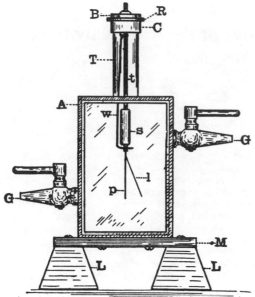

Fig. 1. C. T. R. Wilson electroscope [redrawn from *Boltwood*, 1904*a*]. The air-tight brass case, into which the gas to be tested was introduced via stopcocks (a), was fitted with plate glass windows to allow observation of the gold leaf (b). The leaf was charged by means of a stick of sealing wax, which was rubbed lightly on the clothing and brought in contact with the top of the brass rod (c).

generally a boon to the expansion of scientific knowledge, it also presented some roadblocks. In the winter of 1906–1907, Herman Schlundt, a member of the chemistry faculty at the University of Missouri, began a study of the radioactivity of spring deposit samples from the federal reservation at Hot Springs, Arkansas. At the suggestion of the superintendent of the reservation, the springs in this study [*Schlundt*, 1907], and the earlier study of the radioactivity of the waters at the site [*Boltwood*, 1905], were identified in the published reports only by arbitrary codes (presumably to avoid a rush to certain springs and avoidance of others). Schlundt was therefore not able to correlate his radium determinations from the tufa samples with activity measured by Boltwood in the corresponding water samples when he first presented his results at the October 1907 general meeting of the American Electrochemical Society. However, prior to the publication of Schlundt's report, Boltwood provided him with the official numbers of the springs that corresponded to the laboratory numbers in his paper. With this information (reported in on addendum to the published paper) Schlundt was able to demonstrate that there was no correlation between the radon content of the water and the radium content of the spring deposits. (Boltwood's analyses of evaporated residues from the waters tested showed radium to be present only at concentrations below the detection limit of the analytical technique.)

The most commonly used instrument for the determination of radioactivity was the electroscope. The measurement involved recording the rate of fall of a previously charged metallic leaf. For a 2-liter sample, the lower limit of detection for a typical laboratory instrument in the era around 1920 was about 2 pCi/L [*Skinner and Sale*, 1922; *Perkins*, 1915]. The electroscopes varied in sophistication of design. An electroscope designed by C. T. R. Wilson (Figure 1), best known for his cloud chamber, was used in the 1903–1906 era by Bumstead and Wheeler in Connecticut; by Boltwood at

Hot Springs, Arkansas; and by Schlundt and Moore in Missouri and at Yellowstone National Park, and its use continued into the mid-1920's [*Bohn*, 1930]. Some other units were basically tin cans with mica observation windows [*Shedd*, 1913; *Bradley*, 1922]. One such simple device was used by E. R. Wolcott of the Colorado School of Mines at Glenwood Springs, Colorado. His observations of April 1903 (Figure 2) may have actually predated Thomson's, but Thomson's findings were first announced in a letter to the editor and an article in the April 30, 1903, issue of Nature [*Thomson* 1903*a*, 1903*b*], whereas Wolcott's results did not appear in print until November 1904, and then as an obscure appendix to a Colorado School of Mines report [*Wolcott*, 1904]. Wolcott was, however, probably the first person to suggest the utility of radiochemical analysis of natural waters in prospecting for ores of uranium and thorium.

Bertram Boltwood [1904*b*] was the first to stress the need for quantitative measurements. At this time, radium salts of known and established purity were not available outside of the laboratories of the Curies and perhaps a few others in Europe. Boltwood suggested as a standard, the quantity of radon released when a known weight of uranium, in the form of a natural mineral, is dissolved in a suitable reagent, such as aqua regia. The results were expressed in terms of grams of uranium per liter. Boltwood generously provided other early investigators [e.g., *Moore and Schlundt*, 1905] with uranium mineral samples for calibration purposes. Others [e.g., *Ramsay*, 1915*a*] used an empirical formula developed in the Curie laboratory by Duane and Laborde which required only the measurement of the current produced in an electroscope. With the coming of the International Radium Standard, prepared by Madame Curie in 1911, and the distribution of secondary standards in the United States by the National Bureau of Standards beginning about 1914, calibration procedures became more uniform.

As a result of the various measurement and calibration procedures used in the early years, the radioactivity of water—specifically radon-222 and radium-226—was expressed in terms of a variety of units:

a. grams of uranium, following the procedure and nomenclature of Boltwood.

b. grams of radium—to express either the concentration of radium, or the quantity of radon in radioactive equilibrium with a given weight of radium. This dual usage created opportunities for confusion [see, for example, *Eve*, 1910] as to whether reported data referred to radium or radon concentrations and although widely-used, required a clear statement as to sample handling and analytical methods.

c. curies—while now used for all radionuclides, early usage was, by definition [*Rutherford*, 1913, p. 479], restricted to radon.

d. mache unit—named for Heinrich Mache of the Vienna Radium Institute, the unit was widely used in Europe (outside of England and France), especially among those interested in the therapeutic properties of mineral waters [*Lester*, 1917]. It was defined as the amount of radon in 1 liter that will produce a saturation current of 0.001 electrostatic units of current. One mache unit was equivalent to 364 pCi/L.

e. eman—a unit equivalent to 100 pCi/l of radon, it was used to some extent during the 1920's and 1930's [*Bohn*, 1930, p. 461; *Mann*, 1962].

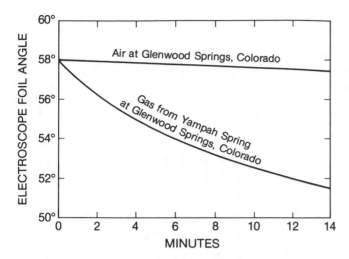

Fig. 2. E. R. Wolcott's April 1903 radioactivity measurements at Glenwood Springs, Colorado [redrawn from *Wolcott*, 1904].

Purging of the radioactive gases, generally referred to as "emanations," was accomplished either by a boiling apparatus [e.g., *Boltwood*, 1904] or by shaking the water sample in a sealed can [e.g., *Ramsay*, 1915a]. In some cases, particularly in remote areas, and where sampling of spring gases was attempted, the measurements were done in the field. Where analyses were done in the laboratory, the short half life of radon required minimal delays in analysis. Field sites were chosen that were close to the home laboratory, or "express" shipment of air-tight, sealed bottles was used. In this pre-overnight delivery era, "express" meant, for example, an average 7-day shipment period in getting samples from Hot Springs, Arkansas, to Boltwood's New Haven laboratory. The identification of the gas as radon (Rn-222) was based on one or more of the following criteria:

a. a half-life of the gas of about 3.8 days.
b. a half-life of the nongaseous daughter products—the so-called "active deposit"—of about 27 minutes.
c. a molecular weight, estimated on the basis of diffusion rates through a porous plate of unglazed porcelain, of about 200 [*Bumstead and Wheeler*, 1904].

The test for thoron (Rn-220), with its half-life of 55 seconds, was possible only with spring gases, and involved the measurement of activity immediately upon collection. At Yellowstone, Schlundt and Moore collected gas samples at 82 localities with an inverted funnel apparatus connected to an electroscope and observed the rapid fall-off of activity during the first minute which is diagnostic of thoron, at 16 of these sites. The presence of radium in water samples was radiometrically tested either by:

a. evaporation of the sample, and then examination of the residue,
b. storage of the sample for prolonged periods to allow for the decay of radon, or purging of radon by boiling, and then examination of the water, or
c. coprecipitation of any radium in the water with barium sulfate and then examination of the precipitate.

Again there were dual interests in such data. The presence of radium in waters was of interest both to scientists and to mineral water bottlers who, in response to the truth in labelling requirements of the U.S. Food and Drugs Act of 1906, desired to show that the purported radioactivity of their wares persisted with shipment and storage—that is, after the rapid decay of the radon [*Skinner and Sale*, 1922].

The plethora of investigations in Europe and America using a variety of measuring devices, standards (or lack thereof), and units created many problems. In 1917, an obviously frustrated *O. C. Lester* [1917, p. 235–236] would write:

Among investigations in the radioactivity of mineral springs, and in particular among those on European mineral springs, there can be found often the results of several observers on the same water or gas. It is rarely that these results agree closely and those of one observer may range anywhere from many times to a fraction of those given by another. With precautions field work can be made practically as accurate as that done in the laboratory. Hence discrepancies in the work of equally careful observers have often been attributed to variations in the activity of the source. On the other hand, there are springs which have shown no appreciable variation in activity when examined systematically at different times of the year by the same observer using the same apparatus. Undoubtedly some springs do vary in activity but the question of their variability and even the amount of their activity can scarcely be determined from the work of different observers so long as there is no uniformity in standards, in methods, and in the nature and the number of the corrections to be applied to the observations. This is particularly true of results expressed in mache units based upon ionization currents. In many cases mache units are apparently calculated from the observed ionization current and not from the saturation ionization current when all radiation is absorbed in the air of the chamber. In the first case the mache unit is dependent upon the dimensions of the particular apparatus used and upon the potential applied to the insulated system which is clearly not intended by its definition.

For the reasons just mentioned the work of European observers in general presents an almost hopeless confusion when accurate comparisons are attempted. It is true that much work had been done before suitable units and methods were devised, and we find therefore many results expressed in terms of the fall of the leaf in volts per unit time or in units even more arbitrary. Such results can not be compared with other work. Still other units used are the Milligram-Second, Milligram-Minute, Gram-Second, etc., meaning the amount of emanation produced by a given amount of radio-active substance in the specified time. The substance is usually the element radium or a radium salt, and when this is specified, as well as its degree of purity, measurements based upon such units can be reduced to curies.

The presence of uranium in water received little attention during the first two decades of the twentieth century. The lack of sensitive analytical techniques precluded the determination of uranium in most natural waters. Some simple laboratory experiments were done around 1918 on conditions conducive to the transport of precipitation of uranium in ground water as a model for economic geologists interested in the genesis of carnotite deposits [*Notestein*, 1918]. By 1930, analytical methods had advanced to the point where the lower limit of detection was less than 1 microgram per liter [*Weeks and Leicester*, 1968, p. 271].

Because the radioactive character of waters and other earth materials was a virgin territory in the early twentieth century, the measurement and reporting of concentrations of radionuclides at various localities was, of itself, a major scientific contribution, and indeed this was the sole focus of many of the early papers. Few conclusions regarding hydrologic and hydrogeochemical processes, other than indications of their complexity, were to be gleaned from those early studies. Springs in close proximity to one another had widely differing radionuclide contents. Attempts at correlating radium and radon concentrations with each other, or

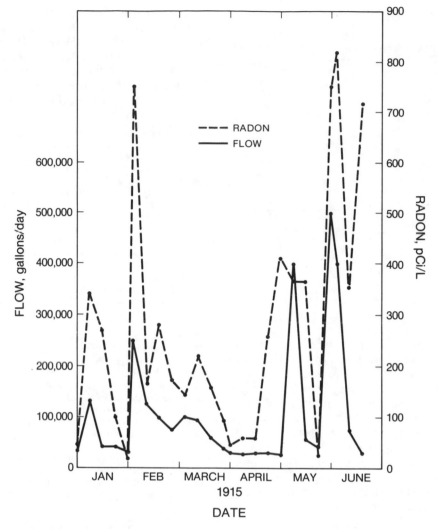

Fig. 3.   Flow and radon concentration of water at Illinois Central spring, near Bloomington, Indiana, during 1915 [plotted from data in *Ramsay, 1915b*].

with temperature, pH or bulk solute chemistry were often made and were generally unsuccessful. However, at Saratoga Springs, a rough correlation was noted by *Moore and Whittemore* [1914] between barium and radium—not surprising in light of their chemical similarities. *Scholl* [1916] examined well waters from glacial and alluvial drift and loess deposits in Illinois, and found a surprising linear correlation (r = 0.86) between calcium and radon concentrations. There was some speculation as to the source rocks of the observed radioactivity in waters but, except for a few laboratory experiments by *Boltwood* [1904b] on the release of radon and radium to water from ground uraniferous (largely uranophane) ore, little study was done in this area.

Spring deposits offered an opportunity to study the accumulation of long-lived, nongaseous radioactive constituents of water, and were studied by many early investigations. About 1904, chemist and mineralogist William P. Headden at the Colorado Agricultural College (now Colorado State University) studied a spring near Hotchkiss, Colorado, where barium sulfate sinter was being deposited. This unusual occurrence prompted his interest as to whether radium was also accumulating. Lacking even a rudimentary electroscope, he concentrated the radium by the same basic method

used with uranium ore by Madame Curie [*Headden*, 1905, p. 29–30].

I took 13 pounds of sinter. It was not all collected from the same spring, but was a mixture from Springs II, V, and VI, or the Birds' Nest, the Bath Tub and the Drinking Spring. I fluxed it with sedic carbonate, washed and dissolved in hydrochloric acid, separated the silicic acid and iron by usual methods and separated the baric from calcic chlorid by crystallization. The yield of crude baric chlorid was eight pounds. This baric chlorid, after the removal of the last of the iron present, was subjected to fractional crystallization, four crops of crystals being removed from each solution. A little practice sufficed to enable me to recover two-thirds of the quantity dissolved in the first three crops of crystals. This was continued until the weight of the three crops when united was two ounces. The last crystallizations were made from hydrochloric acid solutions. I make no pretence to having extracted all of the radium in the sinter. I know on the contrary that my mother liquors and reserve salts contain radium, but I believe that the requirements of my present work did not demand the recovery of all the radium. The crystals of radiferous baric chlorid were at first colorless, but have gradually acquired a yellow tinge. This is an observation which has been repeatedly made.

After allowing the sample to stand 15 days to accumulate its power to act on the plate, I submitted a photographic plate to its action for 2½ days. The plate was covered with two thicknesses of black paper. The distance between the film and the salt was between 0.25 and 0.5 centimeter. The result was a strong, sharp, negative, comparable in its density to negatives obtained with pitchblende or carnotite and not at all with those obtained with the original sinter.

The presence of a radioactive substance was thus qualitatively demonstrated. *Schlundt* [1914] later showed a sample of the sinter to contain 1480 picocuries of radium per gram, which is about the radium content of a 0.5 percent uranium ore. Commercial exploitation of the sinter as a radium ore was apparently never considered, probably because the amount of sinter was small and the radium content was low by the ore standards of the day. However, during the mid-1930's a sinter deposit with a comparable radium content was commercially mined in southwestern Germany at Bad Kreuznach as a source of isolated radium salts [*Spence*, 1936]. Interest has persisted in the springs that Headden studied, and an extensive sampling and analysis of the water and sinter deposits was recently undertaken by the U.S. Geological Survey to investigate this surficial radioactive anomaly as a geochemical indicator of the possible occurrence of buried, uranium-mineralized rock in the area [*Cadigan, Felmlee and Rosholt*, 1976]. In considering mechanisms for the removal from solution of radium at discharging springs, the Headden case of a barite sinter in Colorado noted by Headden was the most clear cut. Other investigators speculated on the possible role of algae [*Schlundt and Moore*, 1909] and manganese oxides [*Schlundt*, 1907].

The presence of increased radon concentration in ground waters in the vicinity of fault zones was noted in the mid-1920's by graduate students at the California Institute of Technology, and was used to map the concealed extension of a fault in the Pasadena area [*Bohn*, 1930; *Engel and Bohn*, 1930]. This observation was a spinoff from efforts to find lake waters of low radioactivity in which Nobel laureate Robert Millikan was to make electroscopic measurements which were to clearly demonstrate the cosmic, rather than terrestrial origin, of what we now call "cosmic rays." Physicist *Robert Ramsay* [1915b, 1916] at Indiana University examined a spring issuing from a coarse gravel deposit in the Bloomington area. The flow varied as a function of rainfall, and the radon concentration in the spring water function of the flow volume (Figure 3); this relation demonstrated the flushing action of the percolating water in carrying radon from the soil pores in the recharge zone.

Most of the early investigators were physicists and chemists. Their focus on water was often brief, and many would go on to make contributions to the developing science of radioactivity that were far afield of hydrology. Richard Moore became involved in research and development efforts aimed at decreasing the cost of production of radium from uranium ores [*Parsons et al.*, 1915]. Herman Schlundt investigated the excretion of radium by dial painters [*Schlundt and Failla*, 1931], and other individuals, and *William Headden* [1923] studied the phosphorescence of irradiated minerals. Despite the brevity of their involvement, their work formed the cornerstone of our understanding of the behavior of naturally occurring radionuclides in the hydrosphere, and the application of this knowledge to mineral exploration and environmental monitoring.

Acknowledgments. The assistance of Judith A. Schiff, Chief Research Archivist of the Yale University Library, in supplying materials related to the Silliman Memorial Lectureship, and of Wilfred B. Mann of the National Bureau of Standards, in supplying reference materials on radioactivity units and standards is gratefully acknowledged.

REFERENCES

Bohn, J. L., Radioactive properties of rocks, soils, crude oil and waters from southern California, *J. Franklin Inst.*, 210, 461–472, 1930.

Boltwood, B., On the ratio of radium to uranium in some minerals, *Am. J. Sci.*, 18 (4th ser,), 97–103, 1904a.

Boltwood, B. B., On the radio-activity of natural waters, *Am. J. Sci.*, 18 (4th ser.), 378–387, 1904b.

Boltwood, B. B., On the radio-active properties of the waters of the springs on the Hot Springs Reservation, Hot Springs, Ark., *Am. J. Sci.*, 20 (4th ser.), 128–132, 1905.

Bradley, W. W., Radioactivity in thermal gases at the geysers, Sonoma County, California, in *California State Mining Bureau Ann. Report*, 18, pp. 545–550, 1922.

Buehrer, T. F., The radioactivity of the thermal waters of Castle Hot Springs, Arizona, *Am. J. Sci.*, 13, 445–449, 1927.

Bumstead, H. A. and Wheeler, L. P., Note on a radio-active gas in surface water, *Am. J. Sci.*, 16 (4th ser.), 328, 1903.

Bumstead, H. A. and Wheeler, L. P., On the properties of a radio-active gas found in the soil and water near New Haven, *Am. J. Sci.*, 17 (4th ser.), 97–111, 1904.

Cadigan, R. A., Felmlee, J. K., and Rosholt, J. N., Radioactive mineral springs in Delta County, Colorado, *Open File Rept. 76-223*, U.S. Geol. Survey, 1976.

Engel, R. and Bohn, J. L., Relations between geologic problems and the radioactivity of rocks and waters (abstract), *Bull. Geol. Soc. of Amer.*, 41, 154, 1930.

Eve, A. S., On the amount of radium and radium emanation present in the water and gases of the Caledonia Springs, near Ottawa, *Trans. Roy. Soc. Canada*, 4 (3rd ser.), 53–54, 1910.

George, R. D., Curtis, H. A., Lester, O. C., Crook, J. K., and Yeo, J. B., Mineral waters of Colorado, *Bull. 11*, 474 pp., Colo. Geol. Surv., Boulder, 1920.

Headden, W. P., The Doughty Springs, a group of radium-bearing springs on the North Fork of the Gunnison River, Delta County, Colorado, *Proc. Colo. Sci. Soc.*, 8, 1–30, 1905.

Headden, W. P., Deportment of calcites toward radium radiations, *Am. J. Sci.*, 6 (5th ser.), 247–261, 1923.

Humphris, F. H. and Williams, L., *Emanotherapy*, 188 pp., William Wood and Company, Baltimore, 1937.

Lester, O. C., On the calibration and the constants of emanation electroscopes, *Am. J. Sci.*, 44 (4th ser.), 225–236, 1917.

Mann, W. B., Radioactivity units, in *Encyclopaedic Dictionary of Physics*, v. 6, J. Thewlis (ed.), pp. 71–73, Pergamon, Oxford, 1962.

Moore, R. B. and Schlundt, H., On the radio-activity of some natural waters of Missouri, *Trans. Am. Electrochemical Soc.*, 8, 291–295, 1905.

Moore, R. B. and Whittemore, C. F., The radioactivity of the waters of Saratoga Springs, New York, *J. Ind. Eng. Chem.*, 6, 552–553, 1914.

Notestein, F. B., Some chemical experiments bearing on the origin of certain uranium-vanadium ores, *Econ. Geol.*, 13, 50–64, 1918.

Parsons, C. L., Moore, R. B., Lind, S. C., and Schaffer, O. C., Extraction and recovery of radium, uranium and vanadium from carnotite, *Bull. 104*, 124 pp., U.S. Bureau of Mines, Washington, D.C., 1915.

Perkins, P. B., Radio-activity of underground water in Providence and the vicinity, *Science*, 42 (N.S.), 806–808, 1915.

Ramsay, R. R., Radioactivity of spring water, *Am. J. Sci.*, 40 (4th ser.), 309–313, 1915a.

Ramsay, R. R., The variation of the emanation content of certain springs, *Philos. Mag. (London)*, 30 (6th ser.), 815–818, 1915b.

Ramsay, R. R., The cause of the variation of the emanation content of spring water (abstract), *Physical Rev.*, 7 (ser. 2), 284, 1916.

Rutherford, E., *Radioactive Substances and Their Radiations*, 669 pp., Cambridge University Press, 1913.

Satterly, J., and Elworthy, R. T., Mineral springs of Canada, Part I, The radioactivity of some Canadian mineral springs, *Bull. 16*, 60 pp., Canada Dept. of Mines, Ottawa, 1917.

Schlundt, H., Electroscopic determination of the radium present in some "tufa" deposits from Hot Springs, Ark., *Trans. Am. Electrochemical Soc.*, 12, 247–253, 1907.

Schlundt, H., The radioactivity of some Colorado Springs, *J. Phys. Chem., 18*, 662–666, 1914.

Schlundt, H. and Failla, G., The detection and estimation of radium in living persons. (III) The normal elimination of radium, *Am. J. Roentgenol., 26*, 265–271, 1931.

Schlundt, H. S., and Moore, R. B., Radioactivity of the thermal waters of Yellowstone National Park, *Bull. 395*, 35 pp., U.S. Geol. Surv., Washington, D.C., 1909.

Scholl, C., Radioactivity of Illinois waters, in *Univ. of Ill. Water Surv. ser. no. 14*, pp. 114–139, Urbana, 1916.

Shedd, J. C., Radioactivity of the mineral springs of Manitou, Colorado, *Proc. Colo. Sci. Soc., 10*, 233–263, 1913.

Skinner, W. W., and Sale, J. W., Radioactivity of miscellaneous waters examined in the Bureau of Chemistry, *J. Ind. Eng. Chem., 14*, 949–950, 1922.

Spence, H., Radium and uranium, in *The Mineral Industry during 1935*, ed. by G. A. Roush, pp. 520–531, McGraw-Hill, New York, 1936.

Thomson, J. J., Radio-active gas from well water (letter to the editor), *Nature, 67*, 609, 1903a.

Thomson, J. J., Radium, *Nature, 67*, 601–602, 1903b.

Thomson, J. J., On the existence of a radio-active gas in the Cambridge tapwater, *Proc. Cambridge Philos. Soc., 12*, 172–174, 1903c.

Thomson, J. J., *Electricity and Matter,* 162 pp., Scribner's, New York, 1904.

Wolcott, E. R., Radio-activity and some radio-active minerals and springs of Colorado, in *Biennial Rept. of the Colo. Sch. of Mines*, appendix (pp. 26–36), 1904.

Weeks, M. E., and Leicester, H. M., *Discovery of the Elements (7th ed.)* 96 pp., Journal of Chemical Education, Easton, Pa., 1968.

E. R. Landa, U.S. Geological Survey, Mail Stop 432, Reston, VA 22092.

History of Thought on the Origin of Subsurface Sedimentary Brines

JEFFREY S. HANOR

Department of Geology, Louisiana State University, Baton Rouge, Louisiana 70803

The remains of ancient salt works around brine seeps stand as evidence that Prehistoric man not only knew that some ground waters are salty, but took commercial advantage of this resource. Pre-Socratics, such as Anaxagoras [ca. 450 B.C.], speculated that the surface waters of the earth were derived by evaporation of subsurface waters, a process which would leave a salty residue. *Lucretius* [ca. 60 B.C.] advocated a subterranean filtering out of brine as seawater was cycled back from the oceans into the continents to form fresh water springs and rivers. Medieval and Renaissance cosmologists also believed in the subterranean cycling of seawater, but more often called upon distillation as a means for removing salt. The body of knowledge concerning brines improved in the late 1600's as drilling and mining activities established the spatial proximity of some brine springs with bedded rock salt. It was generally believed by the early 1800's that brines resulted from the subsurface dissolution of salt.

In 1859, T.S. Hunt proposed that subsurface salty waters are actually fossil sea water and that the elevated Ca to Na ratio in these pore fluids reflects an elevated calcium concentration in ancient oceans. Thus was born the notion of a connate origin for formation waters. Much of the current thought regarding the origin of brines has come from the study of waters co-produced with oil and gas. The most popular brine-forming mechanism of the early 20th century, subsurface evaporation of pore water into a methane gas phase, was shown by Russell on mass-balance grounds in 1933 to be impossible. Most discussion today centers on one or more of the following mechanisms: membrane filtration, infiltration of subaerial brines, and subsurface dissolution of evaporites.

INTRODUCTION

Most pore waters in sedimentary basins are salty, in fact, deep basinal brines often have salinities several times that of sea water (Figure 1). Where such waters occur in proximity to salt domes or to bedded salt, a plausible explanation for their origin is obvious. Salty waters are known, however, from basins apparently lacking evaporites, and here their origin is less clear. The origin of high salinity is not the only problem confronting one who would hope to understand the origin of subsurface waters: the relative proportions of various dissolved species in most deep waters are unlike those in any waters formed at the earth's surface (Figure 2).

Most of what we know about the occurrence and properties of subsurface salty waters is directly due to the fact that these brines have played an important role in international trade and commerce for the past several thousand years. While Ancient and Medieval cosmologists were speculating on the origin and movement of subsurface fluids on theoretical and theological grounds, an unwritten body of empirical field data was being generated by the master salters who were collecting brine from springs or wells and boiling it down to make salt (Figure 3). In our own generation brines continue to be of economic interest, in part because they are intimately associated with the generation, migration, and entrapment of oil and gas. Most of the body of modern information we have on the nature of fluids in the deep subsurface, in fact, has come from the analysis and study of what are commonly called "oil-field brines," that is, formation waters co-produced with oil and gas.

The purpose of this essay is to provide a brief review of the history of thought regarding the origin of subsurface salty waters from Prehistoric times to the present. A detailed account of the history of more recent research on subsurface

brines during the period 1933–1983 has been given in an earlier paper [*Hanor*, 1984], and this discussion will emphasise earlier work. While many contemporary geochemists and hydrologists would restrict the term "brine" to a water containing over 100,000 mg/L total dissolved salts, I will use term much more loosely here, without reference to any particular lower limit of salinity.

PREHISTORIC UTILIZATION OF BRINES

Europe

Prehistoric man in Europe was not only aware that some groundwaters and springs are salty, but took commercial advantage of this fact. The remains of Neolithic and Bronze Age saltworks have been discovered at numerous western European brine spring localities in what are now Austria, Germany, and France (Figure 4). The names of various towns and cities in this region of the continent reflect the importance that salt played in their ultimate location and subsequent commercial development: Hallein and Hallstatt, for example, in Austria; Halle in eastern Germany; and Fontaines Salees, Salies du Salat, and Salins in France.

Nenquin [1961] has proposed that the development of commercial exploitation of salt in Prehistoric Europe resulted from the shift from a hunter population which derived its nutritional salt from meat to an agrarian society which required salt from other sources to supplement a diet dominated by carbohydrates. An additional use of salt, even in Prehistoric times, was in the preservation of food. At Halle, for example, one of the most extensively documented of the Bronze Age sites, the presence of buried heaps of fish scales has been interpreted to represent the remains of an ancient fish-pickling industry [*Nenquin*, 1961, pp. 45–49].

The salt industry played an important role in the economy of Prehistoric Europe and dictated in part the location of

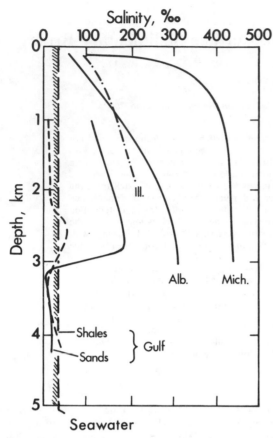

Fig. 1. Summary of variations in maximum values of salinity observed with depth for the Illinois, Michigan, Alberta, and South Louisiana Gulf Coast sedimentary basins in North America. Trends have been generalized. Modified from *Hanor* [1983].

early, transcontinental trade routes. Salt-producing communities were prosperous and important trade centers. The artifacts from the graves of local chieftains of Hallstatt, for example, are of such exceptional quality, that the name of this salt-mining center has been given to the whole period of European prehistory which extended from 900 to 400 B.C.

Salt at Halle was manufactured by boiling down brines containing up to 24 percent by weight salts. In many parts of Europe, however, springs less salty than sea water were utilized for their salt. Although inadequate sunshine required the use of great quantities of fuel to affect evaporation, many of these marginal salt works persisted well into the 19th century.

China

The utilization of saline ground water as a source of salt is as ancient a practice in China as it is in Europe. The principal salt-producing area in China has been the Szechuan province in the southwestern part of the country. Chinese drilling technology was considerably in advance of European methods, and would remain so until the early 1800's. Most of the brine used to make salt was thus derived not from springs, but from wells, some of which had been drilled to depths as great as 600 m [*Multhauf*, 1978]. Some of the wells in Szechuan yielded flammable gas. These wells were capped and the gas transported by bamboo pipe to remote firing pans where brine was evaporated to make salt.

Chinese philosophers undoubtedly speculated on the na-

ture and origin of these salty waters. Most of the written literature on salt generated during this early period, however, such as the treatise by *Huan K'uan* [ca. 73 B.C.], deals more with legal matters, such as regulation and taxation, than cosmological matters, such as origin.

ANCIENT GREECE AND ROME

Anaxagoras and Aristotle

The existence and common properties of rock salt, salty springs, and salt were well known to the writers of classical antiquity. It was during this period that many of the first systematic speculations were written on the properties of matter, the origin of the earth and its oceans, and on the mechanics of what today we call the hydrologic cycle. The earliest written explanation for the origin of subsurface brines exists in a quote from a surviving fragment of the writings of Anaxagoras of Klazomenai [ca. 500–428 B.C.]. In describing the earliest history of the earth, Anaxagoras proposed:

> Of the moisture on the surface of the earth, the sea arose from the waters in the earth (for when these were evaporated the remainder turned salt), and from the rivers which flow into it [*Burnett*, 1930, p. 270].

Anaxagoras, of course, was more concerned here with explaining the origin of the seas than the origin of subsurface brines or rock salt. Clearly, however, the general processes of removal of water by evaporation and the concentration of residual salts were well understood at this time. The other surviving fragments of Anaxagoras' writings do not permit us to deduce how or if salty ground waters or salty springs played a role in his general concept of the hydrologic cycle. He apparently believed that after an initial dewatering of the earth's interior, river and sea water were recycled primarily through runoff from rain and from meteoric waters which

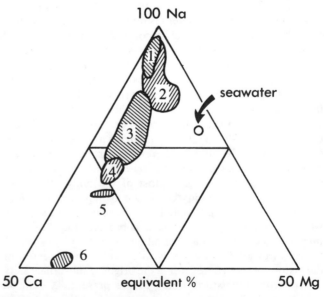

Fig. 2. Variations in proportions of dissolved Na, Ca, and Mg in brines from : 1. Texas; 2. California; 3. Kansas and Oklahoma; 4. and 5. Appalachia; and 6. Arkansas. Modified from *The diagenesis of oil-field brines* [*DeSitter*, 1947].

had infiltrated into the earth during winter months and were stored temporarily in great cavities:

> Rivers take their being both from the rains and from the waters in the earth; for the earth is hollow and has waters in its cavities. And the Nile rises in summer owing to the water that comes down from the snows in Ethiopia [*Burnett*, 1930, p. 270].

Aristotle [384–322 B.C.], while also a believer in the importance of evaporation and meteoric precipitation in recycling of waters on the earth's surface, criticized Anaxagoras' notion of episodic, seasonal storage of waters in the earth's interior on mass balance grounds. Aristotle contended that a single reservoir capable of storing all of the waters which flowed continuously in rivers would have to be larger than or nearly the size of the earth itself [*Biswas*, 1970, p. 60]. Aristotle called upon a more continuous recycling of water, with river waters derived primarily from rainfall which had percolated into the earth and from water formed

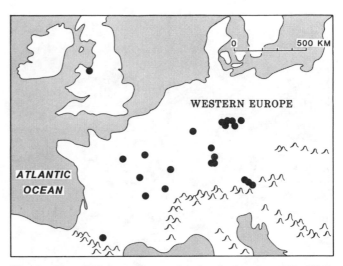

Fig. 4. Map of Western Europe showing the location of Neolithic and Bronze Age salt works centered around brine springs. Locations from *Nenquin* [1961].

by the condensation of air which had made its way into subterranean cavities. A third mechanism for producing river water was the condensation of rising, subterranean vapors from sources unspecified. Perhaps Aristotle would have considered the origin of salty springs to have been related in some way to the vaporization of deep, subterranean fluids. Although he addressed the nature of sea salt, which he believed to be recycled through evaporation and precipitation over the oceans, his extant writings do not explicitly address the origin of salty ground waters.

Lucretius

Roman thought differed from the Greek on the nature of the hydrologic cycle. Lucretius [ca. 99–55 B.C.], the Roman Epicurean, proposed in his treatise, *De Rerum Naturum*, a new mechanism for recycling river and sea water. While Lucretius recognized the importance of evaporation and precipitation in the cycling of surface waters, he also advocated a subterranean cycling of ocean water into continents and up and back out toward the sea as river water. In his explanation of this cycling process, he provides a mechanism for producing subsurface brines:

> Lastly, the earth is of an open texture and is contiguous with the sea, encircling its shores on every side. Therefore, just as the water enters the sea from the land, so must it trickle into the land from the briny gulf. The brine is filtered out, and the main bulk of the water flow back to reassemble in full at the fountainhead. Hence it flows overground, a steady column of sweet liquid marching down the highway already hewn with liquid foot for the guidance of its waves [*Lucretius*, On the Nature of the Universe, translation of *Latham*, 1958, p. 236].

The general concept of a filtration process as a means of separating dissolved salt and water would be reintroduced nearly 2000 years later, this time in the guise of membrane filtration or reverse osmosis [*Russell*, 1933].

FROM THE MIDDLE AGES TO THE INDUSTRIAL REVOLUTION

Ecclesiastical Cycling and Albemic Distillation

Cosmological thought of the Christian Middle Ages saw a

A—SHED. B—PAINTED SIGNS. C—FIRST ROOM. D—MIDDLE ROOM. E—THIRD ROOM. F—TWO LITTLE WINDOWS IN THE END WALL. G—THIRD LITTLE WINDOW IN THE ROOF. H—WELL. I—WELL OF ANOTHER KIND. K—CASK. L—POLE. M—FORKED STICKS IN WHICH THE PORTERS REST THE POLE WHEN THEY ARE TIRED.

Fig. 3. A woodcut showing brine wells in Saxony in the mid-sixteenth century. Porters carry casks of brine to boiling sheds where the brine will be evaporated to make salt [*Agricola, De Re Metallica, Book XII*, 1556, translated by *Hoover and Hoover*, 1912].

Fig. 5. Figure showing the nature of the hydrologic cycle as it was generally conceived of during the Middle Ages and early Renaissance. Whirlpools mark openings in the sea floor into which ocean water rushes. Subterranean channels carry this water into the continents where it rises into hollow caverns called *hydrophylacia*. Water is discharged from the hydrophylacia as springs, the springs give rise to rivers, and the rivers flow into the sea, thus completing the cycle. Somewhere in this process, salt is removed from sea water, resulting in the formation of subsurface brines. Figure from *Mundus Subterraneus* [*Kircher*, 1678].

cold cavernous spaces called *hydrophylacia*, that were thought to make up the interior of mountains, and ultimately trickled out as fresh water springs (Figure 5). Mountains and mountain ranges were considered to be natural analogues to the alembic, the distillation device used by alchemists (Figure 6). A by-product of this process of natural distillation was salt or salty brine. Indeed, the known existence of rock salt and salty springs was evidence favoring the alembic theory of sea water cycling.

These ideas persisted through the Renaissance and well into the 17th century and culminated, at least graphically, in the richly imaginative plates of the folios of Athanasius Kircher. Kircher's book, *Mundus Subterraneus* [1678], contains an intricately detailed account of the interior workings of the earth, including the interaction of the production of heat and the flow of waters (Figure 7). This treatise, which was translated into several languages during Kircher's lifetime, was the most influential geology and geophysics text of its time.

Perrault's Criticisms

The late seventeenth century marks a pivotal time in the history of thought on hydrologic processes in general and on the origin of salty waters in particular. At approximately the same time Kircher was writing his account of subterranean cycling, Pierre Perrault in France was demonstrating for the first time, through experimental investigation, that rainfall is adequate to sustain streamflow [*Biswas*, 1970]. In his famous book, *The Origin of Springs*, published in Paris in

hydrologic cycle dominated, not by meteoric evaporation and precipitation, but by subterranean recycling of sea water back through the continents [*Baker and Horton*, 1936; *Adams* 1938, pp. 432–445]. The quoted authority for such thought was not the Epicurean Lucretius, of course, but the Biblical book of Ecclesiates, Chapter 1, Verse 7:

> All rivers run into the sea yet the sea is not full: unto the place from which rivers come, thither they return again.

It was generally thought at the time that there was insufficient rainfall on earth to account for the large volumes of river water that were observed to flow into the sea. This belief made the idea of subterranean flow of sea water back into the land and up to form rivers not only appealing but absolutely necessary. There were, of course, mechanical problems. What forces could cause salty ocean water to flow into the continents and then appear as fresh water springs at Alpine elevations? Among the numerous explanations proposed during the Middle Ages and Renaissance there were the concepts that the surface of the oceans was in fact higher than land; that subterranean flow occurred as a result of forces produced by high tides and great winds, by the action of air enclosed in the bowels of the earth, or by capillary action, and the straightforward notion that subsurface recycling happened simply in obedience to the Word of God [*Adams*, 1938]. Most pertinent to the origin of salty subterranean waters was the widely-accepted belief that sea water found its way into the interior of the earth and was distilled upward through the crust by local sources of heat. The vapor produced by this distillation process then condensed in the

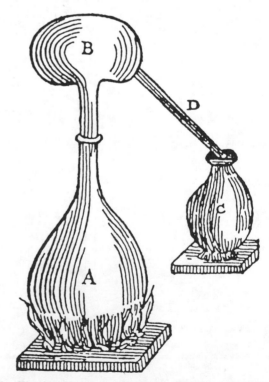

Fig. 6. Woodcut showing an albemic, a distillation device used by Medieval alchemists [*Adams*, 1938]. Distillation of sea water by local sources of heat beneath mountain ranges and the subsequent condensation of water vapor in hydrophylacia were widely considered in the Middle Ages to be the principal forces which drove the hydrologic cycle.

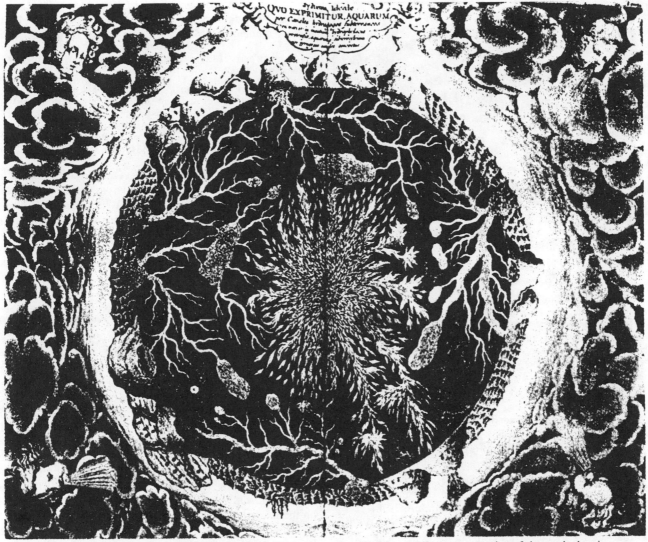

Fig. 7. *Qvo Exprimitur Aquarum*, from *Mundus Subterraneus* [*Kircher*, 1678]. A cross-section of the earth showing the interaction between heat and subsurface waters.

1674, Perrault agrued for the pluvial origin of springs and against subterranean cycling and distillation of sea water:

> . . . since the time that Rivers pour into the Sea fresh and distilled waters, and that all of the salt water that can be in the Sea, must have passed in that time through these underground channels, and have left its salt there in distilling; two things should have happened, one that the sea should no longer be salt; the other that the Earth should be full of salt in great abundance, and it should be found in the bottom of all mountains, more so than sand [*Perruult*, trans. 1967, p. 50].

Perrault's argument against distillation was both simple and compelling. Brine springs and salty water still existed, however. What was their origin?

Subsurface Dissolution

While Medieval and Renaissance cosmologists were arguing on theoretical and theological grounds the fine points of the workings of alembic distillation, owners of commercial salt works were developing a set of empirical field observations that would lead eventually to a radically different notion regarding the origin of salty ground water. The history of the commercial development of the salt works at Cheshire, England provides an illustrative example.

For centuries, saline brines at Cheshire, England provided a commercially important source of salt, not only for England, but for the whole of western Europe [*Bridbury*, 1955]. Archeological evidence indicates that salt works existed at Cheshire in pre-Roman times. Early extraction methods were undoubtedly primitive and probably consisted simply of pouring brine on large piles of burning wood (Figure 8). The Romans introduced open-pan evaporation, a process which required wood as a fuel because the climate was unfavorable for solar evaporation. Wood-fired evaporation continued to be employed for centuries afterward. By the 1600's, England was largely deforested, and coal was substituted as a fuel. In 1670, a coal prospector in the Cheshire area, using primitive drilling techniques, discovered by chance the presence of rock salt at a depth of 32 meters below ground surface [*Multhauf*, 1978]. This and similar discoveries throughout Europe had two important consequences. First, the commercial production of salt shifted away from brine to rock salt as the principal mining commodity, and second, the spatial proximity of rock salt to brine would give rise to the conclusion that salty subsurface waters were the product of subsurface dissolution.

A—TRENCH. B—VAT INTO WHICH THE SALT WATER FLOWS. C—LADLE. D—SMALL
BUCKET WITH POLE FASTENED INTO IT.

Fig. 8. A plate from *Agricola* [1556] [*Hoover* translation, 1912] showing a primitive method of making salt from brine: salty spring water is poured on flaming faggots.

The New World

Inland salt springs of North America were an important source of salt to native Indian and European settler alike. The single most important salt-producing operation in the United States in the period immediately following the American Revolution was located at Kanawha, Virginia (now West Virginia), where coal-fired evaporation of brines produced up to 21 million kg of salt annually [*Multhauf*, 1978].

In 1804, Thomas Jefferson commissioned Sir William Dunbar and Dr. George Hunter to survey the Ouachita River in the newly-acquired Louisiana Territory. Hunter, who may reasonably be regarded as the first geochemist to work in the Louisiana Purchase, made analyses and assessed the potential commercial value of brines collected on the expedition. His journal entries made on November 29, 1804 describe the properties of brines collected from springs just north of what is now the present town of Arkadelphia, Arkansas:

> The specific gravity found by dividing the difference between the weight of the [hydrometer] bulb in Air & salt water, by the difference between its weight in Air & fresh water proves to be of the strongest water in the shallowest hole 1.0272[.] That of the other water 1.22104[.] I afterwards evaporated ten quarts of the strongest water to dryness[;] it yielded ten Ounces Avoirdupois of salt which proved to be deliquesent & developed to the taste besides Sea Salt[,] Muriat of Lime or Magnesia, perhaps both.
>
> . . . I have no doubt that if the ground was perforated to a sufficient depth, water of much greater specific gravity could be obtained.-250 gallons of this water will afford about lbs 50 Salt . . . [*Hunter*, 1804, transcribed in *McDermott*, 1963, p. 99].

While the brine springs analyzed by Hunter never became commercially important, other brine-producing centers flourished in the early decades of the United States. Principal producing areas, in addition to the Kanawha works, were centered at Onandaga, near Syracuse, New York, and at Shawneetown, Illinois. The latter enterprise would eventually fail when the local wood supply was exhausted.

The American geologist, *Edward Hitchcock* [1845], in his popular, introductory geology text, described early 19th-century thought regarding the origin of salt springs:

> In many parts of Europe, salt springs are found rising directly from beds of rock salt; so that their origin is certain . . .
>
> Most American geologists . . . maintain that our salt springs proceed from beds of rock salt, deposited so deep in the earth that they have not yet been discovered: and the fact that the brine increases in strength by descending, which gives strong support to this theory, which is confirmed by the discovery of rock salt in Virginia [*Hitchcock*, 1845, pp. 188–189].

A geologic cross-section of the Onandaga salt basin in New York reproduced from a otherwise unreferenced, "Superintendent's Report for 1857", by Winchell in 1876, clearly shows the spatial association of brines with the subsurface exposure of evaporites of the Salina Group (Figure 9) [*Winchell*, 1876, p. 303]. The origin of subsurface brines was now clear to most geologists. Enter geochemical complications.

GEOCHEMICAL COMPLICATIONS

Good Salt and Bad Salt

During the long period of development of the international salt trade in Medieval and Renaissance Europe, differences in the taste and deliquescent properties of salt from different producing centers gave rise to the notion that there was "good salt" and "bad salt". Cheshire salt, for example, was considered better than French salt for meat, but the French better for salting fish. The salt of Luneberg was better than the salt from Halle. French bay salt was considered bad, but was popular. Perhaps it was cheap. Even the French preferred Spanish or Portuguese salt [*Multhauf*, 1978]. The Dutch peat salt was generally considered to be the best salt on the market, and in 1480, merchants of the Hanse agreed that none other should be employed in the curing of Dutch herring [*Bridbury*, 1955 p. 12].

Some of the differences in the quality of salt were due to presence or absence of physical impurities. It was recognized early on, however, that "salt" varied somehow in its

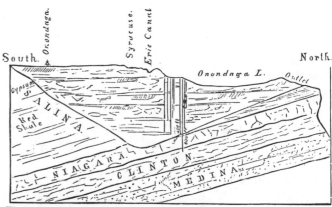

Fig. 92. Longitudinal section of the Onondaga Salt Basin (from Superintendent's Report for 1857), showing the ancient excavation of the outcrop of the Salina group, now filled with gravel and clay, and saturated by an exudation of brine from the old stump of the formation.

Fig. 9. Figure 92 and figure caption from *Sketches of Creation* [*Winchell*, 1876], illustrating the association of subsurface brines with evaporites of the Salina Formation at the Onondaga salt works in New York. Several wells are shown in the center of the figure, the deepest of which is given as 600 feet (200 m).

chemical makeup. We know today, of course, that sea water, subsurface brines, and rock salt itself contain in addition to sodium and chloride, significant concentrations of calcium, magnesium, sulfate, and other components. Many of the differences ascribed to commercial salt of Medieval and Renaissance Europe reflected actual differences in chemical composition of the raw material used to make salt and how lucky a master salter had been in discriminating against undesirable constituents in his salt-making process.

Connate Brines

A natural consequence of the emergence of analytical chemistry as a branch of science in the eighteenth century was the analysis of commercial and geological materials of all sorts, including spring waters and brines. We have seen how Dr. George Hunter, a chemist by training, was able to deduce on the basis of taste and previous experience with known salts, that a brine he had sampled in the Louisiana Territory in 1804 contained not only NaCl, but also $CaCl_2$ and/or $MgCl_2$. Hunter's qualitative field analysis in fact consistent with what modern geochemistry has established brine compositions to be in the region, Na-Ca-Cl brines [Hanor, 1984].

By the mid-1800's, a sufficient body of data had accumulated on the chemical composition of sea water and of subsurface fluids to allow T.S. Hunt, the well-known American geologist, to state in an address before the Geological Society of London in 1859:

> When we examine the waters charged with saline matters which impregnate the great mass of calcareous strata constituting in Canada the base of the paleozoic series, we find that only about one half of the chlorine is combined with sodium; the remained exists as chlorides of calcium and magnesium, the former predominating,—while sulfates are present only in small amount. If now we compare this composition, which may be regarded as representing this of the paleozoic sea, with that of the modern ocean, we find that the chloride of calcium has been in great part replaced by common, salt,—a process involving the intervention of carbonate of soda, and the formation of carbonate of lime. The amount of magnesia in the sea, although diminished by the formation of dolomite and magnesite, is now many times greater than that of the lime; for so long as chloride of calcium remains in the water, the magnesian salts are not precipitated by bicarbonate of soda [Hunt, 1879, p. 11].

Hunt recognized that fundamental differences in chemical composition exist between sea water and subsurface formation waters, at least the waters in Paleozoic carbonates of Eastern Canada. Of more importance is his conclusion that these differences are due to the fact that the formation waters are actually fossil sea water of Paleozoic age, a time when the composition of the oceans must have been significantly different than the composition of today's sea water. Hunt's proposal led to the wide acceptance in the late 19th and early 20th centuries of the notion that formation waters represent fluid trapped in the sediment at the time the sediment was deposited. At the turn of the 20th century, A.C. Lane published a series of papers proposing that calcium chloride waters found in deep mines of the Lake Superior region represent ancient sea water buried in Precambrian lavas. In these papers, Lane introduced the term connate," from the Latin, connatus, "to be born together:"

> Quite different [than rain or magmatic waters] may be the water buried with the beds in the first place, to which we may

fitly apply the adjective connate. The term syngenetic, used in the theory of ore deposits, or cogenital might also be used. [Lane, 1908, p. 502].

Inherent in the original use of the term connate are the tacit assumptions that saline formation waters represent buried sea water or sea water bitterns formed by solar evaporation and that little or no change in chemical composition has occurred in the formation water since the time of its "co-birth" with its host sediment. Truly connate fluids of different ages could, in theory, be used to reconstruct the geochemical history of sea water. With the general subsequent recognition that pore waters undergo significant chemical modification and physical migration after burial, however, the term now has only historical significance.

OIL-FIELD BRINES

Juvenile Chloride

With the rapid development of the oil and gas industry in the early part of the 20th century, new information on the nature of fluids and salt in the subsurface became available at an ever increasing rate (Figure 10). Many oil and gas wells

Composition of Chloride Waters from Oil Fields

	Sea Water	Pennsylvania		Kansas	
	A	B	C	D	E
Cl.............	55.29a	62.31a	161.80b	49,285c	30,066.0c
Br.............	0.19	0.53	0.70	79	....
I..............			0.01	....	8.4	
SO₄............	7.69	0.03	0.05	40	....
CO₂............	0.21	0.27	0.00	0	....
B₂O₃...........				150	....
Na.............	30.59	18.35	64.55	} 2,791	} 4,216
K..............	1.11	1.55	5.16		
Li.............		0.04			
NH₄............		0.23	....		
Ca.............	1.20	13.86	25.19	1,425	2,792
Ba.............			trace	....	
Sr.............			3.55	....	
Mg.............	3.72	2.53	2.48	2,844	6,310
Al₂O₃..........		0.02	0.00		
Fe₂O₃..........				} 56	} 48
Fe.............		0.25	0.16		
SiO₂...........		0.02	0.00	43	85
	100.00	100.00	263.64	56,721	43,517
Ratio $\frac{Cl}{Na}$	1.8	3.5	2.5	18.2 ±	7.5 ±

a. Percentage of total salts.
b. Grams per kilogram of water.
c. Parts per million (?)

A. Dittmar's summary of the principal salts in sea water, from Clarke, Data of Geochemistry, Bulletin No. 491, U.S. Geological Survey, p. 113, 1911. Placed here for comparison.
B. Brine from well 2,667 ft. deep at Conneautsville, Pa. Salinity about nine times that of sea water. Analysis by Robinson and Mabery, quoted by Clarke, loc. cit., p. 174.
C. Brine from depth of 6,300 ft. in well near Imperial, Allegheny county, Pa. Analysis by George Steiger, Journal of the Washington Academy of Sciences, vol. iii, p. 423, 1913. Well record described by White, Bulletin of the Geological Society of America, vol. xxiv, No. 2, pp. 275–282, June, 1913. The salinity is eight times that of sea water.
D. Hudson well, Fredonia, Wilson county, Kan. Depth 400 ft. Analysis by Bailey and Davies, quoted in Water Supply Paper No. 273, U.S. Geological Survey, p. 199 (1911).
E. Flowing salt well in Pennsylvanian strata at Lawrence, Kan., depth 1,400 ft. Analysis by Bartow and Thompson, Kansas Geological Survey, vol. vii, p. 151 (1902).

Fig. 10. A table from Chlorides in oil-field waters, [Washburne, 1914], showing the type of data on subsurface brines which was available to geologists in the early 20th century. Note Washburne's question regarding the concentration units of analysis D.

produced not only hydrocarbons but waters of varying salinity and chemical composition as well. Extensive deposits of bedded salt were found in the course of drilling for oil and gas. Drilling in the Gulf Coast region of the United States revealed the presence of scores of salt domes. The salt domes, in fact, were preferred exploration targets because hydrocarbons were found to be preferentially concentrated around the margins and over the tops of these structures. What was the relation between subsurface brines, salt, and hydrocarbons?

Information on the nature of subsurface pore waters in oilfields brought on a disenchantment with the connate-water hypothesis. Washburne, in a 1914 paper entitled, "Chlorides in oil-field brines," challenged the basic concept that formation waters represented buried seawater:

> The waters of many oil fields have been regarded as buried sea water which has remained in the sediments since the time of their deposition. The preservation of connate water through geologic time has seemed improbable only to a few geologists, but there is room for doubt that buried sea water could remain in strata during their periods of deformation and during the many subsequent epochs of the circulation of meteoric groundwater.

> Chemical analyses of waters associated with oil differ widely from the composition of sea water, requiring extensive alteration of the latter, if the former is truly its derivative. The first noticeable difference is the general absence of sulphates from oilfield waters, but this has been explained satisfactorily through reduction by hydrocarbons and organic matter. The second striking difference is in the high ratio of chlorine to sodium. . . . a large part of the chlorine occurs as calcium and magnesium [Washburne, 1914].

Washburne proposed two working hypotheses to account for the great excess of chlorine over sodium in the water of oil fields. The first, suggested by what Washburn termed the "dryness" of deep sands and by the downward increase in salinity, called for a deep, dry zone, where water was extracted from pore fluid, possibly by the drying action of ascending gases such as nitrogen, carbon dioxide, and methane. As subsurface evaporation continued, NaCl was precipitated out in the pores of the rocks, leaving a residual water enriched in calcium and magnesium chloride. The second hypothesis, preferred by Washburne, was apparently suggested to him by the occurrence of basaltic plugs and dikes in the Gulf coastal plain of Mexico. This hypothesis called for the introduction of calcium and magnesium chloride brines into the subsurface from basaltic intrusions at depth. Washburne went even further to propose that salt domes are precipitated out in place as the result of comingling of sedimentary solutions containing sodium and rising solutions of volcanic chloride. In the jargon of the day, Washburne was thus proposing that subsurface brines were at least in part "juvenile" in origin.

Diagenesis and Diffusion

Like Washburne, *Richardson* [1917a] criticised the notion of a connate origin for oil-field waters, at least in the Appalachian region where he was working. Richardson doubted that a water would remain unchanged in composition throughout geologic time:

> An active solvent like water cannot remain unchanged in composition so long as it is in contact with soluble material [Richardson, 1917a, p. 40].

Richardson proposed as a working hypothesis that two processes were involved in producing brines in the Appalachian region. The first involved prolonged leaching by slowly moving water of great masses of sedimentary beds containing disseminated salt. The second involved upward diffusion of salt from underlying salt beds known to exist in the region. The known increase in salinity with depth made this an attractive suggestion. In 1917, Richardson published the results of theoretical calculations, among the first of their kind for molecular diffusion in sediments, showing that subsurface dissolution and the upward diffusion of dissolved salt could produce a significant column of brine within geologically reasonable times [Richardson, 1917b]. The results of these calculations are shown in Figure 11. In addition to his pioneering work in evaluating diffusion as a mass transport mechanism, Richardson brought attention to the role that formation waters played in what today we would call burial diagenesis:

> Carbonate cannot exist in strong brines [presumably because of their high calcium concentration], yet the former presence of carbonate waters in the oil-bearing rocks is indicated by calcite in the cement of the sandstones. . . . other deep-seated rocks brought up by torpedoing show marked cementation . . . [by] quartz and calcite [Richardson, 1917a, p. 41].

Subsurface Evaporation

The hypothesis of formation of brines by subsurface evaporation, a process proposed by Washburne in 1914, achieved more general acceptance with the publication in 1919 of the well-documented U.S. Geological Survey Bulletin 693 by Mills and Wells, "The evaporation and concentration of waters associated with petroleum and natural gas." Mills and Wells, like many of their contemporaries, were impressed by the common occurrence of salty waters in gas-producing reservoirs. Water does vaporize in the presence of a gas phase, and it seemed reasonable to conclude that salty subsurface waters are the residue formed as a result of the evaporation of pore fluid into gases produced in the subsurface. Mills and Wells added credibility to their arguments by the inclusion of numerous chemical analyses and field observations. The next logical step beyond explaining the origin of subsurface brines was explaining the origin of salt domes:

> It is our belief that salt domes, such as are found in Louisiana and Texas. . . have been formed by the evaporation of saline waters through the agency of escaping gases. Many of the domes occur along faults, and some of the salt masses are situated at the intersections of fault planes. It is also significant that [surface] emanations of the gaseous hydrocarbons are commonly associated with the salt domes [Mills and Wells, 1919, pp. 90–91].

What could be more logical? Gas migration occurs preferentially along faults, and as evaporation of pore water continues, masses of solid salt will eventually be precipitated out along these fault zones.

1933 TO THE PRESENT

In a previous article [Hanor, 1983], I have described in detail the development of thought on the origin and evolution of subsurface sedimentary brines over the fifty-year period, 1933–1983. In the concluding part of this essay, we will look very briefly at just a few representative examples of studies from this period.

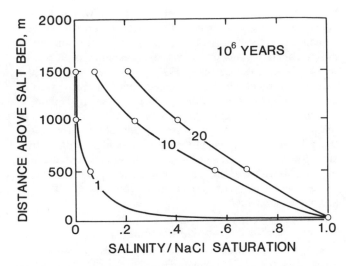

Fig. 11. A graph plotted from data in a paper by *Richardson* [1917*b*] supporting Richardson's hypothesis that a thick column of salty pore water can be generated in geologically reasonable periods of time by dissolution of halite and upward transport of dissolved salt by molecular diffusion. Few of the assumptions which went into the calculations are stated by Richardson, but data apparently represent transient diffusion in a initially salt-free, semi-infinite medium with salt concentration fixed at halite saturation at the base.

The 1930's

We have seen that four mechanisms for the origin of subsurface brines were in vogue at the early part of this century: connate burial of sea water [*Lane*, 1908]; introduction of juvenile chloride [*Washburne*, 1914]; subsurface dissolution and diffusion of salt [*Richardson*, 1917]; and subsurface evaporation [*Mills and Wells*, 1919]. Of these, the latter, subsurface evaporation, was probably the most generally invoked. In 1933, however, W.L. Russell, in a key review article on the subsurface concentration of chloride brines, showed by simple mass balance calculations that impossibly large volumes of methane and methane source rock would be required to produce brines through evaporation. For example, the production of enough 250 g/L brine to fill a 50-meter thickness of sandstone having a porosity of 20 percent by subsurface evaporation would require a volume of methane generated from the alteration of 65,000 meters of bituminous shale. The appearance of Russell's paper marked the end of acceptance of the subsurface evaporation hypothesis.

Russell reviewed several additional brine-forming processes, including molecular settling, more recently invoked by *Mangelsdorf et al.* [1970]; and infiltration of subaerial brines, a process favored by *Carpenter* [1978] for the origin of brines in the northern Gulf Coast. Most intriguing was Russell's hypothesis that "negative osmosis" in some way could produce brines. Sufficient work had been done at the time to show that compacted clays and shales can behave as membranes which would permit the passage of water but inhibit the passage of dissolved salts. Russell correctly predicted that the subject offered a promising field for further research. Reverse osmosis or membrane filtration continues to be in this day one of the principal and more highly debated mechanisms for producing subsurface brines [*Graf*, 1982].

The 1940's and the 1950's

As analytical techniques improved in the decades following World War II, natural waters were analyzed more routinely and reliably for their chemical composition. *DeSitter's* [1947] classic paper on the diagenesis of oil-field brines demonstrated while there is no unique chemical composition for subsurface brines, there are systematic variations. For example, the ratio of dissolved Mg to Ca plus Na is remarkably constant over a wide range of brine compositions (Figure 2). *White* [1957] presented the first systematic review of the variations and controls on the minor and trace element composition of formation waters, and emphasized the role that the early burial diagenesis of seawater plays in modifying pore water composition. White also revived interest in the role sedimentary brines may play as ore-forming fluids.

1960 to the Present

Chave, in 1960, again, and perhaps for the last time, explored the possibility that the composition of ancient sea water could be deduced from the study of brine compositions. He concluded, however, that the degree of post-burial alteration is so great that little useful information on past ocean chemistry is retained. Few, if any, waters are connate. Hitchon and colleagues, in a series of papers on the Alberta basin, Canada, became among the first to attempt to explain the origin of formation waters in the context of regional basinal hydrology [*Hitchon and Friedman*, 1969].

The late 1950's and early 1960's saw the first rigorous applications of chemical thermodynamics to problems of subsurface water composition. Two pioneering studies include *Schoeller's* [1955] systematic review of mineral stabilities in aqueous systems and *Back's* [1961] study of carbonate saturation states in ground water systems. As our understanding of the thermodynamic properties of brines has improved [e.g., *Helgeson et al.*, 1981], so has our ability to relate brine chemistry and mineral diagenesis, as in *Merino's* [1975] study of the Kettleman North Dome, California. The application of high-speed computers in the late sixties and early seventies [*Kharaka and Barnes*, 1973; *Truesdell and Jones*, 1974; *Plummer et al.*, 1975] to equilibrium problems has facilitated the understanding of reaction and mass transfer in complex, multi-component systems. Equilibrium considerations alone, however, are not sufficient to explain the high chloride concentration of most brines because most brines are not saturated with respect to a chloride-bearing mineral phase. Most discussion today focuses in on one of the following three mechanisms for producing high chloride and salinity values: membrane filtration, infiltration of subaerially-produced brines, and subsurface dissolution of evaporites.

Membrane filtration as a mechanism for producing subsurface brines received a great deal of impetus in the 1960's from the results of laboratory experiments [reviewed by *Berry*, 1969] which showed that compacted clays and shales can indeed behave as semi-permeable membranes and from the results of theoretical calculations by *Bredehoeft et al.* [1963] which were intended to show that sufficient differences in hydraulic head to drive waters across membranes apparently can exist in some basinal settings. *Graf* [1982] has reviewed in detail the research which has been done on membrane filtration.

There are few who would advocate a connate origin for

any subsurface salty fluid. There is evidence, however, that some subsurface brines may have inherited at least their high chloride concentrations from a subaerially-produced precursors. *Rittenhouse* [1967] suggested that variations in dissolved Br and Cl could be used to distinguish between brines formed by subsurface dissolution of halite, which should have low Br/Cl ratios, and brines originally formed by the extensive subareal evaporation of seawater, which should have elevated Br/Cl ratios. *Carpenter* [1978], for example, has suggested, on the basis of their high Br concentrations, that brines in the Jurassic and Lower Cretaceous sediments of the northern Gulf Coast originated as interstitial fluids in evaporite sediments and achieved their high salinities as a result of subaerial evaporation of sea water to carnellite saturation. As a result of compaction, these brines have migrated upward into younger, overlying sediments. *Land and Prezbindowski* [1981] have challenged this interpretation and have suggested that incongruent dissolution of halite in the subsurface is responsible both for the elevated salinity and bromine content of these waters. *Hanor* [1984] has suggested on the basis of the presence of nearly linear salinity gradients in the region that diffusion, not compaction, is the dominant mass transport process currently operating in this part of this region of the Gulf Coast.

In some sedimentary basins there is well-documented evidence for subsurface dissolution of evaporites as an ongoing brine-forming process. *Manheim and Horn* [1968], for example, in a survey of the regional variation in pore water salinity along the Atlantic Coastal Plain found the saltiest waters to be spatially associated with buried evaporites. *Hanor and Bailey* [1983] found in their regional study of pore water salinities in the thick, Tertiary section of the Louisiana Gulf Coast that the saltiest waters there occur in thick, sandy sequences in proximity to salt domes. Plumes of elevated salinity can be traced upward and laterally away from some of these domes, implying the existence of on-going dissolution and mass transport.

SUMMARY

The hypotheses for brine formation currently in vogue have distinguished, but varied, ancestries. *Lucretius* [ca. 60 B.C.] appears to have been the first to invoke in writing a filtration mechanism for removing salt from subsurface waters. This was an entirely intuitive deduction, of course, and it was not until the 20th-century, when the membrane properties of compacted clays became known, that filtration was first seriously proposed as a brine-forming mechanism. The belief that salty subsurface waters could be produced by dissolution of evaporites was well established in the scientific literature by the early 19th-century, but it had its origins in field observations made over the preceeding several centuries. The idea that some brines have evolved from infiltrated sea water bitterns can be traced directly to the ideas Hunt proposed in the mid-19th-century. Few today, however, would believe that any of these brines are strictly connate.

The general notion that brines can be produced by subsurface evaporation or distillation was long popular but has not fared well. The idea was intuitively appealing to the Classical and Medieval cosmologists, who knew from first hand experience that evaporation or boiling of seawater left behind a salty residue. The concept was also appealing

centuries later to the first oil-field geologists, who noted the coexistance of natural gas and salty formation waters. Acceptance of subsurface evaporation as a brine-forming mechanism effectively ended with the publication of Russell's mass balance calculations in 1933.

Although much has been learned about the properties of subsurface sedimentary fluids over recorded time, there is still some disagreement regarding the relative importance of different brine-forming processes. Study of brines will continue, however, because of their present and potential intrinsic value as sources of salt, bromine, dissolved methane, and heat, and because of the fundamental role these fluids play in the geochemical, geophysical, and economic evolution of sedimentary basins.

REFERENCES

Adams, F.D., *The Birth and Development of the Geological Sciences*, Reprint of 1938 Edition, 506 pp., Dover Publications, New York, 1954.

Agricola, G., *De Re Metallica* [1556], translated by H.C. Hoover and L.H. Hoover, 638 p., Mining Magazine, London, 1912, reprinted by Dover Publications, New York, 1950.

Back, W., Calcium carbonate saturation in ground water from routine analysis, *United States Geological Survey Water Supply Paper, 1535-D*, 55 pp., 1961.

Baker, M.N., and R.E. Horton, Historical development of ideas regarding the origin of springs and ground-water, *American Geophysical Union Transactions*, Pt. II, 395, 1936.

Berry, F.A.F., Relative factors influencing membrane filtration, *Chemical Geology, 4*, 295–301, 1969.

Biswas, A.K., *History of Hydrology*, 336 pp., North-Holland Publishing Company, Amsterdam-London, 1970.

Bredehoeft, J.D., C.R. Blyth, W.A. White, and G.B. Maxey, Possible mechanism for concentrating brines in subsurface formations, *American Association of Petroleum Geologists Bulletin, 47*, 257–269, 1963.

Bridbury, A.R., *England and the Salt Trade in the Later Middle Ages*, 198 pp., Oxford University Press, London, 1955.

Burnett, J., *Early Greek Philosophy*, Reprint of Fourth Edition of 1930, 375 pp., Meridian Books, New York, 1957.

Carpenter, A.B., Origin and chemical evolution of brines in sedimentary basins, *Oklahoma Geological Survey Circular, 79*, 60–77, 1978.

Chave, K.E., Evidence on the history of sea water from chemistry of deeper subsurface waters of ancient basins, *American Association of Petroleum Geologists Bulletin, 44*, 357–370, 1960.

DeSitter, L.U., Diagenesis of oil-field brines, *American Association of Petroleum Geologists Bulletin, 31*, 2030–2040, 1947.

Graf, D.L., Chemical osmosis, reverse chemical osmosis, and the origin of subsurface brines, *Geochimica et Cosmochimica Acta, 46*, 1431–1448, 1982.

Hanor, J.S., Fifty years of development of thought on the origin and evolution of subsurface sedimentary brines, in *Revolution in the Earth Sciences: Advances in the Past Half-Century*, edited by S.J. Boardman, pp. 99–111, Kendall/Hunt, Dubuque, 1983.

Hanor, J.S., Variation in the chemical composition of oil-field brines with depth in Northern Louisiana and Southern Arkansas: Implications for mechanisms and rates of mass transport and diagenetic reaction, *Gulf Coast Association of Geological Societies Transactions, 34*, 55–61, 1984.

Hanor, J.S., and J.E. Bailey, Use of hydraulic head and hydraulic gradient to characterize geopressured gradients and the direction of fluid migration in the Louisiana Gulf Coast, *Gulf Coast Association of Geological Societies Transactions, 33*, 115–122, 1983.

Helgeson, H.C., D.H. Kirkham, and G.C. Flowers, Theoretical prediction of the thermodynamic behavior of aqueous electrolytes at high pressures and temperatures: Part IV, *American Journal of Science, 281*, 1249–1516, 1981.

Hitchcock, E., *Elementary Geology*, Third Edition, 351 pp., Mark H. Newman Publisher, New York, 1845.

Hitchon, B., and I. Friedman, Geochemistry and origin of formation waters in the western Canada sedimentary basin—I. Stable isotopes of oxygen and hydrogen, *Geochimica et Cosmochimica Acta, 33,* 1321–1349, 1969.

Huan K'uan, *Discourses on salt and iron: a debate on state control of commerce and industry* [circa 73 B.C.], 204 pp., translated by E.M. Gale, Ch'eng-Wen Publishing Co., Taipei, 1973.

Hunt, T.S., *Chemical and Geological Essays,* 489 pp., Osgood and Company, Boston, 1879.

Hunter, G., Journal of an excursion from Natchez on the Mississipi [sic.] up the River Ouachita, 1804–1805, in *The Western Journals of Dr. George Hunter, 1796–1805,* edited by J.F. McDermott, *Transactions of the American Philosophical Society, 53,* 71–122, 1963.

Kharaka, Y.K., and I. Barnes, SOLMNEQ: Solution-mineral equilibrium computation: *National Technical Information Service Report, PB-215-899,* 82 pp., Springfield, Va., 1973.

Kircher, A., *Mundus Subterraneus,* Amsterdam, 1678.

Land, L.S., and D.R. Prezbindowski, The origin and evolution of saline formation water, Lower Cretaceous carbonates, south-central Texas, *Journal of Hydrology, 54,* 51–74, 1981.

Lane, A.C., Mine waters and their field assay, *Geological Society of America Bulletin, 19,* 501–512, 1908.

Lucretius, *On the Nature of the Universe* [circa 60 B.C.]. 254 pp., translated by R. Latham, Penguin Books, Ltd., Middlesex, 1951.

Mangelsdorf, P.C., F.T. Manheim, and J.M.T. Geiskes, Role of gravity, temperature gradients, and ion-exchange media in formation of fossil brines, *American Association of Petroleum Geologists Bulletin, 54,* 617–626, 1970.

Manheim, F.T., and M.K. Horn, Composition of deeper subsurface waters along the Atlantic coastal margin, *Southeastern Geology, 8,* 215–236, 1968.

Merino, E., Diagenesis in Tertiary sandstones from Kettleman North dome, California—II. Interstitial solutions: Distribution of aqueous species at 100°C and chemical relations to diagenetic mineralogy: *Geochimica et Cosmochimica Acta, 39,* 1629–1645, 1975.

Mills, R.V., and R.C. Wells, The evaporation and concentration of waters associated with petroleum and natural gas, *United States Geological Survey Bulletin, 693,* 100 pp., 1919.

Multhauf, R.P., *Neptune's Gift, A History of Common Salt,* 325 pp., The Johns Hopkins University Press, Baltimore, 1978.

Nenquin, J., *Salt, A Study in Economic Prehistory,* 159 pp., De Tempel, Brugge, 1961.

Perrault, P., *On the Origin of Springs* [1674], 209 pp., translated by A. LaRoche, Hafner Publishing Co., New York, 1967.

Plummer, L.N., D.L. Parkhurst, and D.R. Kosiur, MIX2: A computer program for modeling chemical reactions in natural waters, *United States Geological Survey Water-Resources Investigations, 76-13,* 68p., 1975.

Richardson, G.B., Note on Appalachian oil-field brines, *Economic Geology, 12,* 37–41, 1917a.

Richardson, G.B., Note on diffusion of sodium chloride in Appalachian oil-field waters, *Washington [D.C.] Academy of Science Journal, 73–75,* 1917b.

Rittenhouse, G., Bromine in oil-field waters and its use in determining possibilities of origin of these waters, *American Association of Petroleum Geologists Bulletin, 51,* 2430–2440, 1967.

Russell, W.L., Subsurface concentration of chloride brines, *American Association of Petroleum Geologists Bulletin, 17,* 1213–1228, 1933.

Schoeller, H., *Geochimie des Eaux Souterraines,* 213 pp., L'Institut Francais du Petrole, Paris, 1955.

Truesdell, A.H., and B.F. Jones, WATEQ, a computer program for calculating equilibria of natural waters, *United States Geological Survey Journal of Research, 2,* 233–248, 1974.

Washburne, C.W., Chlorides in oil-field waters, *American Institute of Mining Engineers Transactions, 48,* 687–693, 1914.

White, D.E., Magmatic, connate, and metamorphic waters, *Geological Society of America Bulletin, 68,* 1659–1682, 1957.

Winchell, A., *Sketches of Creation: A Popular View of Some of the Grand Conclusions of the Sciences in Reference to the History of Matter and of Life Together with a Statement of the Intimations of Science Respecting the Primordial Condition and Ultimate Destiny of the Earth and Solar System,* 459 pp., Harper and Brothers, Publishers, New York, 1876.

J. S. Hanor, Department of Geology, Louisiana State University, Baton Rouge, LA 70803.

The "Physics" of Soil Water Physics

Garrison Sposito

Department of Soil and Environmental Sciences, University of California, Riverside

Some aspects of the underlying conceptualizations (as opposed to experimental methodologies or mathematical algorithms) in soil water physics are reviewed. Contemporary issues relating to the symmetry properties of the Richards Equation, the status of the energy picture of soil water, and the theoretical description of coupled heat and water flows in soil are raised to exemplify as yet unresolved problems in the "physics" of soil water physics. Four basic questions which formalize these problems are posed as suggestions for future research.

One of the ways of stopping science would be only to do experiments in the region where you know the law.

R. P. Feynman [1967]

The Beginnings of Soil Water Physics

The Buckingham Flux Law

The study of water in soil as a subdiscipline of physics can be reckoned from the year 1905, when Edgar Buckingham completed his first and only research on the equilibrium and flow behavior of soil water. The published report of this research [*Buckingham*, 1907] provided a physical basis for the presently accepted conceptual picture of isothermal soil water processes. *Buckingham* commenced the theoretical part of his study by defining a "capillary potential" $\psi(\theta)$, at a given water content (θ), temperature, and bulk density of soil, to be the reversible work per unit mass required to transfer water from soil to a pure water reservoir. He noted that the capillary potential would be equal to zero in saturated soils but that otherwise, $\psi(\theta)$ would vary among soils even if their temperature, water content, and bulk density were arranged to be the same. Realizing the informality of his definition, he added that "... a rigorous treatment of the subject, with no restrictions imposed on either the water content or the soluble salt content of the soil, would have to use thermodynamic reasoning." Experience since has shown the truth of this prediction [*Sposito*, 1981].

Buckingham [1907] reported the first measured values of the capillary potential, known at present (with opposite sign convention) as the soil water matric potential [*Hillel*, 1980], as a function of water content at constant temperature and applied pressure. His experimental method was based on the application of an equilibrium condition, that the reversible work required to bring about an infinitesimal change in the vertical position of water in a soil profile should be compensated by that required to bring about a concomitant infinitesimal change in water content. Therefore shifts in the soil water matric potential will balance those in the gravitational potential, and the equilibrium condition is expressed:

$$(\partial\psi/\partial\theta)_{T,P} \, d\theta = -g \, dz \tag{1}$$

where $g[L\,T^{-2}]$ is the gravitational acceleration; $z[L]$ is a vertical position coordinate, measured positive upward; and $T[K]$ and $P[M\,L^{-1}\,T^{-2}]$ refer to temperature and applied pressure, respectively. A rearrangement of (1), namely,

$$\frac{d\theta}{dz} = \frac{-g}{(\partial\psi/\partial\theta)_{T,P}} \tag{2}$$

establishes a theoretical basis for measuring $\psi[L^2\,T^{-2}]$ with data on the position dependence of $\theta[L^3\,L^{-3}]$ at equilibrium [*Buckingham*, 1907]. Equation (2), which contains the tacit assumption that the soil is not deformable [*Sposito*, 1981], is known as the Buckingham Equation.

After establishing the measurability of $\psi(\theta)$, *Buckingham* [1907] went on to postulate a constitutive relationship for the soil water flux vector which involved the matrix potential in an essential way. He reasoned that the soil water flux vector was a kind of "capillary current density," and therefore that soil should exhibit a "capillary conductivity" logically akin to the electrical conductivity shown by a metal wire supporting an electrical current density. The fruit of this seminal physical analogy cannot be expressed better than in his own words [*Buckingham*, 1907]:

> Let Q be the capillary current density at any point—i.e., the mass of water which passes in one second through 1 sq. cm. of an imaginary surface perpendicular to the direction of flow. Let ψ be a quantity which measures the attraction of the soil at any given point for water. Then the gradient of attraction, which we may denote by S, is the amount by which ψ increases per centimeter in the direction of the current, by reason of the fact that the water content of the soil decreases in that direction. Let λ denote the capillary conductivity of the soil. Then we may write, in formal analogy with Fourier's and Ohm's laws,
>
> $$Q = \lambda S.$$

In a notation more conventional today, the Buckingham flux law would be written in the form

$$\mathbf{J} = -K(\theta)\nabla\psi \tag{3}$$

where $\mathbf{J}[M\,L^2\,T^{-1}]$ is the soil water flux vector, and $K[M\,L^{-3}\,T]$ is termed the hydraulic conductivity [*Hillel*, 1980]. Commonly, ψ in (3) is divided by g to give it the dimensions of length and K is multiplied by g/ρ_w, where $\rho_w[M\,L^{-3}]$ is the mass density of liquid water, to give it the dimensions of velocity [*Kirkham and Powers*, 1972]. The definition $\mathbf{J} \equiv \rho_w\mathbf{J}_w$ then eliminates ρ_w from the flux law and introduces the volumetric water flux density $\mathbf{J}_w[L\,T^{-1}]$.

Buckingham [1907] reported limited experimental measurements of the quantity $K(\partial\psi/\partial\theta)_{T,P}$, known now as the soil water diffusivity [*Childs and George*, 1948; *Kirkham and Powers*, 1972], but he did not investigate the hydraulic conductivity directly, ostensibly because he could not envision a suitable apparatus to control $\psi(\theta)$. He did note, however, that $K(\theta)$ should be strongly dependent on the water content of the soil, another prediction that experience since has verified amply [*Hillel*, 1980].

Buckingham [1907] did not mention the groundwater flux law discovered by the civil engineer, Henry Darcy [*Darcy*,

1856] at any point in his discussion of the soil water flux law, (3). Since Buckingham was educated entirely as a physicist [*Hersey*, 1970; *Philip*, 1974], it is unlikely that he knew anything about the Darcy flux law. He was an expert in thermodynamics [*Buckingham*, 1900] and he makes it clear in his discussion of (3) that the equation was inspired by the linear flux laws of Ohm and Fourier, particularly that of Ohm. Thus the quantitative study of soil water began with a physicist and its development properly can be regarded as that of a branch of physics concerned with transport phenomena [*Sposito*, 1984].

Philip [1974] has recounted the facts surrounding the near total neglect of the Buckingham flux law by practicing soil physicists for some 20 years after its discovery. Important to the present review is not the long hiatus but the next forward step, which was a conceptual position paper written by *Richards* [1928]. This paper, inspired by the work of Willard Gardner, resurrected the capillary potential with a full consideration of its physical motivation as presented by *Buckingham* [1907], then went on to formalize the concept by defining the total soil water potential, $\phi[L^2 \, T^{-2}]$,

$$\phi = \psi + gz \qquad (4)$$

whose uniformity in a soil profile at equilibrium is the condition leading to the derivation of (2). Richards described an improved device for the measurement of $\psi(\theta)$, the tensiometer, and presented plots of matric potential against water content for four soils of widely varying texture. He also continued the development of the Buckingham flux law in the form

$$\mathbf{J}_w = -K(\psi)\nabla\phi \qquad (5)$$

where $\mathbf{J}_w[L \, T^{-1}]$ is the volumetric flux density, and $K[T]$ is equal to the hydraulic conductivity in (3) divided by the mass density of liquid water. Richards, fully cognizant of the physical ancestry of (5), noted that K

"... will have to be studied for a large number of soils under different conditions, but this procedure seems to be our best chance for reducing the phenomena of capillary flow to a quantitative basis. This method has met with splendid success with heat and electricity and it should not be any more difficult to make reliable capillary potentiometers [tensiometers] than it is to construct good thermometers or voltmeters."

With these prophetic words he went on to study for a doctoral degree in physics at Cornell.

The Richards Equation

True to his promise, *Richards* [1931] soon published a paper based on what *Gardner* [1972] has since called the best-known Ph.D. dissertation in all of soil physics. In this paper, precise measurements of the hydraulic conductivity based on a simple but ingenious apparatus were reported for the first time. The apparatus permitted control of the matric potential at each end point of a thermostatted soil column by means of tensiometers whose pure water reservoirs could be maintained under applied pressures less than atmospheric [*Richards*, 1931]. Measurement of the steady flux of water through the column then permits the calculation of the hydraulic conductivity through a direct application of (5) restricted to one dimension. Values of $K(\psi)$, including the effect of hysteresis in $\psi(\theta)$, were determined for three soils of differing texture. The measurability of the hydraulic conductivity thus was established firmly and the Buckingham flux law verified experimentally.

Richards [1931] also produced the culminating step in the development of soil water physics as a predictive science. Invoking the law of mass balance in the form

$$\nabla \cdot \mathbf{J}_w = -\left(\frac{\partial\theta}{\partial\psi}\right)_{T,P} \frac{\partial\psi}{\partial t} \qquad (6)$$

where $(\partial\theta/\partial\psi)_{T,P}$ was termed the "capillary capacity" (now called the "water capacity"), he incorporated the Buckingham flux law (5) to derive the partial differential equation

$$\left(\frac{\partial\theta}{\partial\psi}\right)_{T,P} \frac{\partial\psi}{\partial t} = \nabla \cdot (K\nabla\psi) - g\frac{\partial K}{\partial z} \qquad (7)$$

Equation (7) is a fundamental equation governing the isothermal, isobaric transport of water through unsaturated soil. It is known today as the Richards Equation [*Swartzendruber*, 1969].

Although critical to predictive applications of the Richards Equation, the numerous improvements in both laboratory and field methods of measuring K and ψ [*Hillel*, 1980] and the many refinements in mathematical methods for solving (7) [*Philip*, 1969] subsequent to the appearance of Richards' dissertation are not intrinsic to the "physics" of soil water physics as considered in the present paper. These kinds of innovations belong properly to "normal science," in the sense of *Kuhn* [1970], since they serve to test essential physics, not to create it. There is, however, a relatively unstudied property of (7) that does belong to the physics of soil water despite its overt mathematical appearance. This property of the Richards Equation may be termed its "symmetry character." Speaking precisely, one asks what groups of transformations of the independent variables in (7) leave its mathematical form invariant [*Birkhoff*, 1960].

Two simple examples will serve to illustrate how the symmetry properties of the Richards Equation are investigated. Suppose that (7) is restricted to one spatial dimension and that the water capacity is absorbed into the time derivative on the left side to produce the partial differential equation

$$\frac{\partial\theta}{\partial t} = \frac{\partial}{\partial z}\left(K\frac{\partial\phi}{\partial z}\right) \qquad (8)$$

This one-dimensional Richards Equation is expressed relative to a coordinate system fixed (let us say) in a laboratory frame of reference and the tacit assumption has been made that the one-dimensional form of (5) applies in that frame. If the soil is deformable, this tacit assumption is false because of a covariance principle stating that (5) refers strictly to the flow of water relative to the solid material in soil [*Raats and Klute*, 1968; *Sposito and Giráldez*, 1976]. If (5) is understood in this way, (6) can be transformed to the frame of reference of the solid material (which, in a deformable soil, can move relative to the laboratory frame) to produce the generalized Richards Equation [*Raats and Klute*, 1969; *Sposito and Giráldez*, 1976]:

$$\frac{\partial\theta_R}{\partial t} = \frac{\partial}{\partial z_R}\left(K\frac{\partial\phi}{\partial z_R}\right) \qquad (9)$$

where

$$\theta_R = \frac{\rho_{bo}}{\rho_b}\theta \qquad (10)$$

$$dz_R = \frac{\rho_b}{\rho_{bo}}dz \qquad (11)$$

and ϕ is now understood to include a term representing the effect of soil deformability on the total soil water potential [*Sposito*, 1981]. In (10) and (11), $\rho_b[M \, L^{-3}]$ is the actual dry bulk density of soil at some time after "time zero," and ρ_{b0} is the dry bulk density of soil in some arbitrary reference state at time zero. It is evident that (9) reduces to (8) when the soil is not deformable. Otherwise, (8) and (9) illustrate the invariance of the one-dimensional Richards Equation under a transformation from laboratory coordinates to material coordinates.

As a second example, consider the following transformation of the independent variables in (8):

$$t' = \beta t \qquad z' = \gamma z \qquad (12a)$$

where γ and β are positive real numbers. It is evident that the set of position and time transformations generated by (12a) includes an identity transformation ($\gamma = \beta = 1$) and inverse transformations ($\gamma_{inv} = \gamma^{-1}$, $\beta_{inv} = \beta^{-1}$), and that $\gamma_3 = \gamma_2\gamma_1$ and $\beta_3 = \beta_2\beta_1$ is a possible transformation if (γ_1, β_1) and (γ_2, β_2) are. A set of associative transformations with these properties is called a group [Birkhoff, 1960]. A special case of the group of transformations generated by (12a) is defined by the equations [Sposito and Jury, 1985]

$$T = (\alpha\omega^2/\theta_s)t \qquad Z = \alpha z \qquad (12b)$$

where θ_s is the water content at saturation and $\alpha[L^{-1}]$ and $\omega^2[L\ T^{-1}]$ are positive constant parameters. With the help of (12b), (8) can be written in the dimensionless form

$$\frac{\partial\hat{\theta}}{\partial T} = \frac{\partial}{\partial Z}\left(\hat{K}\frac{\partial\hat{\psi}}{\partial Z}\right) - \frac{\partial\hat{K}}{\partial Z} \qquad (13)$$

where

$$\hat{\theta} = \theta/\theta_s \qquad (14a)$$

$$\hat{K} = gK/\omega^2 \qquad (14b)$$

$$\hat{\psi} = \alpha\psi/g \qquad (14c)$$

Soils which are described by (13) with the same scaled, dimensionless values of $\hat{\theta}$, $\hat{K}(\hat{\theta})$, and $\hat{\psi}(\hat{\theta})$ are said to be "Warrick-similar" [Sposito and Jury, 1985]. Warrick-similar soils have the remarkable property, epitomized in (12b) and (14), of transforming soil water behavior among themselves solely through the three scale factors, θ_s, α, and ω. For these soils, the Richards Equation is invariant under the group of similarity transformations specified by (12b) and the scaling relations (14).

THE ENERGY PICTURE

Internal Energy

Gardner [1972] has attributed the fecundity of Richards' soil water research to "... his continuing interest in one of its central problems, that of the energy status of soil water." Indeed, the original Richards Equation is expressed in what may be termed the "energy picture," as opposed to the "mass picture," introduced by Childs and Collis-George [1950], which features the water content as the dependent variable [Swartzendruber, 1969]. In the energy picture, the soil water matric potential is the dependent variable, and solutions of (7) are sought once particular, explicit equations relating ψ to the water capacity and the hydraulic conductivity are prescribed.

There is, however, a curious aspect of the derivation of (7) from (5) and (6). If (7) is to be interpreted as an equation governing the space and time dependence of the energy variable, then it seems strange to employ a differential equation of mass balance (equation (6)) to derive it. Why is a differential equation of energy balance not used? One possible response is

that (7) is nothing more than a mathematical transformation of an equation for the water content [Philip, 1969]. If this point of view is correct, then (5) and (6) should be written in the mass picture forms [Swartzendruber, 1969]

$$\mathbf{J}_w = -D(\theta)\nabla\theta \qquad (15)$$

$$\nabla \cdot \mathbf{J}_w = -\frac{\partial\theta}{\partial t} \qquad (16)$$

where

$$D = K\left(\frac{\partial\psi}{\partial\theta}\right)_{T,P} \qquad (17)$$

is the soil water diffusivity, and the Richards Equation should be expressed

$$\frac{\partial\theta}{\partial t} = \nabla \cdot (D\nabla\theta) - g\left(\frac{\partial K}{\partial\theta}\right)_{TP}\frac{\partial\theta}{\partial z} \qquad (18)$$

Equations (15), (16), and (18) exhibit a self-consistency that is lacking in (5), (6), and (7). At issue once again is the physics of the Richards Equation: if (6) is only a mathematically transformed version of (16), then water content is a more fundamental physical variable than is matric potential.

The physical loose end uncovered here has to do only with (6). Both (5) and (7) are rooted firmly in the energy picture, but (6) was derived from mass balance, i.e., the mass picture. To tie up the loose end, (6) must be shown also to express energy balance without any direct appeal to mass balance. The resolution of this problem can be had through consideration of the partial specific internal energy of water in soil [Sposito and Chu, 1982]. Since the transport process to which (7) refers is isothermal, the first law of thermodynamics applied to this internal energy has the form

$$d\bar{U}_w = Td\bar{S}_w + d\phi \qquad (19)$$

where $\bar{U}_w[L^2\ T^{-2}]$ is the partial specific internal energy, and $\bar{S}_w[L^2\ T^{-2}\ K^{-1}]$ is the partial specific entropy of soil water (see, for example, Denbigh [1981, chapter 2]). Equation (19) describes the infinitesimal changes in the internal energy of soil water that occur in response to infinitesimal processes that shift the total soil water potential ϕ, given by (4), and produce the isothermal heating, $Td\bar{S}_w$. The latter quantity is the heat transfer that must accompany the small change in potential $d\phi$ in order that it be an isothermal change [Nielsen et al., 1972; Sposito and Chu, 1982]. The development of (19) into a differential equation of internal energy balance will provide the missing physical link between (5) and (7).

Energy Balance

A differential balance law for $\bar{U}_w$ can be derived under the assumptions that the solid material in soil is incompressible and that soil water has the general properties of a viscous, heat-conducting fluid [Hassanizadeh and Gray, 1979, 1980]. Given these two assumptions, the internal energy balance equation is [Sposito and Chu, 1982]

$$\rho_w\theta\frac{d\bar{U}_w}{dt} = -\rho_w\theta^2\left(\frac{\partial\psi}{\partial\theta}\right)_{T,P}\nabla \cdot \mathbf{v}_w - \nabla \cdot \mathbf{J}_{iso} + \rho_w\theta g\frac{dz}{dt} \qquad (20)$$

where $\mathbf{v}_w = \mathbf{J}_w/\theta$ and $\mathbf{J}_{iso}[M\ T^{-3}]$ is a heating flux density vector. The first term on the right side of (20) represents the rate at which stresses acting on soil water change its partial specific internal energy. The nondissipative part of these stresses is closely related to the soil water matric potential [*Raats and Klute*, 1968; *Hassanizadeh and Gray*, 1980; *Sposito and Chu*, 1982]. The dissipative part of these stresses, under isothermal conditions, contributes to the rate of heating expressed in the second term on the right side of (20). Gravitational contributions to the rate of internal energy change are represented in the third term.

Upon combining (19) with (20), noting (4) and the physical interpretation of $Td\bar{S}_w$, one derives the following differential equation:

$$\frac{d\psi}{dt} = -\theta\left(\frac{\partial\psi}{\partial\theta}\right)_{T,P} \nabla \cdot \mathbf{v}_w \qquad (21)$$

The time derivative in (20) and (21) is evaluated in a frame of reference that follows the mean motion of the water relative to the frame of reference of the solid soil material [*Sposito and Chu*, 1982]. Therefore

$$\frac{d}{dt} \equiv \frac{\partial}{\partial t} + \mathbf{v}_w \cdot \nabla \qquad (22)$$

and (21) can be written in the form

$$\begin{aligned}\frac{\partial\psi}{\partial t} &= -\mathbf{v}_w \cdot \nabla\psi - \theta\left(\frac{\partial\psi}{\partial\theta}\right)_{T,P} \nabla \cdot \mathbf{v}_w \\ &= -\left(\frac{\partial\psi}{\partial\theta}\right)_{T,P} \mathbf{v}_w \cdot \nabla\theta - \theta\left(\frac{\partial\psi}{\partial\theta}\right)_{T,P} \nabla \cdot \mathbf{v}_w \end{aligned} \qquad (23)$$

Finally, one can invoke the definition of v_w to produce from (23) the partial differential equation (compare (6)):

$$\frac{\partial\psi}{\partial t} = -\left(\frac{\partial\psi}{\partial\theta}\right)_{T,P} \nabla \cdot \mathbf{J}_w \qquad (24)$$

Equation (21) expresses one way in which the matric potential changes in response to stresses exerted on soil water from the adjacent phases in soil: it is an energy balance equation consistent with the first and second laws of thermodynamics applied to isothermal processes. Equation (24) is an equivalent form of the energy balance equation that can be combined with the Buckingham flux law to derive the Richards Equation without making a direct appeal to the law of mass balance. The Richards Equation thus can be derived entirely within the energy picture and the equal fundamental physical status of the energy picture and the mass picture is thereby established.

COUPLED HEATING FLUX AND WATER FLOW

The Heating Flux

The heating flux density vector that appears in (20) represents a heating flux borne by soil water when it moves under isothermal conditions. This vector is related directly to the volumetric flux density vector in (5) (see, for example, chapter 5 in the work by *Nielsen et al.* [1972]):

$$\mathbf{J}_{iso} = \rho_w Q_w' \mathbf{J}_w = Q_w' \mathbf{J} \qquad (25)$$

where Q_w' is called the "heat of transfer" (see, for example, chapter 11 in the work by *de Groot and Mazur* [1962]). Experimental values of Q_w' have been compiled by *Nielsen et al.* [1982]; typically, Q_w' is very small when soil water flow involves principally the liquid phase.

More generally than in (20), the balance of internal energy depends on the divergence of a heating flux density vector $\mathbf{J}_q[M\ T^{-3}]$ that can be represented by a constitutive relationship known as the Fourier law [*Truesdell*, 1984]:

$$\mathbf{J}_q = -\lambda\nabla T \qquad (26)$$

where λ, a function of the temperature and composition of a soil, is the thermal conductivity. Besides the problem of divining the composition and temperature dependence of λ in field soils [*Kimball et al.*, 1976; *Pikul and Allmaras*, 1984], there is an aspect of the physics of (26) as applied to soil that is of fundamental concern in the study of energy balance and soil water. This aspect has to do with the definition of J_q on the left side of (26). For example, following *Miller* [1974], one would state that

$$J_q \equiv -\frac{1}{A}\frac{dQ}{dt} \qquad (27)$$

where A is the cross-sectional area of the soil conduit in a plane perpendicular to the direction of J_q and dQ (an inexact differential) represents an infinitesimal quantity of heat transported into the soil. On the other hand, following *de Groot and Mazur* [1962], one would propose that the equation

$$\rho_{bw}\frac{d\bar{Q}}{dt} \equiv -\nabla \cdot \mathbf{J}_q \qquad (28)$$

where $\rho_{bw}[M\ L^{-3}]$ is the wet bulk density, should be used to define the heat per unit mass $\bar{Q}[L^2\ T^{-2}]$ transported into the soil. The vector $\mathbf{J}_q$ then should be defined as the dissipative part of the internal energy flux density vector. These two conflicting proposals from recognized experts in transport phenomena illustrate the point, championed perhaps most vigorously by *Truesdell* [1984], that a universal concensus as to the fundamental meaning of the left side of (26) does not exist.

Coupled Flux Equations

The piquant ambiguity in the interpretation of (26) becomes even more acute when the coupled transport of heat and water in soil is considered explicitly. Most of the popular theoretical descriptions of this phenomenon can be based on a special case of the equation of entropy production developed by *de Groot and Mazur* [1962]:

$$T\sigma = -\mathbf{J}_s \cdot \nabla T - \mathbf{J} \cdot \nabla\phi \qquad (29)$$

where $\sigma[M\ L^{-1}\ T^{-3}\ K^{-1}]$ is the rate of entropy production per unit volume; $\mathbf{J}_s[M\ T^{-3}\ K^{-1}]$ is the entropy flux density vector, $\mathbf{J}[M\ L^{-2}\ T^{-1}]$ is the water flux density vector, and $\phi[L^2\ T^{-2}]$ is defined by (4) [*Chu et al.*, 1983]. Following *Groenevelt and Bolt* [1969] and *Nielsen et al.* [1972], one can define a heating flux density vector $\bar{q}$:

$$\bar{\mathbf{q}} \equiv T(\mathbf{J}_s - \bar{S}_w\mathbf{J}) \qquad (30)$$

With this definition incorporated, (29) takes on the form

$$T\sigma = -\bar{\mathbf{q}} \cdot (\nabla T/T) - \mathbf{J} \cdot (\nabla\phi)_T \qquad (31)$$

where the gradient of ϕ now is evaluated with the temperature held constant [*de Groot and Mazur*, 1962; *Chu et al.*, 1983]. Equation (30) defines a "conduction heating flux density vector" because the convective transport of entropy by soil water has been subtracted from the total entropy flux. Thus $\bar{q}$ should be a logical candidate to represent $\mathbf{J}_q$ on the left side of (26) when gradients in ϕ are absent [*Nielsen et al.*, 1972].

Model approaches to coupled heat and water flow in soil, however, often have used a definition of the heating flux density vector different from (30) [*Kimball et al.*, 1976; *Jury and Letey*, 1979; *Milly*, 1982; *Pikul and Allmaras*, 1984]. A "total heating flux density vector" $\mathbf{q}$ can be defined by adding to $\bar{\mathbf{q}}$ the enthalpy transported by soil water:

$$\mathbf{q} \equiv \bar{\mathbf{q}} + \bar{H}_w \mathbf{J} = T(\mathbf{J}_s + \mu_w \mathbf{J}) \tag{32}$$

where $\bar{H}_w[L^2\ T^{-2}]$ is the partial specific enthalpy of soil water and μ_w is its chemical potential [*Sposito*, 1981]. The second equality in (32) comes from (30) and the relation [*Denbigh*, 1981]

$$\mu_w = \bar{H}_w - T\bar{S}_w \tag{33}$$

The additional thermodynamic equation [*Denbigh*, 1981]

$$(\partial(\mu_w/T)/\partial T)_{P,\theta} = -\bar{H}_w/T^2 \tag{34}$$

and (32) permit (29) to be rewritten

$$T\sigma = -\mathbf{q} \cdot (\nabla T/T) - \mathbf{J} \cdot [T\nabla(\mu_w/T) - \mathbf{g}] \tag{35}$$

where $\mathbf{g} = -g\hat{\mathbf{z}}$, $\hat{\mathbf{z}}$ is a unit vector pointing along the positive z axis, and the relation [*Sposito*, 1981]

$$\nabla\phi = \nabla\mu_w - \mathbf{g} \tag{36}$$

has been introduced. The right side of (32) specifies a heating flux density vector that includes both the transport of entropy and the convective transport of chemical energy by soil water. *de Groot and Mazur* [1962] have argued that it is $\mathbf{q}$ which is accessible directly to measurement in a coupled flow experiment. They note also that (26) applies to $\mathbf{q}$ when gradients in ϕ are absent. In fact, (26) applies to $\bar{\mathbf{q}}$ and $\mathbf{q}$ not only when $\nabla\phi$ vanishes but also when $\mathbf{J}$ vanishes and, in three of the four possible scenarios produced by these two conditions, λ will take on different values [*de Groot and Mazur*, 1962].

Jury and Miller [1974] have used yet another definition of the heating flux density vector in their study of the simultaneous flow of heat and liquid water through a sand. Their definition is [*Chu et al.*, 1983]

$$\mathbf{q}_h \equiv \bar{\mathbf{q}} - \mathbf{J}_{iso} = T\left[\mathbf{J}_s - \left(\bar{S}_w + \frac{Q_w'}{T}\right)\mathbf{J}\right] \tag{37}$$

This heating flux density vector will vanish whenever the transport of entropy in soil is produced solely from the convective transport of entropy and of the heat of transfer by soil water. If the conduction heat flux is induced only by the isothermal transport of water, this condition is met. Just like the flux densities $\bar{\mathbf{q}}$ and $\mathbf{q}$, $\mathbf{q}_h$ can be represented by (26), but in this case (26) applies regardless of the magnitude of $\nabla\phi$ or $\mathbf{J}$ [*Chu et al.*, 1983].

Since each of the three definitions of the heating flux density vector given here can be used to replace $\mathbf{J}_s$ in (29) to provide a valid expression of the entropy production, none of them is more fundamental than the others insofar as coupled heat and water flow is concerned. Any of the heating flux density vectors can be substituted into (26) to verify the Fourier law. In fact, an infinitude of heating flux definitions, related to one another through linear transformations, is possible and perfectly compatible with the physics of entropy production in soil as epitomized in (29) [*Chu et al.*, 1983].

FOUR FUNDAMENTAL QUESTIONS

The present essay is by no means a comprehensive review, but it will have served a useful purpose if it helps dispel the notion that the physics of soil water physics was a settled scientific problem after 1931. Some merit might be accorded the proposition that in fact, little enough work on the physics has been done during the past 55 years. The present discussion can be considered in support of this proposition because it has raised, at least implicitly, three basic issues that demand resolution before our understanding of soil water physics can be regarded as satisfactory.

1. *What are the possible groups of similarity transformations of the Richards Equation and how may they be used to classify the behavior of water in soils?* The practical significance of this question can not be overestimated. In the example represented by (13), the implication is that if water movement is investigated experimentally in any one soil in the class of Warrick-similar soils, water movement in all other soils in the class can be predicted [*Warrick et al.*, 1985].

2. *What is the most general form of the law of internal energy balance for soil water that is consistent with the Richards Equation?* The derivation of the right side of (20) and therefore of (21) depends on reasonable but nonetheless special assumptions about the solid and fluid phases in soil. A more satisfying foundation for (24) and the energy picture of soil water would involve a derivation of (20) that included all possible energy transport mechanisms for isothermal water movement.

3. *What definition of the heating flux density vector will lead to a predictive model of coupled heat and water flow in soil that is both self-consistent and experimentally testable?* The key issue here is whether any one expression for $\mathbf{J}_q$ compatible with (26) and (29) can be accorded a privileged status in the absence of model assumptions about the coupled transport of heat and water in soil. If no expression for $\mathbf{J}_q$ is more physically correct a priori than any other, then experimentation must decide the matter by providing data for models of the coupled transport process, and the correctness of "theories" based on (29) must be evaluated by testing the models, not by testing candidates for the definition of $\mathbf{J}_q$.

Of course, these basic questions certainly do not exhaust the list of important queries that can be made relating to the physics of soil water physics. Nothing has been said, for example, about coupled flows among water, heat, and dissolved solutes, and more questions can be raised about deformable soils, or about soils for which the hydraulic and thermal conductivities must be represented by second-rank tensors. An additional question, heretofore scarcely alluded to, perhaps should be added explicitly because it is allied so strongly to the principal leitmotiv of contemporary physics outside of soil water physics:

4. *How does the microscopic or the molecular behavior of water in soil lead to macroscopic transport equations and to the observed values of macroscopic transport coefficients?* An abundant literature relating to this question already exists, but it is neither rigorous nor comprehensive enough to provide a satisfactory answer.

Perhaps there is an element of heresy in the suggestion that much of soil water physics research in the past 50 years has not been directed toward the physics of soil water. Perhaps also there is an element of orthodoxy in this claim, since it implies a return to the basic issues that so long ago preoccupied Buckingham and Richards. The remarkable brillance of their achievements has sustained two generations of soil physics research which has, for the most part, left fundamental questions unattended, being content instead to deal with practical matters. It is indeed fortunate that the physics of soil water physics, like the lilies of the field, flourishes on a very deep substratum and, therefore, like them, survives in spite of the viscissitudes of cultivation.

Acknowledgments. Much of the author's research summarized in this paper was supported by the National Science Foundation under grant number CEE-79-20778. Gratitude is expressed to S.-Y. Chu and W. A. Jury for their collaboration in that effort.

REFERENCES

Birkhoff, G., *Hydrodynamics*, Princeton University Press, Princeton, N. J., 1960.

Buckingham, E., *An Outline of the Theory of Thermodynamics*, Macmillan, New York, 1900.

Buckingham, E., Studies on the movement of soil moisture, *Bur. of Soils Bull. 38*, U.S. Dep. of Agric., Washington, D. C., 1907.

Childs, E. C., and Collis-George, N., The permeability of porous materials, *Proc. R. Soc. London, Ser. A, 201*, 392–405, 1950.

Childs, E. C., and George, N. C., Soil geometry and soil-water equilibria, *Discuss. Faraday Soc., 3*, 78–85, 1948.

Chu, S.-Y., G. Sposito, and W. A. Jury, The cross-coupling coefficent for the steady flow of heat in soil under a gradient of water content, *Soil Sci. Soc. Am. J., 47*, 21–25, 1983.

Darcy, H., *Les Fontaines Publiques de la Ville de Dijon*, Dalmont, Paris, 1856.

de Groot, S. R., and P. Mazur, *Non-Equilibrium Thermodynamics*, North-Holland, Amsterdam, 1962.

Denbigh, K., *The Principles of Chemical Equilibrium*, Cambridge University Press, New York, 1981.

Feynman, R. P., *The Character of Physical Law*, MIT Press, Cambridge, Mass., 1967.

Gardner, W. R., The impact of L. A. Richards upon the field of soil water physics, *Soil Sci., 113*, 232–237, 1972.

Groenevelt, P. H., and G. H. Bolt, Non-equilibrium thermodynamics of the soil-water system, *J. Hydrol., 7*, 358–388, 1969.

Hassanizadeh, M., and W. G. Gray, General conservation equations for multi-phase systems, 2, Mass, momenta, energy, and entropy equations, *Adv. Water Resour., 2*, 191–203, 1979.

Hassanizadeh, M., and W. G. Gray, General conservation equations for multi-phase systems, 3, Constitutive theory for porous media flow, *Adv. Water Resour., 3*, 25–40, 1980.

Hersey, M. D., Edgar Buckingham, in *Dictionary of Scientific Biography*, edited by C. C. Gillispie, pp. 565–566, Charles Scribners' Sons, New York, 1970.

Hillel, D., *Fundamentals of Soil Physics*, Academic, Orlando, Fla., 1980.

Jury, W. A., and J. Letey, Water vapor movement in soil: Reconciliation of theory and experiment, *Soil Sci. Soc. Am. J., 43*, 823–827, 1979.

Jury, W. A., and E. E. Miller, Measurement of the transport coefficients for coupled flow of heat and moisture in a medium sand, *Soil Sci. Soc. Am. J., 38*, 551–557, 1974.

Kimball, B. A., R. D. Jackson, R. J. Reginato, F. S. Nakayama, and S. B. Idso, Comparison of field-measured and calculated soil-heat fluxes, *Soil Sci. Soc. Am. J., 40*, 18–25, 1976.

Kirkham, D., and W. L. Powers, *Advanced Soil Physics*, John Wiley, New York, 1972.

Kuhn, T. S., *The Structure of Scientific Revolutions*, University of Chicago Press, Chicago, Ill., 1970.

Miller, D. G., The Onsager relations: Experimental evidence, in *Foundations of Continuum Thermodynamics*, edited by J. J. Delgado-Domingas et al., pp. 185–214, Macmillan, New York, 1974.

Milly, P. C. D., Moisture and heat transport in hysteretic, inhomogeneous porous media: A matric head-based formulation and a numerical model, *Water Resour. Res., 18*, 489–498, 1982.

Nielsen, D. R., R. D. Jackson, J. W. Cary, and D. D. Evans, *Soil Water*, American Society of Agronomy, Madison, Wisc., 1972.

Philip, J. R., Theory of infiltration, *Adv. Hydrosci., 5*, 215–296, 1969.

Philip, J. R., Fifty years progress in soil physics, *Geoderma, 12*, 265–280, 1974.

Pikul, J. L., and R. R. Allmaras, A field comparison of null-aligned and mechanistic soil heat flux, *Soil Sci. Soc. Am. J., 48*, 1207–1214, 1984.

Raats, P. A. C., and A. Klute, Transport in soils: The balance of mass, *Soil Sci. Soc. Am. J., 32*, 161–166, 1968.

Raats, P. A. C., and A. Klute, One-dimensional, simultaneous motion of the aqueous phase and the solid phase of saturated and partially saturated porous media, *Soil Sci., 107*, 329–333, 1969.

Richards, L. A., The usefulness of capillary potential to soil-moisture and plant investigators, *J. Agric. Res., 37*, 719–742, 1928.

Richards, L. A., Capillary conduction of liquids through porous mediums, *Physics, 1*, 318–333, 1931.

Sposito, G., *The Thermodynamics of Soil Solutions*, Oxford University Press, New York, 1981.

Sposito, G., Buckingham, Richards, and the Leipzig connection: The beginnings of soil water physics (abstract), *Eos Trans. AGU, 65*, 875, 1984.

Sposito, G., and S.-Y. Chu, Internal energy balance and the Richards Equation, *Soil Sci. Soc. Am. J., 46*, 889–893, 1982.

Sposito, G., and J. V. Giráldez, On the theory of infiltration in swelling soils, paper presented at Proceedings ISSS Symposium on Water in Heavy Soils, Int. Soc. of Soil Sci., Bratislava, Czechoslovakia, Sept. 8–10, 1976.

Sposito, G., and W. A. Jury, Inspectional analysis in the theory of water flow through unsaturated soil, *Soil Sci. Soc. Am. J., 49*, 791–798, 1985.

Swartzendruber, D., The flow of water in unsaturated soils, in *Flow Through Porous Media*, edited by R. J. M. DeWiest, pp. 215–292, Academic, Orlando, Fla., 1969.

Truesdell, C., *Rational Thermodynamics*, Springer-Verlag, New York, 1984.

Warrick, A. W., D. O. Lomen, and S. R. Yates, A generalized solution to infiltration, *Soil Sci. Soc. Am. J., 49*, 34–38, 1985.

G. Sposito, Department of Soil and Environmental Sciences, University of California, Riverside, CA 92521.

R. E. Moore and Yolo Light Clay

Jim Constantz

U.S. Geological Survey, Menlo Park, California

For half a century the extensive use of the water retention and flow characteristics of Yolo Light Clay has established it as a benchmark soil for comparison of water flow models. The characteristics of Yolo Light Clay have been used to model infiltration, evaporation, drainage, and nonisothermal flow processes by researchers throughout the world. Surprisingly, the actual experimental work involving Yolo Light Clay consists of a single experiment performed by R. E. Moore as part of his dissertation work at the University of California, Berkeley, from 1934 to 1937. Furthermore, additional experimental work cannot be performed on Yolo Light Clay, because Moore's description of the soil's location is too general for recollection of the original materials.

Moore's experiments utilized tensiometers in conjunction with horizontal soil sampling tubes to compare matric potential and water content values in one meter high soil columns during steady evaporation. From these experiments, Moore was able to estimate the relationships between the unsaturated hydraulic conductivity, the matric potential, and the soil water content for Yolo Light Clay and five other soils. By using the word 'light', Moore chose an unorthodox nomenclature for Yolo Light Clay, which now traces all references back to this single experiment. After receiving his Ph.D. in soils, Moore went on to a career as an irrigation engineer for the U.S. Department of Agriculture primarily in Latin America, and never performed laboratory experiments again. However during the 1950's, the data from one of Moore's experiments with Yolo Light Clay was used as a primary data set in several papers which have since became standard references in unsaturated zone hydrology. As a result of these innovative papers, this single data set for Yolo Light Clay is still frequently used as a data base for testing unsaturated zone models.

In the field of hydrology, no soil has been cited more frequently than Yolo Light Clay. First studied almost fifty years ago, the number of references to Yolo Light Clay now approaches a thousand, and its continued citation attests to its current value to researchers in the area of soil water physics. The abundance of citations to Yolo Light Clay can be attributed to two distinct factors. First, the original experiment performed by R. E. Moore in 1936 and 1937 on Yolo Light Clay and five other soils still represents one of the most complete data sets concerning the influence of water content and soil texture upon the water retention and transmission properties of soils. Second, one of Moore's primary data sets for Yolo Light Clay was used as an illustrative example in several innovative papers in the 1950's, all of which have now become cornerstones of research in their respective areas of hydrology. Today the name Yolo Light Clay is familiar to almost every hydrologist concerned with the unsaturated zone. Ironically, many of these same hydrologists are unfamiliar with R. E. Moore, although he continued to contribute to various aspects of water resources throughout his entire life [*A. Moore*, 1966]. Furthermore, Moore was the only researcher ever to perform an experiment using Yolo Light Clay and his site description is too general for recollection of the soil. Consequently, Moore's original data set probably represents the only information that will ever exist for this most popular soil.

The story of R. E. Moore and Yolo Light Clay begins in the fall of 1918. Ross Edgar Moore entered South Dakota School of Mines to study mining engineering. In the summer of 1920, he and a friend left school and worked their way south, living on money they made at various odd jobs along the way. They reached New Orleans during Mardi Gras and subsequently ended up on a freighter to Honduras. There, they ran out of money and took jobs as engineers with the United Fruit Company. They were both assigned to general surveying of potentially arable soils which required either irrigation or drainage. By the fall of 1921, they saved enough money to book passage north and reached South Dakota in time to enroll in school. Moore received his B.S. degree in mining engineering in 1923 and took a job with the Homestake Mining Company in Lead, South Dakota. He found the below ground work unpleasant and the industry in general unsatisfying, and soon decided to return to irrigation engineering as a career [*A. Moore*, 1966].

In 1925, Moore was married and he and his wife, Adele, moved to Central America. Moore worked with the United Fruit Company for twelve years in Honduras, Guatemala, Panama, and Colombia, supervising dozens of irrigation and drainage projects. In 1934, he and Adele brought their three children north to attend schools in the United States, and at this time, he elected to enter a graduate program in soils. Moore spent six months with F. G. Veihmeyer in Davis, California, during which time they outlined a Ph.D. proposal concerned with soil permeabilities as a function of water content [*A. Moore*, 1966]. He enrolled in the soils program at the University of California at Berkeley, under the direction of G. B. Bodman and was fortunate to have a committee that included Hans Jenny and B.A. Etcheverry.

These were exciting times in soil water physics: not only had L. A. Richards' paper just been published [*Richards*, 1931], but an important device had recently been invented for the direct measurement of capillary water potentials. It was discovered that when a device called a Livingston Auto Irrigator was attached to a mercury manometer rather than a water supply, a capillary potentiometer or, as Richards called it, a tensiometer was created [*R. E. Moore*, 1938]. Moore realized that this new device would enable the experimental verification of the work of *E. Buckingham*

[1907], *W. Gardner* [1919], and *L. A. Richards* [1931]. Moore's experimental plan was quite direct: induce steady water flux in laboratory soil columns, then use tensiometers to measure the relationship between the unsaturated conductivity and the capillary or matric potential by extending Darcy's relationship to unsaturated flow.

To accomplish this, Moore collected six soils, five along Cache Creek in Yolo County and a sixth near the town of Oakley, California. He packed eighteen one meter high soil columns, three columns of each soil type, to be used in steady evaporation experiments and subsequent drainage experiments. Each initially air-dry soil column was wetted from below using a metered water reservoir. The columns eventually reached steady-state evaporative flux conditions and Moore measured the matric potential profile with tensiometers and the water content profiles with horizonal sampling tubes inserted along the length of the column. Then the reservoir was removed, the column was allowed to drain, and when flow ceased, the matric potential and water content profiles were determined again.

As a point of interest, by using the word 'light', Moore choose an unorthodox nomenclature for Yolo Light Clay. Presumably, he did this to distinguish it from a Yolo Clay which he had collected for the same series of experiments. This can be concluded from Table 1 in Moore's thesis which describes the textural composition of his six soils [*Moore*, 1938, p. 22]; here the three finer textured soils are called Yolo Clay Loam, Yolo Light Clay, and Yolo Clay. However, when the mechanical analysis is reviewed, it becomes apparent that by the textural convention of the day as well as current convention, Moore's Yolo Clay Loam is actually a loam texture, and that Moore's Yolo Light Clay is actually a clay loam. Consequently, by using this unusual nomenclature Moore inadvertently labelled his 'light clay' with a tracer that follows its use in the literature to this day.

When Moore finished his experimental work in 1937 and sat down to write his thesis, he discovered that *L. A. Richards* [1936] had beaten him to press. That is, Richards had published exactly what Moore had set out to measure and report on, the relationship between the unsaturated conductivity and soil matric potential over a range of water contents. So, possibly because of this paper, Moore chose not to publish his results in an international journal like Soil Science or Transactions of the American Geophysical Union. Instead, he published his results in Hilgardia, a regional journal sponsored by the California Agricultural Experiment Station. By this time, Moore had taken a lecturership at Davis, and within two years, he went to Riverside to work with L. A. Richards at the newly formed U.S. Department of Agriculture (USDA) Salinity Laboratory. In 1941, Moore was offered a position with the Office of International Agricultural Development which the USDA was just creating outside Washington, D.C. Moore served with the USDA as an irrigation engineer, and later as a program planner, in Central and South America for the rest of his life.

The evolution of Yolo Light Clay from merely one of six soils in a poorly publicized experiment performed in the 1930's, to the most familiar soil in hydrology, stems from the combination of two factors. First, Moore's experimental results were excellent and his conclusions are still valid today. Second, the properties of Yolo Light Clay were chosen for illustrative examples by several innovative researchers in papers which have become standard references for isothermal and nonisothermal water flow problems. During the 1940's, Moore's paper in Hilgardia was cited frequently, but none of the six soils was singled out for discussion. During this period, there were two aspects of Moore's results that proved useful to researchers. First, Moore's results showed that at saturation, the hydraulic conductivities of sands were higher than those of finer-textured soils, but at lower saturations the opposite was true. Second, during the wetting process, Moore had noted that a steep water content gradient existed at the wetting front regardless of soil texture. It is Moore's description of this sharp wetting front which interested his previous professor, G. B. Bodman, and his coworker, E. A. Colman, in their pioneering laboratory studies on infiltration into initially dry soils [*Bodman and Colman*, 1944, *Colman and Bodman*, 1945].

However, it was not until 1952 that Yolo Light Clay was specifically cited in the literature [*Klute*, 1952]. Arnold Klute chose the Yolo Light Clay data set entitled 'Wetting and Drying Potentials and Permeabilities as a function of Moisture Content; Yolo Light Clay, Can No. 2', for an illustrative example of the water content profiles over time during horizonal wetting. Shortly after Klute's paper was published, J. R. Philip chose this same data set (Yolo Light Clay, Can No. 2) for his milestone series of papers on infiltration into soils [*Philip*, 1957a]. *Philip* [1957b], *Philip and deVries* [1957], and *deVries* [1958] used this same set of data for Yolo Light Clay for their innovative theoretical models for evaporation and nonisothermal flow in porous materials. Because of the strong impact that these works had on the basic understanding of water flow processes in porous material, Yolo Light Clay was established as a benchmark soil for future researchers who wished to compare the value of new theoretical and empirical models to the work of Klute, Philip, and deVries.

Moore probably never saw the work of deVries, and certainly never knew his Yolo Light Clay data set from Can No. 2 was destined to become a standard data base in hydrology. In 1958, he was on assignment in Honduras, the same country where he had started his work in soil-water relationships thirty-seven years earlier. In November of that year, while on a tour of agricultural experiment stations with visiting scientists from Bolivia, Moore drowned after his boat capsized in a heavy chop on Lake Yahoa in the Honduran mountains [*A. Moore*, 1966].

The author would like to acknowledge the assistance provided by Paul R. Day, L. J. Waldron, Jacob Rubin, and G. B. Bodman in obtaining biographical information.

References

Bodman, G. B. and Colman, E. A., Moisture and energy conditions during downward entry of water into soils, *Soil Science Society America Proceedings*, 8, 116–122, 1944.

Buckingham, E., Studies on the movement of soil moisture, *USDA Bureau Soils Bulletin, 38*, 1–61, 1907.

Colman, E. A. and Bodman, G. B., Moisture and energy conditions during downward entry of water into moist and layered soils, *Soil Science Society America Proceedings*, 9, 3–11, 1945.

deVries, D. A., Simultaneous transfer of heat and moisture in porous media, *Transactions American Geophysical Union, 39*, 909–916, 1958.

Gardner, W., The movement of moisture in soil by capillarity, *Soil Science, 7*, 313–318, 1919.

Moore, Adele, *Yankee Salesman*, Vantage Press, p. 148, N.Y., N.Y., 1966.

Moore, R. E., Water conduction from shallow water tables, Unpublished Ph.D. thesis, p. 102, University of California, Berkeley, January 1938.

Moore, R. E., Water conduction from shallow water tables, *Hilgardia*, *12*, 383–426, 1939.

Philip, J. R., The theory of infiltration.1. The infiltration equation and its solution, *Soil Science*, *83*, 345–357, 1957a.

Philip, J. R., Evaporation, and moisture and heat fields in the soil. *J. Meteorology*, *14*, 354–366, 1957b.

Philip, J. R. and deVries, D. A., Moisture movement in porous materials under temperature gradients, *Transactions American Geophysical Union*, *38*, 222–232, 1957.

Richards, L. A., Capillary conduction of liquids through porous mediums, *Physics*, *1*, 318–334, 1932.

Richards, L. A., Capillary-conductivity data for three soils, *J. American Society Agronomy*, *28*, 297–300, 1936.

J. Constantz, U.S. Geological Survey, Mail Stop 496, Menlo Park, CA 94025.

Charles Sumner Slichter—An Engineer in Mathematician's Clothing

Herbert F. Wang

Department of Geology and Geophysics, University of Wisconsin, Madison, Wisconsin 53706

Charles Sumner Slichter (1864–1946) was an applied mathematician who made important contributions to groundwater hydrology between 1894 and 1912. His most significant scientific paper, "Theoretical Investigation of the Motion of Ground Waters," was published by the United States Geological Survey in 1899. Slichter expressed the analogy of groundwater flow to heat and electrical conduction, as well as to ideal fluid flow. He combined Darcy's law and continuity to produce Laplace's equation under the assumption of homogeneity. He then used the methods of classical potential theory to describe well interference and the effects of irrigation ditches. The seminal value of his work was explicitly acknowledged by M. King Hubbert in 1940, although Hubbert was critical of the use of a velocity potential. Slichter conducted numerous field studies throughout the country, including California, the Rio Grande Valley, Long Island, and southwestern Kansas. He determined flow velocities by injecting electrolytes in wells and observing their appearance in other wells. He also conducted laboratory experiments and concluded that dispersion rather than diffusion was responsible for the distribution of the solute (Water-Supply and Irrigation Paper No. 140). Thus, Slichter may be considered to have conducted the first research into contaminant transport by groundwater.

Slichter's highest earned degree was the B.S. from Northwestern University (1885). He spent his entire career from 1886–1934 at the University of Wisconsin, as instructor, assistant professor, professor, and Dean of the Graduate School. Slichter has been characterized as a reverent iconoclast. The second of Slichter's four sons was Louis Slichter (1896–1978), a highly honored geophysicist.

Especially important is the history of your own specialty.
Charles S. Slichter [1938, p. 161]

Introduction

The mathematical description of groundwater flow as a problem in potential theory was recognized by Charles Sumner Slichter and published by the United States Geological Survey in 1899 under the title "Theoretical Investigation of Ground-Water Motion." Slichter was a mathematics professor at the University of Wisconsin and was brought into the employ of the USGS for his mathematical expertise [*Slichter*, 1899, 1902, 1905*a,b*, 1906; *Slichter and Wolff*, 1906]. Slichter is occasionally cited as a geologist or earth scientist [*Hall*, 1954; *Sposito*, 1984], probably because he conducted his work under the auspices of the United States Geological Survey. His influence in the early history of soil physics has been cited by *Sposito* [1985] and *Gardner* [1986]. Slichter also contributed to solid earth geophysics [*Slichter*, 1898, 1909]. By profession, however, he was an applied mathematician; by temperament he was a scientist and engineer.

Slichter conducted numerous field studies of groundwater flow throughout the United States, including the Rio Grande, Garden City, Kansas, Long Island, and Los Angeles. Slichter formulated quantitative analyses of well hydraulics and recognized from laboratory experiments the principles of dispersive solute transport. These major contributions to groundwater hydrology were accomplished during a roughly 18-year period between 1894 and 1912. Although the primary focus in this paper will be on the hydrology period, other facets of Slichter's life will be included to give a fuller picture of this talented engineer/scientist. A book-length biography [*Ingraham*, 1972] has been written by a mathematical and administrative colleague of Slichter's. The fourth chapter

entitled "Scientist and Engineer" is rich in anecdotal material covering the period of Slichter's groundwater research.

Biographical Sketch

Charles Sumner Slichter was born April 16, 1864 in St. Paul, Minnesota. His family moved to Chicago in 1869. He attended the Oakland High School and then Northwestern University where he received a B.S. in mathematics in 1885. He was offered a temporary position as an instructor in the mathematics department at the University of Wisconsin in the fall of 1886. He became assistant professor in 1889 and professor in 1892. He became chairman of the mathematics department in 1902 and ultimately Dean of the Graduate School in 1920 until his retirement in 1934 (Figure 1). He died in 1946. He was the father of four sons, all of whom were successful in their own right. The eldest son Sumner was a distinguished economist at Harvard. His second son Louis was a professor of geophysics at MIT in the 1930's and founder of the Institute for Geophysics at UCLA after World War II. Louis was the winner of the American Geophysical Union's Bowie medal and was elected to the National Academy of Sciences in 1944. A grandson Charles is a physics professor at the University of Illinois. But this paper is not entitled the "Slichter Saga," so I return to my principal subject.

Slichter's teaching loads were high by modern standards. At the beginning of his career he was the second member of a two-man math department. Among the courses he taught over his career were basic freshmen courses in algebra, which he taught 40 times, and calculus, which he taught 48 times, as well as graduate courses in potential theory, which he taught 23 times, and theoretical mechanics, which he taught a record 79 times.

Mathematical Theory for Groundwater Flow

Slichter's most important contribution to groundwater

Fig. 1. Charles Sumner Slichter as Dean of the Graduate School [*Ingraham*, 1972].

hydrology was "Theoretical Investigation of the Motion of Ground Waters" published in 1899 as Part II of the 19th Annual Report of the United States Geological Survey. The first chapter contains a theoretical derivation for the hydraulic conductivity of a medium consisting of uniform spheres. In the second chapter Slichter concisely derived Laplace's equation to be the governing equation of groundwater flow. The third and fourth chapters contain specific solutions to horizontal and vertical flow problems, respectively. The concluding chapter deals with interference between artesian wells.

The impetus for Slichter's incursion into groundwater problems came around 1894 from Franklin Hiram King, a soil physicist in the College of Agriculture. King's paper, "Principles and Conditions of the Movements of Ground Water" immediately precedes Slichter's. It was probably Thomas C. Chamberlin who proposed Slichter's name for consultation with respect to groundwater flow problems [*Ingraham*, 1972]. Chamberlin was a geologist, President of the University of Wisconsin, and later professor at the University of Chicago where with F. Moulton he formulated the Chamberlin-Moulton planetesimal hypothesis for the formation of the solar system. Chamberlin published a very important, if qualitative, paper in 1885 on the geology of groundwater [*Chamberlin*, 1885]. Chamberlin and Slichter later corresponded on problems dealing with the rotation of the earth [*Slichter*, 1909].

Laplace's Equation

Slichter's [1899] own summary of the important second

chapter, "General Laws of the Flow for Ground Waters" is given in his introduction (p. 303):

> I investigate the general problem of the movements of water in soils and rock. I find that the problem is capable of mathematical treatment, and I show that the question is analogous to a problem in the conduction of heat or electricity, or to any other problem involving a transfer of energy. I show that there exists in the case of ground-water movements what is know as a potential function, from which we may derive, in any determinate problem, the velocity and direction of flow, and the pressure at every point of the soil or rock. The existence of the potential function is made the basis of much of the work that follows.

Within Chapter II itself, Slichter (p. 331) comments:

> It seems remarkable that the fact that the solution of any problem in the motion of groundwaters depends upon the solution of [Laplace's] equation has not been pointed out before.

As it turns out, Forchheimer published the derivation thirteen years earlier [*Hall*, 1954]. Slichter was apparently unaware of Forchheimer. His reference list contains papers by Boussinesq, Darcy, Dupuit, and A. Thiem, among others, but not Forchheimer. Furthermore, it is not clear which of these papers were read by Slichter for he says (p. 381):

> The following list of references contains not only title of papers that I have seen, but also includes the titles of about twenty papers which were inaccessible to me, but which are referred to by others as important.

Although Slichter was unaware of previous European work, his own work was to be cited in Europe. While in Munich on a year's sabbatical in 1909–1910, Slichter wrote to Charles Van Hise [*Ingraham*, 1972, p. 263]:

> The work I have done on Groundwaters and my connection with the Reclamation Service has been of the very greatest benefit to me, for I was amazed to find that I was known and my work summarized in their textbooks.

Despite the issue of priority, there is no doubt about the seminal influence that Slichter's 1899 paper exerted on subsequent groundwater research in both Europe and the United States.

Horizontal Flow Example

The influence of *Slichter*'s [1899] work probably stems from his clear exposition of how mathematics translate to field situations. Slichter used the established methods of Fourier integrals, conformal mappings, and images.

Slichter's opening example (Figure 2) is for boundary conditions along the x-axis such that pressure is zero for negative x and one for positive x. The pressure goes to zero at infinity. To give meaning to this problem, Slichter writes (p. 336):

> [W]e may suppose that there is a long ditch dug in a level region to the depth of the surface of the ground water, and divided by a dam O A. Water is maintained at a given height in the part O X, but the water is pumped out of the part O X', so that its level is reduced to the normal level of the ground water. The problem is to determine the flow from one ditch to the other through the surrounding soil.

The equipressure lines are spokes radiating from a point, and the flow lines are circles (Figure 3).

This example has obvious application to seepage loss from

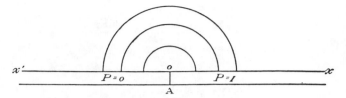

Fig. 2. Horizontal flow example [*Slichter*, 1899].

irrigation ditches, a major problem to which Slichter was to contribute in his work in southwestern Kansas.

Continuing on with this problem, Slichter (p. 338) utilizes the properties of conjugate functions.

> If we interchange the functions p and ψ, we produce an interesting problem which is the inverse of the given problem. In this case the straight lines converging toward O become the lines of flow and the circles become the lines of equal pressure. In this case we may imagine that the ground water is being "created" or "annihilated" at the point O, which point is then designated as a "source" or "sink."

Pressure as Velocity Potential

M. King Hubbert [1940, 1969] was critical of Slichter's use of pressure as the "velocity potential" for the flow. First, the total potential is the sum of a pressure potential and a gravitational potential. Second, the flow lines are not orthogonal to equipressure lines, even in a uniform medium, when a vertical flow component exists. *Hubbert's* [1969, p. 17] assessment of Slichter's work is that

> It is ironical that these two erroneous statements appear to have exercised far more influence upon subsequent writers than all of Slichter's very substantial positive accomplishments.

The basis for Hubbert's statements rests in Slichter's words rather than his equations because *Slichter* [1899, p. 331] specifically pointed out that

> If we assume that an external impressed force, as gravity, acts upon the liquid in the z direction with constant intensity g, and if the density of the fluid be ρ, then . . . the equations of motion with gravity acting are (except for sign [*Hubbert*, 1969, p. 15)])

$$u = \frac{dx}{dt} = k\frac{\partial p}{\partial x}$$

$$v = \frac{dy}{dt} = k\frac{\partial p}{\partial y}$$

$$w = \frac{dz}{dt} = k\frac{dp}{dz} + k\rho g.$$

> These hold, of course, only for the case of steady motion. [Continuity] and [Laplace's equation] are unchanged by the new hypothesis.

Slichter's next paragraph then contains the error.

> After p has been determined by appropriate solution of [Laplace's equation] for a given problem, the equation p = c will give, for different values of c, a series of surfaces upon each of which the pressure has the constant value assigned. These are the equipotential or equipressural surfaces. Orthogonal to this series of surfaces there exists a series of lines in space, along which the particles of liquid actually move. These lines are the lines of flow.

Perhaps Slichter was referring explicitly to horizontal flow. Also, as described in a footnote of *Hall's* [1954]:

> Slichter's publications were not clear about the distinction between pressure and piezometric head. He almost always spoke of "pressure," but clearly meant what is conventionally called piezometric head. On the other hand, equipressural lines appeared correctly identified in some of his drawings although he used the term interchangeably with "equipotential lines."

Vertical Flow Example

Despite the inclusion of the gravity term in his flow equations, *Slichter's* [1899] presentation of a vertical flow problem did not lead him to qualification of the pressure potential. Slichter's chapter on groundwater flow in a vertical plane consists of a single boundary value problem. The boundary conditions are

$$p = 0 \text{ at } x = 0 \text{ and } x = 2a$$

$$p = \text{h at } z = b$$

$$\text{and } w = 0 \text{ at } z = 0.$$

This problem was based on a conceptual model of a vertical tank whose bottom is impermeable and whose sides are seepage faces (Figure 4). The problem was solved for the pressure field by Fourier series, and the result differentiated for the velocity components u and w (Figure 5). Note that the gravity term was included in the vertical velocity component. The pressure field was contoured for the case p = 0 along the top surface (Figure 6). The left boundary in the figure represents the symmetry plane at x = a. My finite difference solution of this problem differed slightly from Figure 6. These results are the overprinted dashed lines. They are in agreement with Slichter's analytical solution when summed out to 21 terms. Slichter used only the first term.

Slichter's [1899, p. 354] interpretation of Figure 6 is based on the concept of pressure being the driving potential.

> A well sunk at M N would probably show an increasing depth of water as the well was dug deeper and deeper.

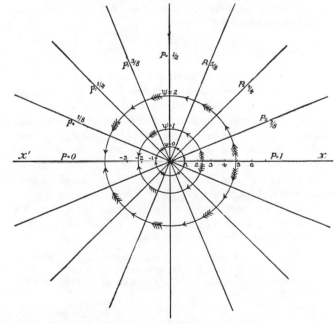

Fig. 3. Equipressure and flow lines for horizontal flow example [*Slichter*, 1899].

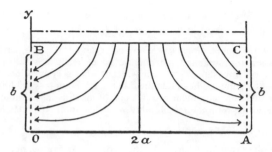

Fig. 4. Vertical flow example [*Slichter*, 1899].

If Slichter had calculated the flow field from his velocity components u and w, he would presumably have seen that the flow lines were not orthogonal to the pressure lines. Furthermore, the pressure lines themselves have gradients that certainly do not agree with intuition about the flow field. The schematic flow field shown in Figure 4 is incorrect because the flow lines converge at the bottom corners. Why with Figure 6 in front of him, did Slichter not recognize the importance of the ρg term in the vertical velocity component? That is a puzzle to me.

SOLUTE TRANSPORT

Water-Supply and Irrigation Paper No. 140 by *Slichter* [1905a] is entitled "Field Measurements of the Rate of Movement of Underground Waters." It contains a full description of direct measurements of groundwater velocity by the technique of salting an upstream well and recording its appearance in a downstream well. The method was applied first in the summer of 1901 along the Arkansas River near Garden City and Dodge City, Kansas. It was later applied in southern California and Long Island. Although intended for flow measurements, Slichter recognized the phenomenon of dispersion (although he did not use the term) from these tests and conducted laboratory studies that showed the essential shape of contaminant plumes [*Anderson*, 1984]. I speculate that Slichter had also formulated the theoretical description of solute transport, but never got around to writing it up.

Field Technique

The experimental configuration is shown in Figure 7. Each downstream well contained a four-foot brass electrode insulated by wooden spools from the well casing. An electric potential was supplied by a battery in series with an ammeter and connected to the well casing. The circuit was completed with the appearance of the electrolyte in the well. The current was recorded as a function of time. Some of the apparatus is shown in Figure 8. The perforated brass buckets were used to lower the electrolyte into the well.

Slichter not only enjoyed the scientific aspects of his groundwater studies, but he also relished the details of the field equipment. Thus, he tells us that

The 1½ inch drive wells are much preferable to the 1¼ inch wells because of the fact that 1½ inch pipe is lap welded, while the 1¼ inch is butt welded, and less capable of standing severe pounding.

And

A driving ram for putting down the drive wells should be about

$$u = \frac{2hk}{a} \sum_{n=1}^{n=\infty} \frac{\cosh \frac{n\pi z}{2a}}{\cosh \frac{n\pi b}{2a}} \cos \frac{n\pi x}{2a}$$

$$+ \frac{4g\rho k}{\pi} \sum_{n=1}^{n=\infty} \frac{1}{n} \frac{\sinh \frac{n\pi(b-z)}{2a}}{\cosh \frac{n\pi b}{2a}} \cos \frac{n\pi x}{2a},$$

$$w = \frac{2hk}{a} \sum_{n=1}^{n=\infty} \frac{\sinh \frac{n\pi z}{2a}}{\cosh \frac{n\pi b}{2a}} \sin \frac{n\pi x}{2a}$$

$$- \frac{4g\rho k}{\pi} \sum_{n=1}^{n=\infty} \frac{1}{n} \frac{\cosh \frac{n\pi(b-z)}{2a}}{\cosh \frac{n\pi b}{2a}} \sin \frac{n\pi x}{2a} + g\rho k.$$

Fig. 5. Infinite series solution for velocity components of vertical flow example [*Slichter*, 1899].

5½ feet long by 5½ inches in diameter, made of heavy oak or other tough wood, with iron bands shrunk on the ends, and bearing two handles of hard wood at each end in order to facilitate the handling of the ram by two men (Figure 9). It is convenient to have these handles placed one about 1 foot from one end, and the other about 2 feet from the other end. By reversing the ram the handles are brought in a more convenient position for driving as the well goes down.

A small nest of drive wells was placed in a typical field configuration as shown at the top of Figure 10. Sal ammoniac (ammonium chloride) was introduced in the upstream well A. The three downstream wells were placed in a fan shape and spaced to capture the electrolyte. The center well was placed along the expected flow line. Downstream distances between four and eight feet were used, the longer distances for higher velocities. Slichter describes the results.

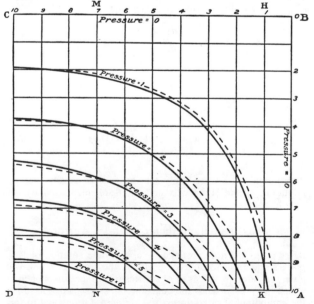

Fig. 6. Pressure field for vertical flow example. Solid lines [*Slichter*, 1899] are for the first term of the infinite series. Dashed lines are for a finite difference solution.

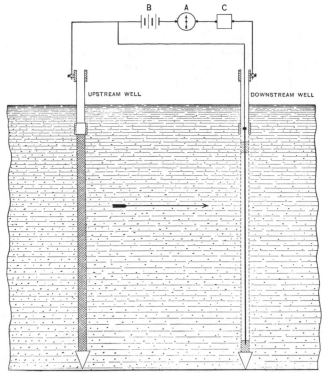

Fig. 7. Electrolyte technique for determining groundwater flow velocities [*Slichter, 1905a*].

The electrolyte does not appear at one of the downstream wells with very great abruptness; its appearance there is somewhat gradual, as shown in the dashed curve in (Figure 10). The time required for the electrolyte to reach its maximum strength in one of the downstream wells (and hence, for the current to reach its maximum value) may vary from a few minutes in a case of high ground-water velocity to several hours in a case of low velocity. The writer formerly supposed that the gradual appearance of the electrolyte at the downstream well was largely due to the diffusion of the dissolved salt but it is now evident that diffusion plays but a small part of the result.

The point of inflection M is used to determine the time of arrival of the electrolyte.

Slichter also recognized lateral dispersion.

Owing to the repeated branching and subdivision of the capillary pores around the grains of the sand or gravel, the stream of electrolyte issuing from the well will gradually broaden as it passes downstream.

A lay description of Slichter's method was recorded at a meeting of Town and Gown [*Ingraham, 1972, p. 63*], an eating club at which Slichter would regale its members with his exploits. Here are the minutes by a non-scientist.

The flow of this water exercised our speaker's ingenuity. He makes a pair of holes in the ground, puts some nasty stuff in the water of one, and makes his attendant drink from time to time the water of the other. Noting the expression of his face, he determines the moment when the water of one hole appears in the other, and ultimately its rate of progress—some 8–20 feet—or was it miles?—per diem.

Field Results

Slichter applied his techniques to measure groundwater flow velocities in several localities around the U.S. Several of his observations are of interest.

Slichter noticed at a station along the Rio Hondo that the current showed several step rises (Figure 11). He interpreted the result in terms of the vertical heterogeneity of aquifers [*Slichter, 1905a, p. 51*].

These indicate different velocities of ground water in the different strata penetrated by the wells. . . . [T]he different porous strata registered themselves on the brass gauze by blackened bands caused by the corroding influence of the electrolyte. In the present case there were three distinct zones marked off on the wells, of about 24, 20, and 8 inches each. The velocities in these strata undoubtedly differed from one another, and hence caused the steps in the ampere curve.

Slichter's field measurements on Long Island were on the south side between the villages of Freeport and Massapequa [*Slichter, 1905a, p. 65*].

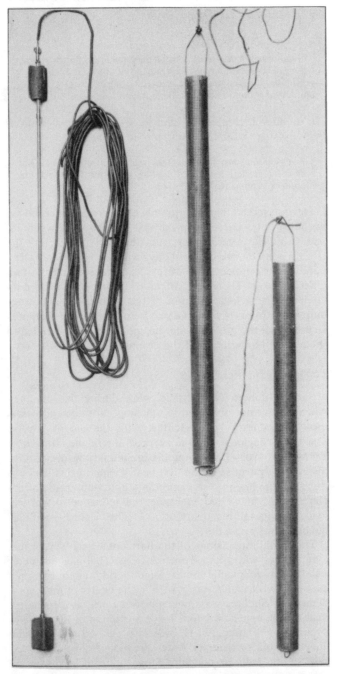

Fig. 8. Field apparatus for electrolyte technique [*Slichter, 1905a*].

Fig. 9.   Driving wells using oak ram [*Slichter, 1905a*].

The purpose of this work was to determine the principal facts concerning the underground drainage of the island, so that a preliminary basis could be secured for an estimate of the amount of ground water available for municipal supply.

He found velocities of 77 and 96 feet/day at two stations below storage ponds, causing him to remark:

These velocities are the highest the writer has determined. They may be regarded as record-making rates for the horizontal motion of ground waters.

He also observed that the groundwater carried a thermal tag to indicate its source. Typical well water was between 58° and 60°F. However, water from the wells just below the storage pond on two different days was 65.8° and 69.5°F. The pond water temperatures were 72.5° and 80°F on the two different days. Therefore, *Slichter* [1905a, pp. 78–79] concluded "that a large portion of the moving ground water must come directly from the pond, and the rate of motion is so great that the ground water has not time to be reduced to the normal temperature of the ground."

Laboratory Studies

Slichter conducted his field work during the summers when he was not obligated to teaching. Not content to idle away the school year Slichter, with the aid of several assistants, began a laboratory program in the winters of 1902–3 and 1903–4 following his preliminary field measurements. The purpose of the first year's experiments was "to ascertain the law of distribution in a horizontal plane of the electrolyte" and "to determine the influence of varying velocities upon this distribution." The second year was devoted to vertical flow.

The inside dimensions of the horizontal tank were 4 feet long, 4 feet wide, and 8 inches deep. Half-inch diameter "wells" were placed on a 6-inch grid and a two-inch diameter "salt well" was placed at the center of the upgradient end. Slichter was quite pleased to be able to adjust floats in the upper tank to achieve a gradient of 18 ft/mile to simulate field gradients. He was also pleased that formalin added to Lake Mendota water prevented clogging of the sand in the tank. He concluded that the formalin prevented the growth of organisms. The result of a typical experiment

is shown in Figure 12. A single well W was salted at 9:30 a.m. and the figure shows the resulting plume, relative to W, at five later times. The size of the circle represents the electrolyte concentration values and the approximate boundary of the plume is outlined. In this example the velocity was 13.2 ft/day.

One of the most remarkable conclusions from the experiments was that diffusion plays but a very small part in the spread of the electrolyte through the ground water. In none of the experiments was it found that the electrolyte extended more than about 3 inches upstream from the large well W. . . . In general, it can be seen that the electrolyte moves downstream in a pear-shaped mass, the width of the stream varying somewhat with the nature of the electrolyte used. The high velocities always gave a stream of electrolyte which was quite narrow and the low velocities gave broader streams.

The vertical tank experiments were carried out in the apparatus pictured in Figure 13. A very small linear water table gradient between 53 and 630 ft/mile was used. The plume for the experiment of February 22, 1904 is followed in a series of diagrams such as in Figure 14. The horizontal velocity was 17 ft/day. Slichter interpreted the elliptical outline of the plume to be "due to the two components of motion, one component being the velocity of ground water to the right, and the other being the downward motion, due to the high density of the solution of sal ammoniac."

Theory of Solute Transport?

The mass of field and laboratory data accumulated by Slichter's solute transport work obviously presented an opportunity to describe them mathematically. With Slichter's successful description of groundwater flow, why didn't he do the same for transport? I think he intended to and may even have known the result.

Slichter published a paper in 1911 entitled "The Mixing Effect of Surface Waves." This work treats mixing to be proportional to the amount of finite shear experienced by the liquid. The liquid motion is assumed to be low so that turbulence is absent. The next to last paragraph of that paper is quoted below.

Although the mixing effect in the slow motion of a liquid is a magnitude of low order, yet there are important cases of motion in which the migration of particles across the lines of flow is very great. An important case occurs in the motion of groundwater. It can be shown in this case that the movement of particles across the lines of flow equals about 30 per cent of the onward movement in the line of resultant motion. This means, for example, that impurities or contaminations are expanded or spread out over wide areas during the motion of underground waters. Diagrams showing some experimental manifestation of this fact will be found in Water Supply Paper No. 140 of the U.S. Geological Survey, pp. 22–68. The consideration of the mixing, or spread of contaminations, in groundwaters lead to the statement of a very general problem of much interest, which the writer will consider in another place.

He never published this intention. I have looked through the archives of Slichter's papers and have found no draft manuscript. However, the typewritten copy contained the words "will take up at another time" which he changed to "will consider in another place." Why did he edit these words? Had he actually considered the problem between when he turned in his handwritten copy to when he received the typewritten copy?

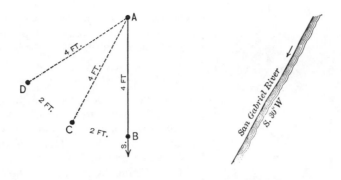

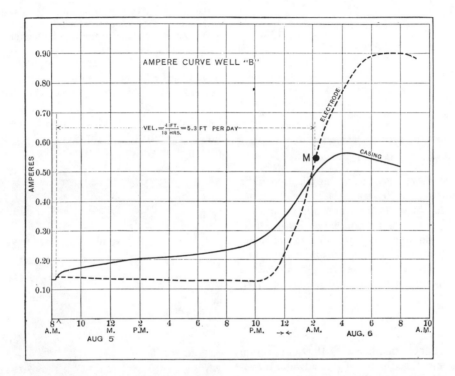

Fig. 10.   Fan geometry for well layout and typical electrical current data [*Slichter*, 1905a]. The curve labeled "casing" is the current flowing between the casing of the upstream well and the casing of the downstream well. The curve labeled "electrode" is the current flowing between the casing and electrode of the downstream well.

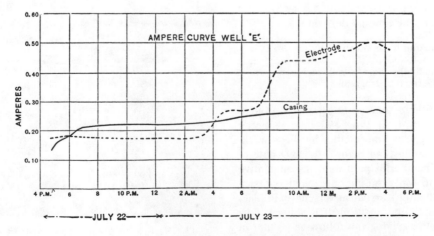

Fig. 11.   Multiple inflection points of electrolyte arrival [*Slichter*, 1905a].

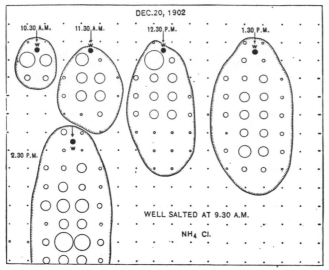

Fig. 12. Electrolyte plume in a horizontal tank [*Slichter*, 1905a]. "W" marks the salted well. Areas of circles are proportional to strength of electrolyte found at their centers.

WELL HYDRAULICS

Flow to wells can be viewed as a specific application of the general governing equations with appropriate boundary conditions. The importance of wells for water supply and the practical aspects of well construction have led to their special consideration. Slichter was interested in the many facets of well hydraulics—drilling, yield, casing, pumps, and economics. These aspects of wells are treated as separate chapters in each of Slichter's major publications of 1899, 1902, and 1905a.

Theory

The fifth and final chapter of Slichter's 1899 publication that set forth the mathematical theory of groundwater movement is entitled "Flow of Artesian Wells and their Mutual Interference." Slichter derives the basic well flow equations from Darcy's law and the reasoning

that the velocity toward the well must vary inversely with the distance from the axis of the well, since the circumferences of concentric circles with their centers on the axis of the well are crossed by equal amounts of ground water in equal times.

A footnote in his 1902 review paper indicates he was not aware of Thiem's work at the time he derived it.

This formula [Thiem equation] was obtained by the writer in 1892. While the paper referred to [1899] was in press he discovered that substantially the same formula had been previously worked out by a German hydrographer.

Ingraham [1972] places the beginning of Slichter's groundwater research around 1894. If the 1892 date is not a typographical error, it suggests that Slichter had been working on the problem for some time before the 1899 date of publication. Because Chamberlin published his qualitative works on groundwater in 1885, the impetus may have been present any time from Slichter's arrival at Wisconsin in 1886.

Slichter considered the superposition of a uniform flow field and a pumping well, deriving the following picture of the flow lines (Figure 15). This same picture appears in

Hubbert's [1940] paper. Also in Chapter V, *Slichter* [1899] superposed two wells and as befits a mathematician he superposed *n* wells.

Specific Capacity

Slichter was interested in the question of well performance. The final three chapters of his 1905a paper that dealt primarily with underground flow were entitled "The Specific Capacity of Wells," "The California or 'Stovepipe' Method of Well Construction for Water Supply," and "Tests of Typical Pumping Plants." *Slichter* [1905a, p. 86] defined the specific capacity of a well as

the amount of water furnished under a standard unit head, or the amount of water furnished under unit lowering of the surface of the water in the well by pumping.

Following this definition is a quaint discussion of units, including the "California miner's inch being one-fiftieth of a second-foot (cubic foot per second), and hence of a very convenient size for the measurement of well capacity." In the next sentence Slichter backs down from endorsing this unit. "However, the different values of the miner's inch prevalent in various sections of the country make this unit of

Fig. 13. Vertical tank for solute transport experiment [*Slichter*, 1905a].

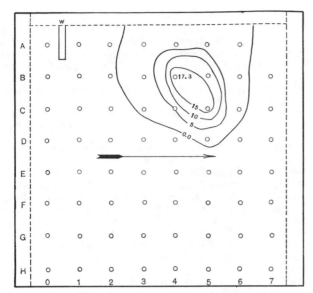

Fig. 14. Electrolyte plume in a vertical tank [*Slichter*, 1905a].

measure undesirable for general use." Slichter was also an astute observer of human nature. After stating that aquifer properties are usually uniform in a given locality, he notes that the discovery

> [T]hat neighboring wells, similarly constructed, yield very different amounts of water, or that water can not be obtained a short distance from a good well, . . . always causes considerable comment, while the numerous cases in which groundwater is found at very uniform depths and in nearly identical material call forth no comment whatever.

Slichter gives the theoretical law for transient rise in well level after cessation of pumping to be

$$t = (A/c) \ln (h/H)$$

where A = area of cross section of the well casing
  H = initial depression of the well level
  c = specific capacity
and h = depression of the well level at time t.

Slichter evidently arrived at this equation by a mass balance whereby dh = (ch/A) dt. Neither the Theis recovery method nor the governing equation for transient flow is foreshadowed in Slichter's treatment. Nevertheless, Slichter's application of the specific capacity concept to actual well data was sufficient for him to discover a well that "showed an expensive waste of gasoline through a hidden leak in the feed pipe" [*Slichter*, 1905a, p. 91].

CONSULTANT AND EXPERT WITNESS

All of Slichter's work for the USGS was done on a WAE (While Actually Employed) basis. The per diem rate was $7/day in 1903 at a time when Slichter's university salary was roughly $16/day and his private consulting rate was $20/day. He also testified as an expert witness. We can picture his aplomb on the witness stand from a letter to his son Sumner in 1922 [*Ingraham*, 1972, p. 101].

> I had a fine time on the stand and had a lot of fun with the lawyers because they were so ignorant of underground waters. The judge is a fine able fellow and enjoys a joke very much, and I had a good many chances to cheer him up. The jury had not heard a joke for three weeks. The lawyer on cross examination asked me the ultimate origin of all waters—rivers, lakes, and springs. He wanted me to say "the rain." I said "the seas." He

then said, "Isn't the ultimate source the rainfall?" I then quoted: "God said, let the waters be gathered together in one place, and the gathering together of the waters called He the sea; and the morning and evening were the third day." The jury roared. He was then foolish enough to read from one of my publications where I said that the source of all surface and subterrane waters was the rainfall. He asked me if that were not true. I said "Who said that." He said, very decisively, "Slichter." I then said, "I have quoted what God said. You have quoted what Slichter said. There is a conflict of authority." I waited a minute, until they had laughed several minutes, and then said, "Slichter is right." I had no trouble with the jury after that.

CLUBS AND ORGANIZATIONS

I found a letter to Slichter from the AGU in 1942 that granted him active membership without payment of dues according to a policy that applied to retired members with 15 years of previous AGU membership. But the AGU should not feel too proud to claim Slichter's membership for he was a joiner. He was active in the American Mathematical Society. He was active in the Chaos Club, a midwestern spoof of the Cosmos Club of Washington. But the Town and Gown Club and the Madison Literary Club were the ones

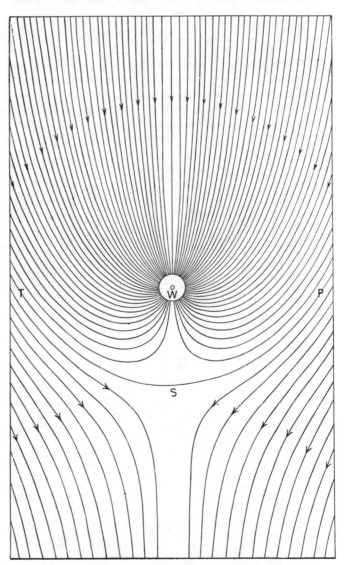

Fig. 15. Flow to a well in the presence of a horizontal gradient [*Slichter*, 1899].

that meant the most to Slichter. His neighbors Charles Van Hise, the geologist, University President, and President of the National Academy of Sciences [*Vance, 1960*], and Frederick Jackson Turner, the American historian who developed the frontier hypothesis [*Billington, 1973*], were members. The Madison Literary Club required presentation of formal papers and Slichter gave one about every five years. Because he was interested in clubs and eating, one of his papers was on the Royal Society Club, also known as the Royal Philosophers. To give you an idea of his literary style, I quote the opening sentences of the essay.

> Not all the heavy eaters and hard drinkers of past centuries have been poets and dramatists, or literary fellows. I propose to show that the men who led scientific progress in England during the seventeenth and eighteenth centuries were men who could and did eat and drink with almost as much gusto as did Shakespeare, Ben Jonson, Marlowe, Donne, Dekker, Dr. Johnson, Boswell, and other luminaries of literature and the arts.

A number of these essays were gathered together in book form under the title *Science in a Tavern*. In the essay "Self-training of a Teacher" Slichter says "Especially important is the history of your own specialty." So I think Slichter would have approved of this *History of Hydrology* volume. In this same essay Slichter wrote the words:

> We are all mentioned in the wills of Homer and Shakespeare.

These now immortal words are blasted into the granite facing of the Memorial Library at the University of Wisconsin.

Another essay in the volume is entitled "Polymaths." A polymath is a scientist for whom knowledge has no compartments. Slichter was a polymath whose will included groundwater hydrology.

REFERENCES

Anderson, M. P., Movement of Contaminants in Groundwater: Groundwater Transport—Advection and dispersion, in *Groundwater Contamination*, pp. 37–45, National Academy Press, Washington, D.C., 1984.

Billington, R. A., *Frederick Jackson Turner; historian, scholar, teacher*, 599 pp., Oxford, 1973.

Chamberlin, T. C., The requisite and qualifying conditions of artesian wells, Fifth Annual Report, United States Geological Survey, 131–173, 1885.

Gardner, W. H., Early soil physics into the mid-20th century, in *Advances in Soil Science*, Vol. 4, edited by B. A. Stewart, pp. 1-101, Springer-Verlag, New York, 1986.

Hall, H. P., A historical review of investigations of seepage toward wells, Journal of the Boston Society of Civil Engineers, *41*, 251–311, 1954.

Hubbert, M. K., The theory of ground-water motion, Journal of Geology, *48*, 785–944, 1940.

Hubbert, M. K., Introduction to *The Theory of Ground-Water Motion and Related Papers*, pp. 9–23, Hafner Publishing, New York and London, 1969.

Ingraham, M. H., *Charles Sumner Slichter*, 316 pp., The University of Wisconsin Press, Madison, 1972.

Slichter, C. S., Theoretical investigation of the motion of ground waters, 19th Annual Report, Part II, United States Geological Survey, 295–384, 1899. Chapter 2 reprinted in *Physical Hydrogeology, Benchmark Papers in Geology*, V. 72, edited by R. A. Freeze and W. Back, pp. 21–25, Hutchinson Ross, Stroudsburg, Pennsylvania, 1983, and *Ground Water, 23*, 396–397, 1985.

Slichter, C. S., The Motions of Underground Waters, Water-Supply and Irrigation Paper No. 67, United States Geological Survey, 106 pp., 1902.

Slichter, C. S., Field Measurements of the Rate of Movement of Underground Waters, Water-Supply and Irrigation Paper No. 140, United States Geological Survey, 122 pp., 1905a.

Slichter, C. S., Observations on the Ground Waters of Rio Grande Valley, 1904, Water-Supply and Irrigation Paper No. 141, United States Geological Survey, 83 pp., 1905b.

Slichter, C. S., The Underflow in Arkansas Valley in Western Kansas, Water-Supply and Irrigation Paper No. 153, United States Geological Survey, 90 pp., 1906.

Slichter, C. S., The rotation period of a heterogeneous spheroid, *Annual Report of the Director Geophysical Laboratory, 5*, 171, 1909.

Slichter, C. S., The mixing effect of surface waves, *Annals of Mathematics*, Second Series, *12*, 170–178, 1911.

Slichter, C. S., *Science in a Tavern*, 186 pp., The University of Wisconsin Press, Madison, 1938.

Slichter, C. S., and H. C. Wolff, The Underflow of the South Platte Valley, Water-Supply and Irrigation Paper No. 184, United States Geological Survey, 42 pp., 1906.

Sposito, G., Buckingham, Richards, and the Leipzig Connection: The beginnings of soil water physics, *Trans. AGU, 65*, 875, 1984.

Sposito, G., Concepts of transient water flow in soil physics, *Trans. AGU, 66*, 880, 1985.

Vance, M. M., *Charles Richard Van Hise; scientist progressive*, 246 pp., The State Historical Society of Wisconsin, Madison, 1960.

H. F. Wang, Department of Geology and Geophysics, University of Wisconsin, Madison, WI 53706.

Contributions of Robert E. Horton

Francis R. Hall

Department of Earth Sciences, University of New Hampshire

Robert Elmer Horton (1875–1945) is probably best remembered by the hydrologic community for his work in infiltration that led to the concept of "Hortonian" overland flow and for his contribution to quantitative geomorphology. Modern texts in hydrology still contain references to his work which now is more than 40 years old. Obviously, he is also remembered for the Horton Award, Medal, and Research Grant which are made possible by the Robert E. Horton Fund of the American Geophysical Union. As impressive as these contributions seem, they would appear to be merely the tip of the iceberg for a professional career that covered nearly 50 years from around the turn of the century until his death in 1945 with posthumous papers appearing in 1948 and 1949. He was author or co-author of over 80 papers that were published in a number of leading journals, and he regularly participated in discussion or letters to the editor sections. He was on the founding committee of the Hydrology Section of the AGU, and he was an active member thereafter. Horton was impressive not only for the breadth of his interests in the rainfall-runoff process but also for his ability to bring quantitative skills to bear on problems that arose. A brief sampling of his publications more or less in chronological order from 1903 to 1949 includes: base-flow analysis, evaporation, snow, rainfall and estimates of water yield, interception, transpiration, history of hydrology, drainage-basin characteristics, infiltration, overland flow, ground-water levels, stream-channel storage, erosion, flood waves, capillarity, and physics of rain and thunderstorms.

INTRODUCTION

Robert Horton (1875–1945) was active in the field of water resources for about a half a century from his first publication in 1896 until his death in 1945 with posthumous papers appearing in 1948 and 1949. In fact, he has been called the father of American hydrology. He made significant contributions as shown by over 80 publications (see Bibliography at end of chapter) and many consulting reports in hydraulic engineering, meteorology, hydrology, and geology. He is probably best remembered today for his work on infiltration leading to the concept of what is commonly called "Hortonian" or "Horton" overland flow and for his work in developing quantitative geomorphology.

Horton appeared to consider himself simply as a civil or hydraulic engineer, but his effectiveness as an engineer and scientist and as an inspiration for young workers are brought out well by Leopold in his Robert E. Horton Lecture to the American Meteorological Society [*Leopold*, 1974] and by Theis in his acceptance of the Robert E. Horton Medal from the American Geophysical Union [*Theis*, 1984]. Both men encountered Horton early in their careers and knew him over the years. He is still a force to be reckoned with in hydrology some 40 years after his death as can be seen by examining recent texts [for example, *Dingman*, 1984] and articles [for example, *Ward*, 1984]. He is also remembered by the American Geophysical Union through the Horton Award, Horton Medal, and Horton Research Grant [*Eagleson*, 1984; *Freeze*, 1984] and by the American Meteorological Society through the Robert E. Horton Lecture Series [*Leopold*, 1974].

His diverse interests along with his extensive list of publications makes it difficult to do justice to Horton in one article. Therefore, I have chosen to give a brief sketch of his life and career and to emphasize his work in hydrology.

BIOGRAPHICAL SKETCH

The information in this section comes mainly from *American Men of Science* (now *American Men and Women of Science*) [*Cattell and Brimhall*, 1982; *Cattell*, 1944] and *Who Was Who in America* [*Anonymous*, 1950] with some material from *Lepold* [1974] and *Theis* [1984]. The first two items are of interest because they undoubtedly were prepared by Horton himself whereas the remaining items show how he was viewed by others. Also, I obtained material about Horton from the Stockwell Memorial Library of Albion College and from the American Geophysical Union.

Robert Elmer Horton was born May 18, 1875 in Parma, Michigan the son of Van Rensselaer W. and Rowena Spencer (Rafter) Horton. He received a bachelor's degree (B. Sc.) from Albion College, Albion, Michigan in 1897, and on June 6, 1932 he received an honorary doctorate (Sc. D.) from the same institution. He was cited for being. . . "brilliant student of engineering and related subjects. . . ." He had high regard for Albion College as shown in 1931, when he donated a number of technical books and some volumes of essays to its Library. These now appear to be in the Horton Collection in the Physics Department. He married Ella H. Young on June 19, 1901, and they were long time residents of Voorheesville, New York. They had no children. Horton died April 22, 1945 of a heart attack. Mrs. Horton died in 1971 [*Leopold*, personal communication, 1985]. Horton left the larger part of his estate to the American Geophysical Union after the death of Mrs. Horton. There were other legacies too. He also left his papers to the American Geophysical Union, and they were placed in the National Archives. Apparently, the American Geophysical Union provided starting funds for the journal *Water Resources Research* knowing that the Horton funds would be coming.

Horton actually began his professional career before graduating from college as he co-authored a paper with his uncle, George W. Rafter in 1896 [*Rafter and Horton*, 1896]. Rafter was a well known hydraulic engineer who was active in New

York State. Rafter had considerable influence on his nephew both in his choice of career and where he chose to begin work. Also, he found or helped Horton find employment in his own field, and Horton moved to New York after graduation. Much of Horton's professional work was in the northeastern United States.

Below, I summarize his career, but a few preliminary comments may be helpful. Soon after moving to New York or perhaps while he was still in college he began work on his well known weir and water wheel experiments which were completed while he was with the U. S. Geological Survey. During some of this period he worked at Cornell University and resided in Ithaca [*Wilfried Brutsaert*, personal communication, 1984]. Subsequently, Horton took up residency in Albany and then later in Voorheesville where he founded the Horton Hydrologic Laboratory probably in the 1920's. The Laboratory was located on eighty acres complete with stream, waterfalls, and an old mill. At about this time or perhaps earlier he also began a long association with H.R. Leach, Richard Van Vlict and George W. Cook. Others, including C.O. Wisler and perhaps S.W. Jens also worked with him at the Laboratory. Finally, after working with state and federal agencies for about thirteen years he became a private consultant for the rest of his life.

I have compiled a summary of Horton's professional career from the sources listed at the beginning of this section. There are a few inconsistencies in dates that I have not been able to reconcile. For example, he is listed as Director/Proprietor of the Horton Hydrological Laboratory from 1942 on whereas the Laboratory was in existence by the 1920's.

Assistant, U. S. Board of Engineers on Deep Waterways, 1898–1899, Ithaca

District Engineer of the New York District, U. S. Geological Survey, 1900–1906, Albany

Engineer in Charge, Bureau of Hydraulics, New York State Barge Canal, 1906–1911

Consulting Practice, 1911–1945, with office in Albany

Hydraulic Expert, Department of Public Works and Attorney General's Department, State of New York, 1911–1925

Lecturer in hydraulic engineering, Michigan, 1914

Engineer in Charge, Delaware River case before U.S. Supreme Court for State of New Jersey, 1922–1930

Consulting Engineer, Board of Water Supply, Albany, New York, 1924–1932

Consulting Engineer, The Power Authority, State of New York, 1932–1933

Member, Advisory Council of Federal Board of Surveys and Maps, 1918–1939

Member, Engineering Board of Review, Sanitary District of Chicago, 1925–1927

Engineer Consultant, National Resources Commission, 1934–1937

Consultant, U.S. Soil Conservation Service, 1939–1941

Consultant, City of Rochester, New York, 1942–1943

Director/Proprietor, Horton Hydrological Laboratory, 1942–1945, Voorheesville

It is interesting to note that during his period with the Soil Conservation Service Horton was associated with or in charge of such prominent engineers and hydrologists as L.K. Sherman, W.W. Horner, H.L. Cook, R.A. Hertzler, L. Glymph, E. Flaxmore, and L.B. Leopold [*Leopold*, personal communication, 1985].

Horton was very active in professional societies not only by membership but by participation in society affairs and in printed discussions of published papers. In fact, some of Horton's better contributions were made in this way. Fortunately, his career came during a time when printed discussions were an important mechanism for scientific advance. In addition to the organizations listed by the sources I have used, I believe Horton was a member of two other organizations I have marked with question marks.

American Society of Civil Engineers
American Water Works Association
New England Water Works Association
American Geophysical Union (A founder of the Hydrology Section)
Institution of Civil Engineers (London)
Institution of Water Engineers (England)
American Meteorological Society (Fellow; President, 1939)
Royal Meteorological Society
American Geographical Society
Geological Society of America (?)
American Association for the Advancement of Science (?)

Robert Horton led an active life outside of professional affairs. For example, he wrote a book of stories called "Apples from Eden" in 1938 which was published by Christopher and sold for $2.00. He was the inventor of a water-level gauge and of a joint for wood stave pipe. He was a member of the Sigma Nu social fraternity, and he listed his political affiliation as Republican!

CONTRIBUTIONS

Before discussing Horton's contributions, I think it worthwhile to briefly consider how he approached things. In many ways, Horton was a problem solver who used empirical relationships as necessary. Nevertheless, he was deeply interested in the processes that were involved. He also appreciated good data. In what in many ways was the qualitative age of hydrology, he liked quantitative methods. In fact, he encouraged others to use mathematical approaches as is indicated by *Theis* [1984]. For example, Theis notes that his U.S.G.S. superior, O.E. Meinzer, was not very appreciative of his quantitative efforts until Horton complimented Theis on his results in the presence of Meinzer. A frustrating characteristic of Horton, however, is that although he utilized equations in publications often he neither derived them nor gave a source. For example, he did graphical base-flow analysis in 1903, and he presented the exponential decay equation for base-flow analysis in 1914 [*Horton*, 1903; *Horton*, 1914]. Also, by 1914 he had used or had derived a nonlinear equation for base-flow separation which is sometimes called the Horton double exponential [*Horton*, 1933a]. In neither case did he give any details about how these relationships were obtained [*Hall*, 1968].

An instructive aspect of Horton's work is that few of his significant papers, particularly those of his later years, came out full blown for the first time. They had precursors, as shown by discussions of published papers of others or as earlier papers of his own some extending back over 20 years. Clearly, he developed his ideas early, and then returned to them as time and inclination permitted. I have attempted to summarize by topic some of his more significant contributions, and I have indicated the approximate range of publication dates for them. He also published on some aspects of topics such as ground water, capillarity, deforestation, erosion, and conservation that I have not listed.

Base flow, 1903–1935
Weirs and water wheels, 1906–1916
Stream channels and hydraulics, 1914–1941
Rainfall-runoff and snow melt, 1914–1945
Infiltration, 1933–1945
Evaporation, transpiration, interception, 1914–1943
"Hydrophysical" drainage basin development, 1921–1945
Floods, 1921–1938
Physics of rain, 1921–1949

Clearly, much of his work was concerned with the major components of the rainfall-runoff process; so it might be argued that there should really only be one major topic. This is true in the broad sense, but it does not help much in understanding how he did things. I believe, however, that his ideas and interests evolved as he solved each specific problem. Then, because of his strong interest in determining and quantifying the physical processes that were involved, he would begin to develop a broader synthesis that would appear in his later works. His work in hydraulics (weirs, water wheels, and some aspects of stream channels) and physics of rain seem to more or less stand on their own although the latter is part of the rainfall-runoff process.

His approach can be illustrated along the following lines. Some of Horton's earliest work was with low flow or base flow of selected streams in New York in which he developed and utilized typical separation techniques [Horton, 1903]. He also realized that ground water was the major source of this kind of runoff. By 1914, he expressed a broader interest in water yield during periods of minimal flow as shown by his discussion of the New England Water Works Association Committee on Yield of Drainage Basins [Horton, 1914]. Then in his discussion of a paper by Meyers on computing runoff he demonstrated that he had put considerable thought into the entire rainfall-runoff process [Horton, 1915].

Horton realized early in his work that the physical characteristics of drainage basins were also important for determining runoff. He introduced the idea of what now would be called quantitative geomorphology but which he called "hydrophysical" in a discussion of the probable variation of annual precipitation [Horton, 1921, as noted in Leopold, 1974]. Leopold also indicates that Horton carried his ideas further in a discussion of a paper by Jarvis on flood flow characteristics [Horton, 1926]. He followed this with a paper on drainage basin characteristics [Horton, 1932] and then produced his classic paper on the erosional development of streams and drainage basins [Horton, 1945]. Therefore, at least 21 years of thinking, testing ideas, and experience went into the final work. Roberts and Cobb [1973] published an interesting follow up to his 1945 paper.

Horton pursued other aspects of the rainfall-runoff process in a series of papers in the 1920's and 1930's with an important contribution being his work on infiltration [Horton, 1933a]. He proposed an exponential relationship that decayed to a limiting value during rainfall. Then he concluded that if rainfall intensity were greater than the limiting value as he thought was likely there would be substantial overland flow. Also, it seemed likely that this would take place over most if not all of the drainage basin. Subsequent work has shown that this is not generally the case in humid regions with which Horton was most concerned [Ward, 1984]. Nevertheless, his concept is still used in practical engineering, and it is incorporated in one way or another in many modern mathematical models for simulating runoff.

Many of Horton's ideas on the rainfall-runoff process seemed well established by the time he published his small book on surface runoff phenomena as Publication 101 of the Horton Hydrological Laboratory [Horton, 1935]. This probably should be called a classic, but unfortunately it is not readily available. This also appears to be the only one in the series put out by the Laboratory although other work was published elsewhere.

Robert Horton had other interests in hydrology as shown by his co-authorship of a paper on the origin of springs and ground water [Baker and Horton, 1936]. He also discovered the relationship of mean stream velocity at 0.6 depth [Veatch et al., 1906, as noted by Leopold, 1974]. He was much concerned with the nature of and the direction of hydrology as shown by his participation on the committee to form the Hydrology Section of the American Geophysical Union [Leopold, 1974] and a 1931 paper related to that endeavor [Horton, 1931]. He also emphasized the importance of vegetation [Horton, 1933b], soils [Horton, 1937a], and hydrologic research in general [Horton, 1937b], and he should be given recognition for his important study on the hydrology of the Great Lakes [Horton, 1927].

Acknowledgments. I am grateful to Luna Leopold for sending me a copy of his 1974 Horton Lecture for the American Meteorological Society and for personal communications. Meridith Ann Compton kindly provided information from the files of the American Geophysical Union, and Marilyn Simons of the Stockwell Memorial Library of Albion College was most helpful in sending material from college records. Allen T. Hjelmfelt, Jr. shared the list of references for Horton that he has compiled, and he provided copies of three hard to find publications that Horton did in cooperation with the Soil Conservation Service. Wilfried Brutsaert also told me about Horton's time at Cornell. A reviewer provided additional references and made helpful comments that have improved the text.

REFERENCES

Anonymous, editor, *Who was Who in America*, 2, p. 263, The A.N. Marquis Company, Chicago, Illinois, 1950.

Baker, M.N. and R.E. Horton, Historical development of ideas regarding the origin of springs and ground-water, *EOS-Transactions American Geophysical Union*, 17, 395–400, 1936.

Cattell, J.M. [Ed.], *American Men of Science*, 7th edition, p. 371, The Science Press, Garrison, New York, 1944.

Cattell, J.M. and D.R. Brimhall [Eds.], *American Men of Science*, 3rd edition, p. 847, The Science Press, Garrison, New York, 1921.

Dingman, S.L., *Fluvial Hydrology*, 383 p., W.H. Freeman and Company, New York, 1984.

Eagleson, P.S., Horton: Award, Medal, and Grant, *EOS*, 65, 66, 1984.

Freeze, R.A., AGU Hydrology Awards, Horton, Horton, and Horton, *EOS*, 65, 1178, 1984.

Hall, F.R., Base-flow recessions,—A review, *Water Resources Research*, 4, 973–983, 1968.

Horton, R.E., in *Annual Report of the State Engineer and Surveyor of New York*, supplement, p. 16, 1903.

Horton, R.E., Discussion of report of Committee on Yield of Drainage Areas, *Journal New England Water Works Association*, 28, 536–542, 1914.

Horton, R.E., Discussion of paper by Meyer on Computing Runoff from Rainfall and other Physical Data, *Transactions American Society of Civil Engineers*, 79, 1056–1224, 1915. [Horton's discussion was originally published in 77, 369–375, 1914].

Horton, R.E., Discussion of the probable variation in yearly precipitation, *Transactions American Society of Civil Engineers*, 1921.

Horton, R.E., Discussion of paper by Jarvis of flood flow characteristics, *Transactions American Society of Civil Engineers*, 89, 1081–1086, 1926.

Horton, R.E. in collaboration with C.E. Grunsky, *Hydrology of the Great Lakes*, Report of the Engineering Board of Review of the

Sanitary District of Chicago on the Lake Lowering Controversy and a Program of Remedial measures, Part III, Append. II, 432, p., 1927.

Horton, R.E., 1931, The field, scope and the status of the science of hydrology, *EOS-Transactions American Geophysical Union*, *13*, 350–361, 1932.

Horton, R.E., The role of infiltration in the hydrologic cycle, *EOS-Transactions American Geophysical Union*, *14*, 446–460, 1933a.

Horton, R.E., The relation of hydrology to the botanical sciences, *EOS-Transactions American Geophysical Union*, *14*, 23–25, 1933b.

Horton, R.E., *Surface runoff phenomena, Part I, Analysis of the hydrograph*, 73 p. Publication 101, Horton Hydrological Laboratory, Voorheesville, NY [published by Edwards Brothers, Inc., Ann Arbor, Michican] 1935.

Horton, R.E., Hydrologic interrelations of water and soils, *Proceedings Soil Science Society of America*, *1*, 401–429, 1937a.

Horton, R.E., Hydrologic research, *Science*, *86*, 527–530, 1937b.

Horton, R.E., Erosional development of streams and their drainage basins, *Bulletin Geological Society of America*, *56*, 275–370, 1945.

Leopold, L.B., Great ideas, great problems, The Robert E. Horton Lecture, Honolulu, 1974, *Bulletin American Meteorological Society*, *55*, 424–426, 1974.

Rafter, George and R.E. Horton, a report for the New York State Engineer and Surveyor, p. 424, 1896.

Roberts, M.C., and D.A. Cobb, Horton's 1945 study—A cartobibliography, *Bulletin Geological Society of America*, *84*, 2733–2736, 1973.

Theis, C.V., 1984, Robert E. Horton Medal to C.V. Theis- Acceptance, *EOS*, *65*, 436–437, 1984.

Veatch, A.C., C.S. Slichter, Isaiah Bowman, W.O. Crosby, and R.E. Horton, *Underground water resources of Long Island, New York*, 394 p., U.S. Geological Survey Professional Paper 44, 1906.

Ward, R.C., On the response to precipitation of head water streams in humid areas, *Journal of Hydrology*, *74*, 171–189, 1984.

BIBLIOGRAPHY

ailThis represents a fairly comprehensive but incomplete bibliography for Robert E. Horton. For example, it includes only a few consulting reports and a few abstracts. Also, some of his papers, particularly earlier ones, may have been missed because he published in so many places. In addition, there are likely to be errors in titles and page numbers because of the various sources I have used. His obituary in *Who Was Who* for 1950 notes a series of annual reports on hydrography of New York, 1900–1911, which I have not listed. Also, the obituary mentions a paper on determination of stream flow during the frozen season with H.K. Burrows in 1907 and one on rainfall, runoff, and evaporation with L.K. Sherman in 1933, and I have not found either one. Finally, I have not listed his book of stories "Apples from Eden", 1938.

Baker, M.N., and R.E. Horton, Historical development of ideas regarding the origin of springs and ground water, *EOS-Transactions American Geophysical Union*, *17*, 395–400, 1936.

Beutner, E.L., R.R. Gaebe, and R.E. Horton, Sprinkled plot runoff and infiltration experiments on Arizona desert soils, *EOS-Transactions American Geophysical Union*, *21*, 550–558, 1940.

Horton, R.E., in *Annual Report of the State Engineer and Surveyor of New York, Supplement*, p. 16, 1903.

Horton, R.E., Turbine water-wheel tests and power tables, *U.S. Geological Survey Water Supply and Irrigation Paper No. 180*, 1906.

Horton, R.E., Weir experiments, coefficients and formulas, *U.S. Geological Survey Water Supply and Irrigation Paper 150*, 1906.

Horton, R.E., Weir experiments, coefficients and formulas [revised and republished], *U.S. Geological Survey Water Supply and Irrigation Paper 200*, 1907.

Horton, R.E., Deforestation, drainage, and tillage, with special reference to their effect on Michigan streams, *The Michigan Engineer*, 176–194, 1908.

Horton, R.E., Ebermayer's experiments on forest meteorology, *The Michigan Engineer*, 156–180, 1911.

Horton, R.E., Flood frequency and flood control, *Engineering News Record*, *68*, 505–506, 1913.

Horton, R.E., Discussion of Report of Committee on Yield of Drainage Areas, *Journal New England Water Works Association*, *28*, 536–542, 1914.

Horton, R.E., Evaporation from snow, *Monthly Weather Review*, *42*, 99, 1914.

Horton, R.E., Discussion of paper by A.F. Meyer on Computing Runoff from Rainfall and other Physical data, *Transactions American Society of Civil Engineers*, *79*, 1166–1173, 1915. [Originally published in *77*, 369–375, 1914.]

Horton, R.E., The melting of snow, *Monthly Weather Review*, *43*, 599–605, 1915.

Horton, R.E., Standing-wave experiment, *Engineering News Record*, *75*, 658, 1916.

Horton, R.E., Some better Kutter's formula coefficients, *Engineering News Record*, *75*, 373–374, 1916.

Horton, R.E., A new evaporation formula developed, *Engineering News Record*, *78*, 196–199, 1917.

Horton, R.E., Failure of hydraulic projects from lack of water prevented by better hydrology, *Engineering News Record*, *78*, 490–492, 1917.

Horton, R.E., Rational studies of rainfall data make possible better estimates of water yield, *Engineering News Record*, *79*, 211–213, 1917.

Horton, R.E., Drainage-basin and crop studies aid water supply estimates, *Engineering News Record*, *79*, 357–360, 1917.

Horton, R.E., Determining the regulating effect of a storage reservoir [Differential equation of inflow, outflow and storage relations solved using time interval as independent variable], *Engineering News Record*, *81*, 455–458, 1918.

Horton, R.E., Rainfall interception, *Monthly Weather Review*, *47*, 603–623, 1919.

Horton, R.E., Discussion of the probable variation in yearly precipitation, *Transactions American Society of Civil Engineers*, 1921.

Horton, R.E., Correlation of maximum rain characteristics for long and short time intervals, *Monthly Weather Review*, *49*, 200–202, 1921.

Horton, R.E., Results of evaporation observations, *Monthly Weather Review*, *49*, 553–566, 1921.

Horton, R.E., Accuracy of areal rainfall estimates, *Monthly Weather Review*, *51*, 348–353, 1923.

Horton, R.E., Transpiration by forest trees, *Monthly Weather Review*, *51*, 571–581, 1923.

Horton, R.E., Group distribution and periodicity, *Monthly Weather Review*, *51*, 1923.

Horton, R.E., Rainfall interpolation, *Monthly Weather Review*, *51*, 603–623, 1923.

Horton, R.E., Flood reduction by reservoirs, submitted to Institute of Civil Engineers in 1924 and described in Abstract no. 4483, Session Notices, Institute of Civil Engineers, 1924–25, 1924.

Horton, R.E., Determination of the mean precipitation on a drainage basin, *Journal New England Water Works Association*, *38*, 1–47, 1924.

Horton, R.E., Discussion of paper by C.S. Jarvis on flood flow characteristics, *Transactions American Society of Civil Engineers*, *89*, 1081–1086, 1926.

Horton, R.E. in collaboration with C.E. Grunsky, Hydrology of the Great Lakes, *Report of the Engineering Board of Review of the Sanitary District of Chicago* on the Lake Lowering Controversy and a Program of Remedial Measures, *Part III*, Appendix II, 432p., 1927.

Horton, R.E., The field, scope, and the status of the science of hydrology, *EOS-Transactions American Geophysical Union*, *12*, 189–202, 1931.

Horton, R.E., Drainage-basin characteristics, *EOS-Transactions American Geophysical Union*, *13*, 350–361, 1932.

Horton, R.E., Discussion of the report of the committee on floods, *Boston Society of Civil Engineers Journal*, *19*, 506–514, 1932.

Horton, R.E., The role of infiltration in the hydrologic cycle, *EOS-Transactions American Geophysical Union*, *14*, 446–460, 1933.

Horton, R.E., The relation of hydrology to the botanical sciences, *EOS-Transactions American Geophysical Union*, *14*, 23–25, 1933.

Horton, R.E., Separate roughness coefficients for channel bottom and sides, *Engineering News Record*, *111*, 652–653, 1933.

Horton, R.E., Discharge coefficients for Tainter gates, *Engineering News Record*, January 24, 1934.

Horton, R.E., Water-losses in high latitudes and at high elevations, *EOS-Transactions American Geophysical Union*, *15*, 351–379, 1934.

Horton, R.E., *Surface Runoff Phenomena, Part I, Analysis of the*

Hydrograph, 73 p., Publication 101, Horton Hydrological Laboratory, Voorheesville, N. Y. [published by Edwards Brothers, Inc., Ann Arbor, Michigan], 1935.

Horton, R.E., Maximum ground-water levels, *EOS-Transactions American Geophysical Union*, 17, 344–357, 1936.

Horton, R.E., Natural stream channel-storage, *EOS-Transactions American Geophysical Union*, 17, 406–415, 1936.

Horton, R.E., Hydrologic interpretations of water and soils, *Proceedings Soil Science Society of America*, 1, 401–429, 1937.

Horton, R.E., Hydrologic research, *Science*, 86, 527–530, 1937.

Horton, R.E., Determination of infiltration-capacity for large drainage-basins, *EOS-Transactions American Geophysical Union*, 18, 371–385, 1937.

Horton, R.E., Natural stream channel-storage [second paper], *EOS-Transactions American Geophysical Union*, 18, 440–456, 1937.

Horton, R.E., Hydrologic aspects of streamflow stabilization, *Journal of Forestry*, 35, 1015–1027, 1937.

Horton, R.E., Surface-runoff control, *Headwaters Control and Use, Chapter II*, Papers presented at the Upstream Engineering Conference held in Washington, D. C., September 22 and 23, 1936, 16–41, discussion 41–49, Published by Soil Conservation Service and Forest Service of the United States Department of Agriculture with the cooperation of Rural Electrification Administration, 1937.

Horton, R.E., Channel waves subject chiefly to momentum control, *Contribution from Division of Research, Soil Conservation Service and Horton Hydrologic Laboratory, Voorheesville, N.Y., SCS-TP-16*, 50p., 1938.

Horton, R.E., Analysis of simulated rainfall experiments, *Contribution from Division of Research, Soil Conservation Service and Horton Hydrologic Laboratory, Voorheesville, N.Y., SCS-TP-18*, 16p., 1938.

Horton, R.E., The interpretation and application of runoff plot experiments with reference to soil erosion problems, *Soil Science Society of America Proceedings*, 3, 340–349, 1938.

Horton, R.E., Seddon's and Forchheimer's formulas for crest-velocity of flood waves subject to channel friction control, *EOS-Transactions American Geophysical Union*, 19, 374–382, 1938.

Horton, R.E., Rain wave-trains, *EOS-Transactions American Geophysical Union*, 19, 368–374, 1938.

Horton, R.E., Definition and classification of flood waves, *Bull. Perm. Internatl. Assoc. Navigation Congress, No.25*, 1938.

Horton, R.E., Phenomena of the contact zone between the ground surface and a layer of melting snow. *International Association of Scientific Hydrology, Publ. 23*, 545–561, 1938.

Horton, R.E., Analysis of runoff-plot experiments with varying infiltration capacity, *EOS-Transactions American Geophysical Union*, 20, 693–711, 1939.

Horton, R.E., An approach toward a physical interpretation of infiltration-capacity, *Soil Science Society of America Proceedings*, 5, 399–417, 1940.

Horton, R.E., Suggestions for a comprehensive research program on runoff phenomena, *Deficiencies in Hydrologic Research*, 62–74, National Research Planning Board, Washington, D.C., 1940.

Horton, R.E., Hydrophysical approach to quantitative morphology of drainage basins, *American Association for the Advancement of Science*, Abstract, Section E, Philadelphia, 1940.

Horton, R.E., Sheet erosion - present and past *in* Symposium on dynamics of land erosion, *EOS-Transactions American Geophysical Union*, 22, 299–305, 1941.

Horton, R.E., Virtual channel-inflow graphs, *EOS-Transactions American Geophysical Union*, 22, 811–819, 1941.

Horton, R.E., Flood-crest reduction by channel-storage, *EOS-Transactions American Geophysical Union*, 22, 820–835, 1941.

Horton, R.E., Remarks on hydrologic terminology, *EOS-Transactions American Geophysical Union*, 23, 479–482, 1942.

Horton, R.E., An experiment on flow through a capillary tube, *EOS-Transactions American Geophysical Union*, 23, 534–538, 1942.

Horton, R.E., Simplified method of determining an infiltration-capacity curve from an infiltrometer-experiment, *EOS-Transactions American Geophysical Union*, 23, 570–575, 1942.

Horton, R.E., A simplified method of determining the constants in the infiltration capacity equation, *EOS-Transactions American Geophysical Union*, 23, 575–577, 1942.

Horton, R.E., A discussion of the relation of soil conservation to air and ground-water pollution, *Bulletin American Meteorological Society*, 1943.

Horton, R.E., Evapotranspiration-maps of the United States, *EOS-Transactions American Geophysical Union*, 24, 743–753, 1943.

Horton, R.E., Hydrologic interrelationships between lands and oceans, *EOS-Transactions American Geophysical Union*, 24, 753–764, 1943.

Horton, R.E., Infiltration and runoff during the snow-melting season with forest cover, *EOS-Transactions American Geophysical Union*, 26, 59–68, 1945.

Horton, R.E., Erosional development of streams and their drainage basins, Hydrophysical approach to quantitive geomorphology, *Geological Society of America Bulletin*, 56, 275–370, 1945.

Horton, R.E., Statistical distribution of drop sizes and the occurrence of dominant drop sizes in rain, *EOS-Transactions American Geophysical Union*, 29, 624–630, 1948. [Posthumous publication, arranged by Richard Van Vliet - No. 1 of a series.]

Horton, R.E., Physics of thunderstorms, *EOS-Transactions American Geophysical Union*, 29, 810–844, 1948. [Posthumous publication, arranged by Richard Van Vliet - No. 2 of a series.]

Horton, R.E., Convectional vortex rings - hail, *EOS-Transactions American Geophysical Union*, 30, 29–45, 1949. [Posthumous publication, arranged by Richard Van Vliet.]

Horton, R.E. and J.S. Cole, Compilation and summary of the evaporation record of Bureau of Plant Industries, U.S. Department of Agriculture, 1021–1932, *Monthly Weather Review*, 62, 77–89, 1934.

Horton, R.E., H.R. Leach, and Richard Van Vliet, Laminar sheet flow, *EOS-Transactions American Geophysical Union*, 15, 393–404, 1934.

Leach, H.R., H.L. Cook, and R.E. Horton, Stormflow predictions, *EOS-Transactions American Geophysical Union*, 14, 435–446, 1933.

Rafter, George, Computational works connected with hydraulic tests [involved contribution by R.E. Horton], *Transactions American Society of Civil Engineers*, 64, 1900.

Rafter, George and R.E. Horton, A report for the New York State Engineer and Surveyor, 1896.

Veatch, A.C., C.S. Slichter, Isaiah Bowman, W.O. Crosby, and R.E. Horton, Underground water resources of Long Island, New York, *U.S. Geological Survey Professional Paper No. 44*, 394p., 1906.

F. R. Hall, Department of Earth Sciences, University of New Hampshire, Durham, NH 03824.

Max Leggette, Pioneer of Hydrogeology Consultants

R. G. SLAYBACK

President, Leggette, Brashears & Graham, Inc., 72 Danbury Road, Wilton, CT 06897

R. M. (Max) Leggette, a geology graduate of the University of Chicago, was one of the early employees of the Ground Water Branch of the U. S. Geological Survey under the legendary Oscar Meinzer. His Survey career, starting in 1928, included investigations in 20 states, with extensive work in Pennsylvania, New York and Utah, and culminated as District Geologist for New York and New England from 1935 to 1942. Following service in World War II as a Water Supply Officer in the North Africa campaign, Max Leggette opened shop in 1944 as a consulting ground-water geologist, a new profession. After 8 years as a sole proprietorship, he was joined by Survey "graduates" M. L. Brashears in 1952 and Jack B. Graham in 1955. The demand for services was good, with early projects in 32 states and territories, and foreign work on five continents. Once a rather lonely profession, with competitors in only a few states, consulting hydrogeology has grown to the point that such services are offered in the "yellow pages" of every major city in the United States. The pioneering firm Max founded 40 years ago, continues in the practice of consulting hydrogeology under the name of the three founding partners, with offices in three states. The systematic approach to ground-water investigations with multiple quality-control checks that Max Leggette brought from the U.S.G.S. to his consulting firm remains an active legacy of a pioneering hydrogeologist.

INTRODUCTION

The history of any science or profession is the story of innovators, of key discoveries, and of people who blazed new trails. Max Leggette was a pioneer of another sort, the man who demonstrated, long before the era of public concern about water contamination, that a living could be earned by the full-time practice of consulting in the specialty of ground-water geology.

Today, when one can open the "yellow pages" of any major city in the United States and find hydrogeologic consulting services advertised, that may seem unremarkable. It may be surprising to recall that 1985 marks only the 50th anniversary of the publication by C. V. Theis of the non-equilibrium formula that revolutionized quantitative hydrogeology. Moreover, 1944, only four decades ago, marked the start of the specialty consulting business in ground-water geology by Max Leggette.

Ralph Maxwell Leggette was born on St. Valentines Day in 1899 in Ontario, Canada. He became a United States citizen in 1915, received a baccalaureate in geology from the University of Chicago in 1923, and completed 3 years of graduate study at Chicago.

He taught briefly at Ohio State and joined the Ground-Water Division of the U. S. Geological Survey in 1928. At that time, the total professional staff of the Division of Ground Water was 8 people; 6 geologists and 2 engineers; indeed the infancy of that group that now employs about 500 ground-water scientists. Our first picture of this era is of the staff in 1932, with the Geologist in Charge, Oscar E. Meinzer in the center, and Nelson Sayre, Lee Wenzel, Arthur Piper, Henry Barksdale, David Thompson, Harold Stearns, George Taylor, Stanley Lowman, Vic Stringfield, Al Fiedler, Vic Fishel, Harold Thomas and C. V. Theis among the better-known scientists—a truly remarkable group. Max Leggette, already a bit thin on top, is shown to the right side of Meinzer (Figure 1).

Max's Survey career started in northwestern Pennsylvania, and resulted in his first major publication, aptly titled "Ground Water in Northwestern Pennsylvania". He then worked with Stan Lohman on his study of the ground-water resources of northeastern Pennsylvania, with Lee Wenzel on the Platte River aquifer in Nebraska, and performed a ground-water investigation at Fort Leavenworth, Kansas for the Federal Bureau of Prisons.

1932 brought Max Leggette to Utah and one of the key stages of career and life. He performed ground-water studies with George Taylor of the Ogden Valley and of the Jordan valley near Salt Lake City, resulting in Water Supply Papers 796-D and 1029. He also met the charming Mildred Heist of Salt Lake City and married her in October, like so many of his professional decisions, a wise choice that endured to the benefit of all of their associates.

In 1934, Oscar Meinzer appointed Max to be Chairman of the Survey Committee on Observation Wells, charged with developing a nationwide program of systematic water-level observations. This assignment led to field work in about 10 states, from North Carolina to Washington State and from Texas to Wisconsin. The program led to the publication of Water-Supply Paper 777, "Water levels and artesian pressure in observation wells in the United States in 1935", the first of a long series of basic data reports that were the precursors to the computerized data base we now use.

In 1935, Max became District Geologist in charge of ground-water investigations in New York and the New England states, a position he held for 8 years. This Survey office was based in Jamaica, Queens, on Long Island, one of the most prolific ground-water areas of the nation. During these years he continued his interest in the collection and dissemination of basic data, publishing a series of reports consisting of well logs for the 4 Long Island counties that are still one of the starting points for new hydrogeologic studies. His staff included C. E. Jacob, one of the great innovators of our science, and M. L. Brashears, who succeeded Max as District Geologist and was later to become his partner in the consulting business. An observation of drawdown in obser-

Fig. 1.   Division of Ground Water, U. S. Geological Survey, July 1, 1932.

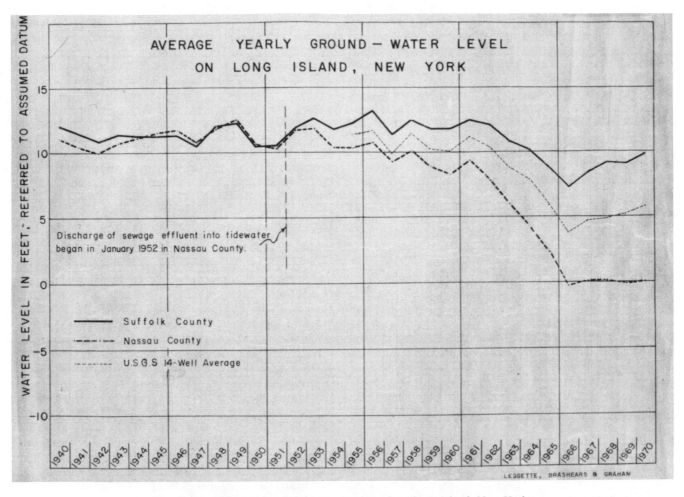

Fig. 2.   Average yearly ground-water level graph on Long Island, New York.

vation wells completed in the Lloyd Sand Member of the Raritan Formation caused by a pumping well more than 7 miles distant became Leggette's most common citation in the literature of hydrogeology.

Max left Long Island and his family in 1942 to serve in World War II with the Army Corps of Engineers. He served as a Water Supply Officer in Algeria and French Morocco during the North African campaign. Many years afterwards, we knew when a client was also a World War II officer when he asked for this most unmilitary of men as Major Leggette. Mustered out in 1944, Max returned to private life at age 45 and decided to see if he could support himself and his family as a consulting ground-water geologist. Today that seems a rather mundane choice but it was, in its time, a risky and trail-blazing move.

Max took office space on Fifth Avenue in New York City. A prestige address remained a part of his formula for conveying an aura of success throughout his consulting career. He consulted his Survey friends about what to charge and settled on a fee of $100 per day. His good friend, Henry Barksdale, told Max that no one was worth $100 a day. Of course, some hydrogeologists now charge $100 per hour, but that is another story. Max shared his first office with several fledgling businessmen. After some costly experiences, he learned to lock his telephone inside his desk drawer when he was out in the field.

The first big job, starting in March 1945, was a water-supply investigation for a dairy and poultry enterprise on the Island of Eleuthera in the Bahamas, a delicate salt-water intrusion problem. Later that year, Max landed an annual retainer from the Suffolk County Water Authority, a newly-formed water-supply agency for the most easterly county on Long Island, an area that was destined for considerable growth in the post-War years. In 1950, he traveled across the country as the AAPG "Distinguished Lecturer", giving talks on "The Fundamentals of Ground-Water Hydrology".

After operating as a sole proprietorship for 8 years, Max found, in 1952, that the demand for specialty consulting services in hydrogeology had grown beyond his individual capabilities to provide. In a relatively short time, he took in M. L. Brashcars as a partner, hired a secretary-bookkeeper, Miriam D. Miller, who was to be the backbone of the firm for 29 years, and hired two professional staff geologists; Ed Simmons, a later President of the Firm, and David W. Miller. Brash brought in new foreign and mine-dewatering work, and the firm prospered. Gene Hickok, Sid Fox and Jim Geraghty joined the professional staff. In 1955, Jack Graham, another Survey "graduate", brought strength to the partnership in water quality and broadened the regional base with extensive contacts in Pennsylvania. Many will recognize that Geraghty & Miller and Gene Hickok moved on to form their own successful consulting firms, based in Long Island and Minnesota, respectively.

The firm became consultants to water-supply companies and authorities; developed large well-water supplies for the paper, metals and brewing industries; dewatered mines in

Canada and Africa; and performed some of the earliest consulting studies involving contaminated ground water.

As a consultant, Max Leggette used his U.S.G.S. training to good advantage. His broad travels and diverse experience had made him a master of sizing up a problem, focusing his efforts on the key points, and yet thoroughly examining all pertinent data. He was driven by a concern for accuracy, major technical content, minor details, and the report language that conveyed his results to the clients. We junior geologists did not look forward to the days when our report drafts were to be reviewed in head-to-head and word-by-word sessions with Max but, in retrospect, the discipline gave us excellent training.

His achievements as a pioneering consultant were many. Those that stand out in my memory include:

1. Drill-stem Sampling

When the Suffolk County Water Authority complained in 1962 of the high cost of treating some of their well water for excessive iron, Max drew on the oil-business, drill-stem test technology. On his recommendation, each new production well site was drilled first by a pilot hole, in which temporary screens allowed water samples to be taken from several depth zones, which commonly varied considerably in iron content. Over a period of years it was found that such short-duration sampling was an exceptionally reliable indicator of the long-term iron content of a production well completed at a given depth. This pre-sampling program is still in use in Suffolk County in areas where iron content is a problem, and is further used to screen for nitrates and pesticides resulting from agricultural practices.

2. Expert Witness Testimony

When the New Jersey Water Policy and Control Council established the first protected ground-water areas in 1947 and established a permit procedure for new ground-water withdrawals exceeding 100,000 gallons daily, Max became the first hydrogeologist to be accepted as an expert witness. Working before a lay council, his testimony was drafted to educate as well as set forth the facts of an application. By exceptional thoroughness, he literally set the standard for such expert witness testimony in New Jersey.

3. Long Island Water Balance

When Nassau County on Long Island first began the systematic installation of sanitary sewers in 1952, with discharge of treated effluent to the ocean, Leggette's experience with the Long Island observation-well program and understanding of the pumpage and recharge balance of the area led him to conclude that a serious imbalance would occur and ground-water levels would progressively decline. As he did in so many other matters, Max devised a simple average water-level comparison between sewered Nassau County and unsewered Suffolk County to convey his concern to the local government officials. This simple graph (Figure 2), first presented in 1954 and updated annually, received considerable attention during the record drought of the mid 1960's.

He also began lobbying for controlled experiments with artificial recharge, using treated sewage effluent to set up a barrier to salt-water encroachment or otherwise restore the recharge-pumpage balance. Those efforts were partially responsible for the classic deep-well injection experiments conducted by the U.S.G.S. at the Bay Park Sewage Treatment Plant, and go on today as scientists study the efficacy of maintaining the water table and base streamflow by return of treated sewage effluent to the upland recharge area in central Long Island.

4. Professional Status

After several years of arguing with the City and State of New York regarding the tax status of the consulting firm, Max went to court and succeeded in establishing that ground-water geology was a profession in the eyes of law. The unanimous decision, rendered on March 4, 1958, noted that "the occupational activities of the taxpayer as a consulting geologist. . . constitutes an occupation or vocation in which a professed knowledge of the science of geology was used by its practical application to the affairs of others and in servicing their interests or welfare in the practice of an art founded on such knowledge. . . That the activities of the taxpayer as a geologist. . . constituted the practice of a profession within the meaning. . . of the tax law." To our knowledge, this was the first such recognition under the law. As noted in the October 1958 GEOTIMES, "Earth scientists owe a debt of gratitude to the defendant for carrying this legal fight to a correct conclusion."

In 1969, at age 70, Max retired from his consulting firm. He and Mil moved to San Diego, where they still are enjoying life and good health.

Leggette, Brashears & Graham has endured and grown, under Brashears, and then Graham, and more recently Ed Simmons. The consulting business in hydrogeology has changed tremendously in the past dozen years, especially with respect to the competition for work involving contaminated ground water. We have added to our tools and knowledge, and have learned how to market professional services in the era of the cattle-call Request for Proposal. Max hung out his shingle, put his professional card in a few journals, and waited for the phone to ring, which it did often enough. And yet, for all of the changes, the firm Max Leggette created retains very much of the personality and professional image of its founder.

Following Leggette's example, there are now several hundred firms that offer hydrogeologic consulting services, as either their sole business or as part of broad engineering services, and they provide employment for a few thousand hydrogeologists, hydrologists, geophysicists and geochemists.

R. Slayback, Leggette, Brashears, and Graham, Inc., 72 Danbury Road, Wilton, CT   06897.